P9-EEP-392

HOW TO HELP OLDER PEOPLE

How to Help Older People

A GUIDE FOR YOU AND YOUR FAMILY

by

JULIETTA K. ARTHUR

WITH AN INTRODUCTION BY
WILMA DONAHUE, PH.D.
CHAIRMAN, DIVISION OF GERONTOLOGY
INSTITUTE FOR HUMAN ADJUSTMENT
UNIVERSITY OF MICHIGAN

J. B. LIPPINCOTT COMPANY

PHILADELPHIA AND NEW YORK

Printed in the United States of America

First Edition

Library of Congress Catalog Card Number: 54-5597

TO MY MOTHER, AND THOSE
MANY OTHER OLDER PEOPLE
WHO INVITED ME TO ASK
QUESTIONS AND GAVE ME
FRANK ANSWERS

. . . To those who have not the means within themselves of a virtuous and happy life every age is burdensome; and, on the other hand, to those who seek all good from themselves nothing can seem evil that the laws of nature inevitably impose. To this class old age especially belongs, which all men wish to attain and yet reproach when attained. . . .

—CICERO, *De Senectute*

Contents

FOREWORD

Many people, of diverse backgrounds and varied points of view, have helped to bring this book from an idea into reality. In writing it, I have had the benefit of consultations with many of the country's most distinguished pioneers in geriatrics and gerontology. At the same time, I have listened to literally hundreds of questions posed by troubled young people. They are trying to understand the old closest to them, and are justifiably concerned with what is in store for them when they, too, are old.

However, the structure and the content of this book is chiefly due to the reaction and comments of old people themselves. I have talked to them in the "laboratories" which old age homes, nursing homes, boarding homes and hospitals afford, and "in the field," living under their own, a relative's, or a stranger's roof. It was they who felt this book would be most worth while if it provided reassurance and sound information for young people caught up in family situations involving two, three, sometimes even four generations. They felt that the young should be directed to the avenues of aid for the old which exist in their own communities. At the same time they felt that young people need to learn more about new measures, both governmental and private, which are opening up for all of us who are aging.

With their comments in mind, chapters in this book, therefore, deal with the principal situations that frequently produce crippling and disabling emotions and attitudes. These include the terrors of loneliness in old age, worry about illness or shelter, anxiety over finances, or the unhappiness which results if one generation infringes on the life of another.

Merely to discuss these sore points, however, would still leave two essential questions unanswered. What concerns us all, first, is what to do for and with the older people who are closest to us?

The second question is equally important but often disregarded in the heat of daily living: How can we best prepare to meet our own old age which almost certainly most of us will experience?

No one book, or set of books, can give categorical answers to either question. We hear and read more about the old today because almost overnight they have ceased to be a minority group too small and too unimportant to reckon with. Books and articles on how to grow old gracefully, or at least without pain, flood the market. The psychological, the physical, and the mental aspects of involution are aired on every radio and television station. Often the speakers are the old, chiefly those who boast they have kept "young," no mean asset in a nation dedicated to the cult of youth.

This book, however, does not attempt to offer an easy, push-button solution to the complicated problems the aging process presents in our time. The reader may even be disappointed to learn that there is no easy solution to any question which affects old people.

It has been a challenging job to give the best answers found by the most eminent authorities, with as little as possible of the technical evidence upon which their conclusions are based. I have tried to bring inert data to life in a way that maintains accuracy and gives factual information, and yet is both readable and intelligible to the layman. Technicalities could not be entirely eliminated, but I have reduced them to the minimum, without, I trust, dealing in popular jargon about the "care of the aged."

This book is intended, then, for the reader who may not have the time, training, or inclination to read the technical volumes and the scientific articles written by men and women who are wrestling with the problems an ever-growing older population presents. It is hoped that for that reader it presents a practical, concentrated, and easily digestible guide to whatever solutions exist today.

IN ACKNOWLEDGMENT

This is the kind of book which could never have been written without the candid revelation of facts on the part of a great many interested individuals and organizations. I regret that I cannot name all those to whom I would like to express my gratitude for encouragement, practical help, and constructive criticism. By no means least, my thanks are due to many courageous older men and women who were not only willing to permit the use of their names and their ages, but also their experiences, good and bad, to help younger people understand the role older ones can play in the family and in our society.

I am deeply grateful to the many experts who listened tirelessly, answered my questions with enthusiasm, and made me rewrite all my favorite passages. I am particularly in the debt of those who read with care those chapters which related to their own special fields and gave me patient counsel. My special thanks are due to the following:

Albert J. Abrams, Director, New York State Joint Legislative Committee on Problems of the Aging; Mrs. Elizabeth Breckinridge, Executive Secretary, Illinois Committee on Aging; Georgene E. Bowen, Director of Recreation for Philadelphia's Older People; Mrs. Jean Wallace Carey, Director, Division of the Aged, Federation of Protestant Welfare Agencies, New York City; Dr. C. Ward Crampton, sub-Chairman of the Committee on Geriatrics and Gerontology, Medical Society of the County of New York; Dr. Robert Felix, Director, National Institute of Mental Health; Mrs. Esther C. Forsstrand, Consultant, Division for the Aged, Philadelphia Health and Welfare Council; Flora Fox, Executive Director, Central Bureau for Jewish Aged, Inc., New York City; Dora Goldfarb, Director, Community Homemaker Service, New York City; Harry

A. Levine, Administrator, Special Services for the Aged, Department of Welfare, City of New York; Mrs. Geneva Mathiasen, Secretary to the National Committee on the Aging of the National Social Welfare Assembly; John M. McGibony, Medical Director, Chief, Division of Medical and Hospital Resources, U. S. Department of Health, Education, and Welfare; Dr. Robert T. Monroe, Director, Geriatric Clinic, Peter Bent Brigham Hospital, Boston; L. H. Millikan, Inspection Section, Indiana Department of Public Welfare; W. G. Scott, National Employment Service, Toronto, Canada; Dr. David Seegal, Director, Columbia University Research Service, Goldwater Memorial Hospital, New York City; Dr. Nathan W. Shock, Chief, Section on Gerontology, National Institutes of Health and Baltimore City Hospitals; Dr. George Stevenson, National and International Consultant, National Ass'n for Mental Health; Dr. Malford W. Thewlis, Secretary, American Geriatrics Society, Wakefield, R. I.; Clark Tibbitts, Chairman, Committee on Aging and Geriatrics, U. S. Department of Health, Education, and Welfare; Miss Margaret W. Wagner, Executive Director, The Benjamin Rose Institute, Cleveland, Ohio; Alice J. Webber, Regional Representative, Federal Bureau of Public Assistance, Region Two, New York City.

INTRODUCTION

Of all the problems which our contemporary industrial society and the increasing longevity of the population are posing, none are of greater significance to the happiness of mankind than those related to the family. Man's major opportunity to form satisfying emotional relationships lies within the family circle. It is here, still, that the deep affections which are to last a lifetime are formed and nurtured. But changing times have made assaults upon our most impregnable institutions and have wrought extensive modifications in them. The family is no exception. However, because the meaning of these changes and of the new attitudes have not yet been made clear to families, many of them are deeply perplexed over their ambivalent feelings and their inadequacies for coping with the emerging crises of three and often four generation relationships and responsibilities.

The extent of these responsibilities and perplexities can be appreciated when we realize that the second fastest growing segment of the population is that which is sixty-five years of age and over, and that of the more than thirteen million who are in this age group, one third has already exceeded the three-quarter century mark. Every day one thousand more people become members of the conventionally defined (65 and over) older group. There is scarcely a middle-aged family in America that does not have one or more of the four parents as its real or psychological obligation. The need for understanding of the new forces at work and of the causes for these changes in the accountability of both younger and older age groups is almost universal.

The explanation is not simple. With industrialization has come about a striking change in social organization of the family. Previously, aging members were able to retain or increase their power and prestige within the kinship group, but today the older generation is finding itself shelved and sometimes stranded by its younger families. That this changed situation is a reflection of the demands of a competitive society in which the younger family must concentrate all its resources upon its children in order that they may take their places successfully in the competitive world, is not understood either by the older or younger generation. To both groups, it appears that there is a dereliction of duty and a weakening of family bonds. Resentments based upon misapprehensions build up in both parents and children, and lead to a transformation of the feelings of mutual love and respect to those of hatred and disappointment, thus embittering the last few precious years a family can have together.

If an industrial society is unkind to the aging, it is equally unkind to the children of the aging. For the older parents, our era has failed to maintain a family structure in which emotional security is a built-in feature; nor has it produced satisfying substitutes for family roles. It has failed to emancipate the younger persons from their sense of obligation to their parents and, at the same time, has denied them the means by which they can meet the obvious material and emotional needs of the older family members. Out of such situations are built the present-day frustrations which, for far too many, have seemed intolerable. Thus are born the tragedies of misunderstanding between the generations, the putting out of sight of the offending older person in some isolating institution, the painful over-protectiveness (killing with kindness) for the relief of guilt feelings, or the monotony of long, sustained, inescapable daily association.

Admittedly, then, the solution of the problems of the several generations is and must be a complex process. Fortunately, most of us have before us prime examples of families who have succeeded in establishing plans equitable to all age levels in the family group. Furthermore, this is not a new area of human relationships for the psychologist and the social worker. For years, they have been confronted with these delicate interpersonal situations of the multi-generation family, and they are now ready, in this time of expanded need, to give us guideposts and benchmarks by which we may chart and measure our course. Communities, aware that family needs are among the most pressing, long ago set up service agencies which are prepared to help children and older people alike. Also, state agencies, voluntary organizations, and governmental units already have programs in operation which can be brought to bear on these problems of guiding the family in its relationships with aging members and of providing services needed to insure that the needs of all age groups are met.

It is because these services and understandings are available, and because, at the same time, the three- or four-generation problem continues to persist and grow, that the publication of this book is of utmost importance to every family and every older person in the United States. It is not a book of prescriptions for palliative measures. Instead, it is a book of specifics for the alleviation, control, and cure of tensions, frustrations, and heartaches. Its theme is prevention. It emphasizes planning and taking steps *before* problems arise, or before they move into the critical phase. The book is designed to assist in the everyday problems of the average family in planning with, and for, its older members: where to live, how to determine whether employment is desirable and how to go about finding a job, how to get financial aid, whom to see when expert counselling is needed, where to go for social experiences and how to develop satisfying leisure-time activities. These and many other questions are discussed and methods for finding answers are outlined.

But, if I were to stop at this point in my description of the value of this Guide, I would do the author, Julietta Arthur, a great injustice, because I would have neglected its most important features. First of these is its practical nature. Mrs. Arthur has never wavered from her criteria to write a book which meets people's practical everyday needs. She believes, and writes accordingly, that what people want and need is information and understandable realistic interpretation. These things she has given in amazing abundance with the true insight of the trained and experienced mind bent on bringing the art of personal adjustment to the working level of the family and the individual. Through concrete example, one can read about his neighbor or see himself reflected in the understanding analysis of the problems of others. One can learn to accept himself and the other members of his family because one gains the sense of the inevitability of the common problems, and receives encouragement that there are sensible and desirable solutions to what heretofore have seemed insoluble difficulties.

The second outstanding achievement of this book, and one which is unprecedented in its field, is that it provides a directory of services which are available to assist every citizen in his pursuit of a solution to his own personal problem. This is not a directory of some faraway service, attainable only by the few who have the means to seek out some obscure specialist. It is, instead, a directory of what exists in your own home town and in your own state. This aspect of the book will make it an invaluable guide not only to the individual family but to the professional worker. A real debt is owed Mrs. Arthur for the incredible amount of research which she has put into collecting the detailed information necessary to provide such a guide.

WILMA DONAHUE
Chairman, Division of Gerontology
Institute for Human Adjustment
University of Michigan

HOW TO HELP OLDER PEOPLE

CHAPTER ONE

GETTING ALONG WITH OLDER PEOPLE

Unless, like H. G. Wells' Mr. Polly, you are going to live in a state of constant civil war, you will have to recognize that a new "breed" of older people is developing before your eyes. The apple-cheeked, snowy-haired grandmother of fiction, arm-deep in flour and pumpkin pies in an old-fashioned kitchen, still appears on Thanksgiving magazine covers. In real life, however, she is much more likely to take as her model, or at least her mouthpiece, a woman like Mary Heaton Vorse. Mrs. Vorse was well in her sixties when she worked as a war correspondent during World War II. When her juniors tried to make much of that fact she brushed it aside.

"It's high time," she said, "that young people stop treating able elderly ones like a nine days' wonder!"

If you want to avoid your own tug-of-war between generations—or bring one to a good end—you must accept this point of view. For it is not only a Mrs. Vorse, a Connie Mack, and an Arturo Toscannini who want to contribute their talents to their country and their wisdom to their children. It is also the old people on your block and mine. Newspapers nowadays report the exploits of septuagenarians, octogenarians, and nonagenarians almost as matter-of-factly as they do wars and threats of wars. The reason is a simple statistical fact. There are so many older people, and there are going to be more. They are increasing more rapidly than any other portion of our population—a fact which is bound to have powerful repercussions on your family life.

Every day, including Sundays and holidays, nearly a thousand men and women pass their sixty-fifth birthday. In 1900 there were only three million people who had lived to that age or more. A half century later when the census was taken, their number had leaped to over twelve million and a quarter. Any startling development in medicine or public health—such as a cure for cancer or the heart diseases, which chiefly attack the aging—would send these figures skyrocketing. (1) *

THIS NEW "BREED"

This spate of statistics is the most powerful incentive any of us can have to live on amicable terms with the generation just ahead. Your parents and grandparents may have been able to take their older relatives for granted. You cannot afford to. The aging people around you, who will probably live ten to twenty years beyond the Biblical three score and ten, are persons to reckon with in ways your father never knew. They probably have healthier bodies; at a comparable age most of them have livelier minds. They are likely to demand more than the back seat their elders were content with (possibly because the time was so short between their elders' maturity and the grave).

When Emma Crittenden left Brooklyn, New York, to take her first plane ride when she was ninety, it was to attend her college class reunion in Michigan. She only stopped teaching music a half-dozen years ago. At ninety-five Charles C. Burlingham, clear-eyed and robust of mien, is an active lawyer in New York City. "The press makes a fuss about my numerous birthdays because they happen to fall in a dull season when there isn't much news," he says placidly. In rural Oklahoma Mrs. Mabel Kalka lives alone. She is in her late seventies. When a youthful reporter comments on the fact that her children live at a distance, she replies briefly, "I'm too busy to think about it." She cultivates four hundred varieties of iris and is licensed to sell them. In her spare time she raises hens and sells their eggs, too.

In 1975 newspapers probably will find such stories too commonplace to print. Statisticians predict that seventeen million people—one out of every ten in the population—will be sixty-

* Notes will be found at end of respective chapters.

five years old or more. By that time, when we shall be old, let us hope our children's children will take it for granted that if we give way to them in some things, our lives need not, therefore, be as empty as a vacant house.

In the meanwhile, we and our elders are caught in a transitional period which accounts for most of our difficulties with them —and their problems. There is much greater tension now between the old and the young than there ever was before, and more reason for it. Unless you are willing to make the effort to find out why, and then act on your discoveries, life with mother or father, or any other older individual, is going to be a continual struggle.

REASON FOR TODAY'S TENSION

Even the most saintly of us have asked at some time or other, "Why are so many people difficult to get along with when they are old?"

Dr. Erwin Ackerknecht of the University of Wisconsin believes he has the answer.(2) He said: "Two-thirds of the old persons in the United States feel unwanted and many of them are right. . . . The attitude toward old age in our country is contradictory and lukewarm at best, often negative and scornful."

This is a harsh indictment, but examine it honestly.

Don't we all take it for granted that every old man or woman would like to drink from the Fountain of Youth if he could? Do you know any young people who long to find the well of wisdom and experience which only old age knows? A few rare individuals can be philosophic about their place in the world, but don't expect them to enjoy the role of an ancestor.

A wit once said, "A child has no objection to being a child because he knows he will soon get over it. But a person who has been dreading old age all his life knows it will not only continue but grow worse."

This is one of those smart-aleck sayings which sting because there is truth in them. Psychologically, our country is geared to its young. Movies, sports, advertisements, fashions, and every other facet of our life emphasize the importance of youth as the highest boon any of us can have. Our society, which regards youthfulness as its top asset, nevertheless puts emphasis on an ever-increasing life span. It is expecting millions of old people to be added to the present millions—yet gives them less of a role to play than any other older generation ever had.

In educational circles much emphasis is put on "discovering the child." We have succeeded so well we are quite self-conscious about the frustrations and complexes of small boys and girls and their adolescent brothers and sisters. But what about the complexes and frustrations of their grandparents and great-grandparents?

If your elderly relative is unhappy and is "taking it out" on his family, it is probably because he is one of millions of aging men and women baffled by the swiftness with which family life has altered in just one generation. As the American young people have moved from the farm into the tight-packed city, more and more older people find themselves alone. We have changed radically from the three- or four-generation family to the two-generation unit, and there is little room to expand in a city apartment or a small town house.

If you are under fifty you accept this as the order of our day because in most cases you have known nothing else. For the same reason you can take it in your stride if business claims uproot you so that next year you expect to be in the California desert—or The Gobi—though this year you may live in Boston. Jet flights, in the brief time since World War II, have annihilated distances on this planet. But project yourself forward twenty years or so. If your small son or daughter is an average child of our time he or she is playing with toy "space ships." By the time he is old enough to vote there may be rocket flights to the already projected space stations in the upper atmosphere—or to the moon. Could you face the undoubted change in living conditions complacently—that is, if you were invited to share them at all?

This is not a far-fetched comparison plucked from the comic books your child probably reads. Any individual who has lived to be seventy is living in a world which never existed when he was born, when telephones were curiosities and airplane travel as much a scientist's dream as space flights are now. He has had to undergo vast technological, cultural, and social changes which elders in his own youth never had to face. Yet he is expected to be able to adapt to all of them, without murmuring, during those "golden years" (for which *we* have furnished the rhapsodic name) which in many cases have the gilt rubbed off.

Fifty, or even twenty-five years ago, three or four generations could live together, and like it, under a single, spacious roof. Today if we make room for them, it may not be grudgingly, but quite frequently it is at a sacrifice. Any sensitive old person feels this painfully.

It is not only at home that the older person's services are seldom needed or wanted. Economic conditions have so changed in his lifetime that there is a premium on speed and quantity production in which the old lag, and little place for the crafts and slow handwork in which he was trained. Even in the professions accumulated knowledge is quickly outdated.

In more primitive cultures the problem of what to do with the old was faced matter-of-factly. If a tribal society could not afford to support its aged, the old man or woman was eliminated, and accepted his disposal with equanimity as being for the good of the community. If, on the other hand, he was regarded with respect by reason of the years in which he had gathered experience and wisdom, he was elevated to the post of magician, priest, or sage. In either case, there was finality to the solution.

We are not so realistic. Though we no longer put our old out to die, we expect them to continue to strive to be youthful. A popular columnist summed up this national attitude when he said: "We Americans have little real devotion for our old people. . . . We do everything for them; we are fond of them, we tolerate them, we take care of them, we speak jokingly of their crotchets and frailties—we do everything but respect them."

BURDEN OF UNDERSTANDING ON YOUNG

If you are going to help your relative find himself you will need both imagination and sensitivity. The gulf between any two generations is so vast that, as Booth Tarkington said once when he was already in his sixties, "By the time we reach middle-age we think of our own youthful days as the experience of a generally absurd stranger."

The great-grandmother who is still an active farmwife in Vermont, the cotton broker in New York who swam happily on his ninety-third birthday, the "young" pilot who still goes up in his plane at sixty-two—these are in the minority, though their number is growing. If your relative is as yet lagging with the majority of old people, he is a bewildered individual in a world which revolves chiefly around the young. You can't expect him to cope with his frustrations, unaided. Unless you do help him overcome them, you, and everyone who comes in contact with him, will also be a loser.

This puts the burden of understanding on you. If you are like the rest of us, there are times when you resent it and show your resentment. You may sigh enviously when you read the almost universal annual article in a woman's magazine. Its title usually runs something like "Why My Daughter-in-Law Loves Me." The author generally claims to be a dear old lady or gentleman who makes a cheerful martyr out of himself by sleeping on a bumpy davenport in the living- or dining-room. When company comes for the card-playing, dancing younger generation, the older one effaces himself, of course. Usually he retreats to the kitchen. If he is a man, he mixes marvelous drinks; if a woman, she makes equally marvelous sandwiches or cakes. In either case the story ends happily because he wins everybody's admiration.

A much better idea would be to see to it that your old encumbrance, if he is that, can have the opportunity which a ninety-two-year-old woman in Clyde, New York, enjoys. She lives a life of her own. She still inhabits her own home, does her own cooking, takes complete care of herself, and says to her neighbor: "I'm not going to get old and stiff like some people do!"

WHAT OLDER PEOPLE WANT

We all believe we know what children are like because we have already lived through their growing pains. But old age is an unknown terrain. The day when some older person's attitudes or actions come in conflict with your own is the day to stop and ask this question: *Just what is it that older people want to get out of life?*

If you say it only because you are exasperated with an old woman's complaints, or bored with an old man's tales of his past glories, you'll get nowhere. If you really want to close the gap between your generation and theirs, find out what lies behind their dominant desires, especially when they are at odds with your own.

Once you take your attitudes toward aging firmly in hand, you'll find that you will be much more likely to achieve a happy relationship. One reason is that you will not be so ready to label the actions and reactions of an older person as abnormal, or, at the least, inconvenient. They may be perfectly fitting from his point of view. This key, which enables you to measure an older person against the standards and values of his own generation, not yours, will not unlock all the painful mysteries in family kinships, but it can show you the way.

The story of young Mrs. Marchand and her pressure cooker is a good illustration. Her mother-in-law came to live with her soon after her son's departure for the army. The older woman refused to use the young bride's electrical attachments or her pressure cooker. This sensible girl quietly put them away and let her mother-in-law putter about with the iron pots and kettles she brought with her. She realized the old lady's protests grew largely out of two fears—fear of not being useful, and fear of being displaced in her son's affections. When the young man returned from the battlefields, he was distraught, suspicious, and for a while, difficult to live with. Mrs. Marchand, Jr. reaped her reward when she found an affectionate, loyal ally in her old-fashioned mother-in-law.

Not all situations can terminate with such a storybook ending. Nevertheless, if, in your turn, you can figure out why some older man is egocentric or why some woman is "mulish," you may be able to make a compromise which will preserve their dignity without endangering your own. At the same time you will be taking a long look ahead to the time when you, too, will need understanding.

NEEDS OF THE AGED

Years ago the Society of Friends summed up the basic needs of the aged simply and succinctly: "Somewhere to live, something to do, and someone to care."

These are the things that all old people have always wanted, and always will want. But if you want to know in detail what your own elderly friends and relatives expect from you and from life, all you need to do is to keep an ear cocked to hear what their contemporaries have to say.

The residents of a Home for Aged Jews in Chicago speak for their fellows in and out of institutions when they say in one issue of their magazine: "We would like to begin by saying that we are people—people like you, and like all other people. Having lived longer than you does not make us different, and we still like to be considered as individuals."

Remember this the next time you speak of "Sally's aunt" or "John's mother," or "the children's grandfather." We are all inclined to think of older people only in relation to *ourselves.* (The most rebellious escape this role and sometimes the only way left to them is the one they take. They kick up a row about something, which shows they are still persons, not merely ancestors.)

If you need any proof that all older people everywhere long for the same satisfactions, reflect on what twenty-one hundred grandmothers set down as their formula for success and happiness. (Their age range was from thirty-six to ninety-one.) For a New York newspaper they listed, in order of their importance: health, financial independence, separate living arrangements from their children, friends of their own, a hobby or a job, and exchange of love and services with younger people.

Everyone from Cicero to a Commitee of the United Nations has attempted to set down a "bill of rights" for the old, but what have the old to say for themselves?

Mrs. Martini, a sprightly elderly visitor on one of the "Old Craftsman" radio programs in San Francisco, declaimed this "Bill of Rights" for herself and all other old men and women:

"The right to be treated as a person
The right to be treated as a grownup
The right to have our say about our own life
The right to a fair chance on our merits
The right to a future
The right to have fun and companions
The right to be romantic
The right to the help of one's family in becoming interesting to that family
The right to professional help whenever necessary
The right to be old."(3)

Which ones will your own relative regard as first in importance? And how are you going to help him get them?

You'll find some hints in the answers which a psychologist collected when he interviewed men and women, ranging in age from sixty to ninety. They thought most old people could be kept off the highroad to gloom and unhappiness if they had these compensations:

Bodily health: This came first. The fear of being helplessly bedridden and dependent is not confined to any age group, but it can be more poignant when life's satisfactions are nearly at an end.

Health of the spirit: This was named as a close second. Other studies have proved that the hunger to be at peace with one's self, to discover justification for the world's ills and man's inhumanity to man, is a regular and striking accompanient of that phase of life we term growing older. This need may or may not be met by organized religious activity. Many elders in this and other groups complain that houses of worship, like employers and their own families, push them aside and disregard their assets.

A cheerful state of mind: This stood third on the list. A great many considered that it was important to accept what we cannot alter. The words "be patient" occurred often. (Possibly with the younger generation.)

Money: It is a rare old person who has not learned early in life that money will not purchase his happiness in old age. Nonetheless, this appeared fourth among the list of sources of contentment because it was found to be a matter of deep concern. What these and all other aging people want is to have enough to cover their bare necessities and be free of concern for the future. (This is natural enough when you consider the figures disclosed in the 1950 census. More than three-fourths of all persons over sixty-five years old, who lived alone or with non-relatives, had a cash income of less than $1,000 annually. Nearly forty per cent had less than $500.)

Friends: This word appeared often. Its use is based on the sad fact that the longer we live the more friends and relatives we survive. It also is a result of the equally sad law of life that we, who as youngsters looked for love and support from our elders, seldom need either when they are old and we ourselves are adult.

Work to do: Every normal person wants an occupation as long as he lives, and dreads idleness. The whole gamut of desires in this field is summed up in the remark of one octogenarian. Mr. X., aged eighty-two, protested against being forced to be idle against his will, and accepted a pension with reluctance. "Working hard," he declared, "playing hard, loving hard—that's what makes people happy!"

Pleasant family relationships: Those who had once enjoyed the warmth and intimacy with close kin and no longer had it felt, as one man says, "like trees left to face the elements unprotected." All of them voiced the same old cry—they wanted to be treated as an active part of the world, living and struggling with the rest of us. "My family," said one septuagenarian, "instead of giving me things to do, pampers me, treats me like china just too fragile for use."

A chance to watch young people develop: All older people confessed their pleasure and interest in their grandchildren, and other people's children—when they were on good terms with them. As one seventy-five-year-old man said, "It gives a person satisfaction to be able to see his children and his grandchildren grow up and know you have had some part in shaping their lives. It makes him feel that when he dies, he will not altogether leave this world."

Doing things for others: Not every person in this or any other group recognizes services as a compensation of old age. But those who had always found pleasure in thinking of others named this quality ninth on their list, and considered it an important means of continuing to "belong" to society.

Kindness and consideration: A number said this was all they sought—and seldom received.

The question for which you will have to find a permanent answer if you want to live in peace, is this: *How can you help your relatives fulfill these basic desires without encroaching on the rights of a younger generation?*

It is not a trite phrase to say you can do nothing at all unless you put yourself in an older person's place. To do so, you have to rid yourself of the misconceptions concerning old age that most of us had hammered into us in childhood. The chief of them is that to be young is a virtue; to be old is deplorable.

MISCONCEPTIONS ABOUT OLD AGE

Old age makes people different. This is the commonest misconception of all.

Most of us fall into the pit of assuming that putting on grandmotherhood or grandfatherhood automatically assures a halo of sweetness and light. Or we take the opposite view, and our differences with older people occur when we try to fit them into a mold in the belief that old age makes them crabbed.

Two thousand years ago, Cicero had an answer for this. He said: "The complaints on this score, as well as the trouble with relatives, may all be referred to one cause, and that is not the age . . . but the character of men. . . . As it is not every wine, so it is not every disposition that grows sour with age."(4)

If we have had pleasant experiences with old men and women in our childhood we accept the stereotype when we are adult and think of the aged as docile, unselfish. If we remember unpleasant episodes, we believe, as did the majority in Cicero's time, that the common description of all old people is "morose, troubled, fretful, and hard to please."

Actually, the only thing you can be really sure of is that any elderly man or woman has taken a long time to get the way he is, and he is going to remain that way. The father who was a young autocrat at the breakfast and every other table will remain so. The mother who was frivolous and vain in her twenties and thirties is not going to turn into a sweet, self-effacing old granny. And, of course, the opposite has to be true. The man or woman who has always pulled his own oar is going to try to keep on doing it, and he will have regard for the rights of everybody else. He'll probably be like the sturdy seventy-year-old ex-school teacher who told a Chautauqua audience: "I don't want to be re-tired; I just want to be re-treaded!"

The old like to be in a safe and cozy nest. This is the second major misconception most of us hold, and probably accounts for more unhappy relationships than all the rest.

No older person likes to have his life planned for him, whether his children tuck him away in an old people's home, or put him in a gilded cage they preside over themselves. Naturally, if you have been going to great lengths to protect your father and mother from draughts and grocery bills, or "fuss" when they wet their feet or go shopping alone, they will become used to your silken chain. They may be resigned to it in time—or even learn to like it.

Dr. Lillien J. Martin, who entered the field of old age counselling when she herself was past sixty-five, and continued in it till she died at the age of ninety-two, used to say many older people are forced into loss of self-assurance by their own offspring.

"Children," she said, "may coddle aged parents, not only out of concern for their health and well-being, but also because they really want their parents to live restricted lives so they will not interfere with young people's conduct of their own lives and families."

Most older people, Dr. Martin found, are remarkably tough and capable, even if they have physical limitations—where their independence has not been blunted by over-solicitude.

A man like Ira E. Bennett, for instance, at the age of eighty was still considered a good enough writer and newspaperman to be named staff consultant of the House Foreign Affairs Committee. This kind of push and drive is not necessarily limited to one sex.

Mrs. Lillian S. Loveland—who would never describe herself as an unusual woman—found seventy-seven years no deterrent to adventure. When she went around the world in a freighter, she wrote of her travels with such gusto that a leading Boston newspaper printed them and eventually she won a journalism award for her homely, heart-warming reports.

If your family members have this kind of initiative, preserve it. The chief breeding-ground of friction is the absence of something to do which will seem important in the eyes of the old and commands respect from those—as one youngster said—who think of old age as "the wilted butt of a burned-out cigarette."

Don't expect an older person to accept a seat on the side-lines with good humor. It is no easier at eighty to be told you are "too old" for something than it was for you to give up thumb-sucking at one or two because you were told you were "too old" for that pastime. It is more difficult, in fact. For to sit back and accept direction—very often correction—from those you used to have authority over in the diaper and romper stage, is a soul-trying process and very few can be philosophical about it.

Old people expect too much. This is the third major misconception which most of us hold. When we say "tolerance must be mutual," we usually mean we expect older people to leave off some cherished activity which interferes with one of ours. We would also like them to do so without making us feel guilty or uncomfortable.

The daughters and sons of Mr. Manetti, the Italian grocer, were perfectly right when they said the huge, clumsy furniture he and his dead wife had brought from the "old country" would clutter up their apartments. His fellow-countryman from Sorrento, now a barber in an obscure neighborhood in New York, had more understanding. He knew the meaning and associations those old pieces had for the bereaved widower. So when the old gentleman left for good or ill to live in a more fashionable neighborhood with one of his daughters, he was allowed to install a nearly ceiling-high clothes press and a towering grandfather clock in the back of his friend's barbershop. There the two old cronies meet occasionally to smoke together and talk—there Mr. Manetti really lives.

Not all of us can achieve the Olympian point of view. Yet most of us can say of a fourteen-year-old boy or girl who has difficulty in adjusting to life: "Well, it is just because he is an adolescent. He'll get used to things." We ought to know that people of seventy or eighty are also entitled to have periods of adjustment. The reason is obvious. They have already spent a lifetime accumulating habits and patterns.

It is true that almost any man or woman can be uprooted late in years, even against his will, and take on the color and tempo of a new life. But if, while he is doing it, his opinions seem outrageous, or his actions irritating, exercise self-control. You ought to be able to do it because you are more pliable, more adaptable, and above all, more *used* to this hectic existence which is all anyone under fifty knows.

It means believing that if an old man refuses to change his socks or stop smoking in bed, or an old woman won't change the fashion of her clothes or her cooking, neither is doing it, like the baby in *Alice in Wonderland,* merely to annoy and tease you. They may be biologically too old to change their ways, or they may be making an effort to adjust themselves and haven't yet succeeded. If you force them beyond their strength the result is likely to be a dejected individual, bitter because he thinks himself useless and unwanted, often so miserable he places everybody around him in the same lower depths.

No old person is like any other old person, but there is one thing on which they all agree. No matter where they live, whether in luxury or in poverty, they don't want to relinquish their own identity. If this seems to you to be "asking too much," consider that, if you live, you yourself will be old some day. It will help you be more tolerant of what you see now as the old-foginess of your elders.

TO LIVE OR NOT TO LIVE TOGETHER?

Should you be willing to share your home with your parents, or your spouse's parents?

This is one of the most difficult problems in family relationships that any of us have to solve. There are thousands of families which include grandparents who live happily with their offspring and the latter's children. Generally speaking, however, the comment of one spry seventy-six-year-old woman sums up the real (though often unexpressed) attitude of the person most affected.

When Mrs. Matthews was asked whether she lived with her son and daughter-in-law, she answered, "No, *they* live with me, and I can tell you there's a world of difference between those two situations!"

There is no reason to feel guilty if you are apprehensive about sharing your home. There are other ways of honoring your father and mother besides giving them a place around your fireside. Nor is there any reason for you to feel you must do for your older relatives what they did for theirs. Two or three generations had a much better chance fifty or even thirty years ago of living amicably together. When households overflowed with children and space, there was always ample work and ample room for a spinster aunt or an aging uncle. In communities which lacked the distractions of radio, television, moving pictures, automobiles, and airplane travel, home life was more placid and more close-knit. The older person of either sex could, figuratively, rock the cradle with one hand and chop wood with the other, and in addition, be a social asset.

Today, if someone is needed to help with the housework or the children it usually is not on the full-time, living-in basis. Nursery schools and machine-housekeeping have taken away that solace of the old.

You may be a loving daughter or an affectionate son with tender memories of a sheltered childhood, and still find an older person in the house a burden. To ask anyone in the last third of his life to live where he has to compete for attention, as it were, with labor-saving devices and a streamlined life, or where he is "beholden" for extra attentions, is to invite friction where none existed before.

ADVANTAGES VS. DISADVANTAGES

The mother-in-law jokes probably had their inception in the fact that people of different ages are better off if they live apart.

On the other hand, they can live together successfully if there is an "even exchange." It may be the practical advantage of a single overhead with reduction in cost of food, service, repairs and taxes. Many a young couple can keep up with the Joneses only because someone living with them fattens their bank account. Or there may be good points about sharing work and responsibilities. No older person is a dead weight if he adds his strength in time of trouble or shares interests in time of joy.

We need to bring back to our children one of the things we moderns have been deprived of. Too many of us lack the feeling that the "family" is many people, with the peace and security this gave our grandparents when they leaned on younger generations, and were leaned on, in turn.

In Pierre Loti's autobiography of his childhood, *Le Roman d'un Enfant,* he describes the happiness and the serenity he derived from the presence of his two grandmothers, his great-aunt Berthe, and his Aunt Claire, each with her own little room. How his mother got along with these four extra women he does not say, but to him, at least, they were a source of endless comfort.

Something of this warm security and well-being can be preserved even today, as the remarks of one little five-year-old boy show. In a forced "merger" during the last war, the Forrest household consisted of Mrs. Forrest's mother, her sister, a hitherto-unknown ten-year-old niece from England, Mr. and Mrs. Forrest, and their two small boys. It was the youngest who said one Sunday morning, looking around the expanded breakfast table, "I *like* living like this. It's cozy!"

Large dividends like this require large capital, and to make a success of a mixed household requires mutual esteem, mutual respect for each other's privacy as well as joy in each other's company. Without all these ingredients nothing will result but turmoil.

From the point of view of the older person himself the picture is also hazardous. Even a room with a view and a bathroom all his own can never compensate for a step down from independence. He may think he *ought* to like living with his loving children and still make them conscious that he resents the restrictions on his freedom which inevitably must follow.

If your mother or mother-in-law can do what Mrs. Harcourt did, the problem is greatly simplified. She was tired of living in an apartment hotel. She offered to lend her son some of her capital if he would build a house (which she knew her daughter-in-law wanted), and fit up a separate, small cottage for her, a quite small one. The son, who was short of cash, readily agreed. Today the Harcourts live near each other on five acres of ground, but separately. Mrs. Harcourt's income is enough to support her in the tiny apartment which is a converted garage. She has what every older person really wants—her own home, her own meals how and when she chooses, her own friends, her family close at hand—but no children underfoot, unless she herself wants them, which, happily, is often. She is a willing (but entirely voluntary) baby-sitter.

Lacking this ideal situation, the next best method of achieving mutual support is compromise. It usually exists where two people who have arrived at different stages along life's road are willing to admit openly to each other they'd rather live separately, but since they can't, they'd better make the most of it. As jolly Mrs. Finlandia said, when she'd had to move in with her daughter-in-law after her husband's death, "I gif up my European way of cooking, and Anna, she let me rock the baby the old-fashioned way, so we get along!"

OLDER PEOPLE'S RIGHTS

If, however, your own relative hates the idea of being shipped from one place to another, stand up for him. It's not easy to see why an old man prefers a shabby furnished room to luxury under someone's gilded roof, or to accede to an old woman's desire to stand on her own two feet in a decrepit neighborhood. But it is better than browbeating them into a move they protest against.

If it is you who fear friction, steel yourself to look for another place for a relative to live, even if you have to face family criticism. It's more than possible your own distaste for too close proximity is shared.

If you need to bolster your conviction by some unassailable

facts, examine these results from some recent surveys. They may bring about a change of mind in others of your family if they are mistaking "duty" for what is right.

All grandfathers and grandmothers do not want to be around their children or grandchildren all the time.

When the Florida State Improvement Commission asked eight hundred retired persons in St. Petersburg what their preferences in living arrangements were, these were the answers: (*a*) About forty-five per cent said they preferred to associate exclusively with people their own age. (*b*) Some twenty per cent preferred the society of younger adults. (*c*) None preferred the society of children. (*d*) Only twenty-eight per cent wanted to associate with people of all ages.(5)

Older people value their own homes first, and privacy at all costs anywhere.

When the housing likes and dislikes of fifty aging people in Manhattan, Kansas, were investigated, this was the interviewer's conclusion: "These aged couples were reluctant to face the problem of where and how to live in the event that maintaining their own homes was no longer feasible. Actually, living in their own homes was the only preference they could be persuaded to voice. If this arrangement was not possible, even with the services of a companion, they wanted *separate quarters* in the home of a son or daughter."(6)

The best place in the gamut of living arrangements for older people is wherever they want to stay.

This may be—but often is not—with their relatives.

When Dr. Ruth Shonle Cavan studied their living arrangements, she scored elderly people on how well they adapted to various situations. She found that twenty-nine per cent of the men and thirty per cent of the woman who lived in their own homes were well adjusted. Of those who lived in someone else's home, the proportion of those who had made a good adjustment (based on a ten-item, composite score) was eleven per cent of the men and twenty-four per cent of the women. The rating of those who called rooming or boardinghouses or hotels home was only slightly different. Just twelve per cent of the men and thirty-two per cent of the women who lived in this impersonal environment had adjusted themselves to it well.(7)

GOOD RELATIONSHIPS AT A DISTANCE

It takes courage of the sort one young bride had to defy tradition and the custom of the family. You need to be prepared for "back talk" and "black looks" as she was.

When a family council was called to discuss how to make "granny" and "gramp" give up their tiny flat in the inelegant neighborhood of the Chicago stockyards, the new granddaughter spoke up and said they ought to stay there. The babel of dissent that followed was led by the prosperous son who had offered his parents a suite of rooms in a hotel.

The new bride, an ex-social worker, held to her opinion. The "in-laws," even her husband, looked askance, but the aged couple blessed her. Encouraged by her firmness, they, too, stood firm. Eventually they were separated by death but before that time came, thanks to a stout-hearted young woman, they had had a few years more together in the one place which to them spelled home.

If you are the one on whose shoulders it will fall to make a decision, there is only one safe rule to follow. If an aging individual doesn't *want* to live with you or someone else, it is more economical, in terms of the eventual strain that will develop on both sides, to help him stay where he wants to be, even if dollars-and-cents expenditure is greater.

Physical or geographical separation is not the same as emotional separation (which can occur even when two bodies occupy the same space, or nearly so.) It is still possible to go to the movies or a play or to church together if you live in the same community. If the older person lives far away, you can make him feel he has a real, not a forced part in your own life by writing to ask his advice about real estate or insurance or by confiding your troubles to him. We all need to learn that where a person lives is not the major consideration. Making him know he is valued for what he is and was is all that counts. You can do this through such a simple gesture as asking an old man to write down his memories of family history, or by helping an old woman cherish family heirlooms for her grandchildren. One woman stimulated her whole community when she asked people over seventy to present, arrange, and talk about their relics of pioneer days for her club. This exhibition, now held annually, gives young people a chance to see and hear about local history and to respect their elders who shaped it.

RULES FOR LIVING TOGETHER

Whatever form it takes, a good relationship is not born; it has to be cultivated. There are circumstances which make living together the only workable solution. If that is your case, look your situation in the face. Before you make the irrevocable decision, be sure you have threshed out all its implications.

A grandmother, who is not an old fogey but an intelligent, cultivated woman in her thinking and in her appearance, sits day after day on a Central Park bench. One day she confided in a park acquaintance, also watching children play.

"I'm wanted in my daughter's home," she remarked, "because 'nice people' have to want to take care of their old parents. But I am not really wanted at all. I'm supposed to act just like a piece of furniture, not to bother anybody, and not to embarrass the family by trying to earn a place for myself in somebody else's home."

The daughter, in her turn, is horrified because her parent proposed to work as someone else's housekeeper (even though that would give her independence in the only way she knows how to earn a living). She thinks her mother unappreciative of the good home she and her husband are offering for the rest of her mother's life.

If you are on the outside of this situation it is not difficult to see that the truth lies somewhere between these extreme points of view. But if it is your problem, you can solve it in advance if you are willing to be entirely frank, not only with yourself (which is hard enough) but with the other person. If you are already on sufficiently good terms to confess that both of you will have to work hard to escape evil consequences, you are well along the way to finding out how to avoid them.

Dr. Mary Fisher Langmuir of Vassar College, who directs the Summer Institute for parents and their children, believes that peace in the family does not mean an absence of conflicts or problems.

"Instead," she says, "peaceful, friendly, and satisfying family life comes about when all members accept problems as normal, and learn to work together toward their solution." Some of the sound rules she advocates imply "accepting all members of the family, from baby to grandparents, as first-class citizens, each with appropriate rights, privileges and responsibilities."

RULE #1: *Discuss grievances openly.*

More than two thousand years ago Socrates said that "the children now love luxury, they have bad manners and contempt for authority. . . ."

Since that time millions of aunts, uncles, parents, and grandparents have played variations on the same theme. It is not always possible to control young folks' irritation when they think they are being criticized or their anger when they think their privileges are being taken away, but it ought to be possible to eliminate the situations that give rise to these emotions.

This is one of those cases where crossing a bridge before you come to it is a precaution. Practise family planning. Bring your own and your children's grievances out in the open. It is not any easier for an older person to hide hurt feelings, if he is termed "too indulgent" with the children or "too strict," than it is for you, if you are called "too extravagant" or "too fond of a good time." But if you encourage informal family conferences where decisions that affect everybody are reached openly after discussion and mutual compromise there is less danger of domination by any one member. Even a benevolent autocrat has enemies, and dictatorship by mother, father, or grandparent falls in the same category.

Start by including older people in conversations. Make them feel they are *part* of the family circle at the outset and their ego won't have to draw attention to itself by being unpleasant.

One grandmother wrote to a leading newspaper deploring the fashion of putting older people out to pasture.

"I simply can't understand," she wrote, "the attitude of the current generation which my own generation produced. It's not disrespect. It's not scorn. Rather it's utter indifference and disregard."

She lived in the home of her son because her small income would not take care of her anywhere else. When she wanted to support herself by taking a job after her husband's death, her son demurred. "What would my friends say?" he demanded.

So Mrs. F. was given a small room at the top of the house, and a place at the family table. No one ever argues with her and no one complains about her. The adults and their children come and go, sometimes telling her their objective, sometimes saying nothing; sometimes taking her with them, more often leaving her behind. As she wrote, somewhat grimly, "I am prepared to be tolerated for the rest of my life. My children and my children's children endure me, but they don't enjoy me."

There are two sides to this story, too. But when you know that sore points gain in exaggerated importance every day they are allowed to be repeated, you can anticipate or get rid of them. In your family conferences make a point of asking old people about household matters that don't arouse irritation in young listeners. It may be nothing more important than what to have for Sunday dinner, or what neighbors to invite to tea. But it will not be so difficult to go on from there to discuss the touchy matter of who is or who is not to be present when young people entertain, or who has first right to the Sunday newspaper or the bathroom.

Granted such things are all unimportant. Nevertheless, most family wars, as well as most international ones, are touched off by nothing more than "incidents."

RULE #2: *Don't turn a blind eye or a deaf ear toward frustrations of older people.*

One woman in her late seventies was transported from her small-town life and kitchen garden to her son's suburban house. She was terrified in this sophisticated "station wagon" atmosphere where everything seemed to be done in a hurry, even the cooking.

This latter-day Cinderella was humiliated to overhear her little grandson comment on her old-fashioned ways when she refused to eat frozen foods. Her offers to help with the housework in this establishment where there are two capable maids evoked only the remark, "Why, mother, we don't expect you to do anything!"

Within a few months this woman, who had been alert and capable enough in her own former limited environment, had deteriorated into a discontented, unhappy scold, whom her grandchildren avoided and her own children resented.

As her son said to his sister when he urged her to take their mother off his hands, "We do everything for her and yet she is never satisfied!"

What he might have said was that everything had been done to cushion the comfort of the old lady but nothing at all to keep her from turning into a futilitarian.

The point needs to be labored. For we are all inclined to take credit for providing grandma and grandpa with an expensive radio or television set of their own. Or we even feel virtuous when we include them in a beach excursion or take them along to the theatre. It is much easier to provide such passive, rich diet of entertainment than it is to bestir ourselves to see that older people have a job in the household that is interesting to them, worth doing for its own sake, and useful to someone else. However, if you do make the effort, no person is going to say, as did one old man with too much leisure, "You do not live longer nowadays; it only seems longer!"

Helping an older person find himself doesn't have to mean martyrdom for the family. If old folks are fussy and you think they interfere too much, encourage them to live their own lives, to keep up an interest in church and clubs, make their own friends, have their own fun. Then they won't hamper yours. If they have a room of their own, or a place to do their own entertaining, however modest, they'll develop fewer irritating habits and mannerisms. If they are invalids or stay-at-homes, you can still turn over some tasks they are competent to handle, real chores that are burdensome to someone else. (Old people can detect "made work" as readily as children.)

One harried mother of five children said to her fellow-club

members when she entertained them, "I couldn't have done this or a good many other things if it weren't for father!"

Father can go no farther than from his bed to his chair. Nonetheless he can shell the peas, peel the potatoes, read aloud to the small non-school child, and help the older ones with their stamp collection or arithmetic. He is always ready to fill in at Canasta or bridge when the elders need an extra hand. He does not think it beneath his masculine dignity to wheel himself into the kitchen to wipe dishes when the younger people are in a hurry to go out, or to clean the silver before a party. He is useful and he knows it; he is loved and he is happy.

Relatives frequently come to an old people's home or a nursing home with a florid picture of their past differences with a cantankerous, overbearing older person in mind. They are very often surprised that in the new environment he is neither hard to live with nor hard to please. His essential nature has not changed. But even a cantankerous man or woman will seem less so when he lives with those who not only allow him to air his opinions, but make him feel that what he has to say is worth listening to, and what he does is worth doing.

Doing your bit to give an older person under your roof a full life is not all on the debit side, by an means. It may be very useful to know there is always someone who will cope with the involved telephone message, the insistent salesman at the door, or to have the assurance that someone *likes* to do the mending, the weeding, or the marketing.

Not all older people are so willing, or so able to adapt themselves to a square hole. Nevertheless, if you want to see whatever capacities an older person has continue at their optimum, and expect him to contribute to your own family life, you must be willing to do what a trained occupational therapist does. She is always trying to find at what level, however low, a patient's energies can be organized and directed into channels of activity from which he will obtain emotional satisfaction.

RULE #3: *Don't have differences over disciplining children.* We expect our parents to be grateful that years have brought

them the privilege of ignoring irksome details that rearing the most beloved of children involve. But their tempers may be short (or they say their hearts are breaking) because they can't stand to see their grandchildren following what they deem is a wrong road. One strong-minded grandfather speaks for a multitude:

"It's difficult to watch a child being brought up in a way you don't approve of. I see these little brats I love coming into a room with muddy shoes, climbing all over guests, marking up furniture, and I think they belong to the wild animal kingdom. Well, I understand I am of the past generation. I don't foist my ideas on my daughter, but I do express myself when I'm asked—though that's all too rarely!"

That plaint would sound familiar to any man or woman in the sixties or seventies who has had a difference of opinion over the way children should be disciplined.

For one of the hardest facts for older people to face is that the ways and methods of their generation may not always be expedient or wise for their children's children. If you are a sensible young person you will take the advice of your elders—with modifications. A great deal of it will be good, but some of it won't fit in with your mode of living. In your grandparents' youth, for instance, there did not need to be rules concerning the etiquette of television use after school, and no arguments could exist about automobiles. These are the types of problems that can best be handled by the generation which evoked them.

The principles of right living, however, go on unchanged from generation to generation. If your parents' teachings have helped you carry the burden of life, you will welcome the chance to have them impart their ethics to your own children.

In the practical, everyday give and take, exercise common sense (with a dash of humor if you can summon it), and you won't live at cross-purposes. Expect your elders to love and cherish your offspring but don't expect them to act as your proxies whenever you want to go out. Nature never intended that a seventy or a seventy-five year old should enjoy the antics of a sixteen-year-old "hot rod" enthusiast or a four-year-old space demon. It is not a sin, either, if they want peace and quiet. An older person needs to have

his meals and his conversations uninterrupted, without pauses to hear you correct a child's manners or to correct them himself. If you are a twenty-five-year-old or even a forty-five-year-old parent, you can stand the noise and confusion and the joyful hilarity of your offspring. You have the nerves and the stamina.

If you do turn the children over to their spinster aunt or their grandparents at frequent intervals while you enjoy a respite, then don't expect them to rear your little rascals the way you think they should be brought up. No fashion changes faster or more radically than the fashion of handling children. Don't look for too much forbearance with today's mode of child-raising from someone whose own childhood is long past.

If you understand this, and make allowances for it, you may even have the pleasant experience of Mrs. Richmond. She had dreaded her mother-in-law's extended visit but did not realize how frankly and how often she had expressed her fears till the school social worker called on her. The worker reported that Bobby's second-grade teacher had heard him tell his neighbor, "Mama tells papa she's going to fight with grandma!"

Three months after Mrs. Richmond, Sr.'s arrival, however, this is what the daughter-in-law wrote the social worker who had counselled patience.

"I never realized till mother came how much petting the children had missed. They were born at a period when we parents were taught to raise them by rule and by book. Since mother arrived I've learned not only to 'play' with Bobby and his two little sisters more, but also with my husband. Mother has taken over some of the housekeeping tasks I used to think came first. My husband and I hope she'll stay all year!"

RULE #4: *Treat damages of old age with tenderness.*

This rule embodies all the rest. Old age doesn't have to be miserable and forlorn but it often is. One of the reasons is that we either make sharp answers when we are provoked "beyond endurance," or we try to "make up" by over-solicitude for what we cannot freely give the elderly, or what they can no longer get for themselves.

What action should you take? Should you ignore the symptoms as mere manifestations of old age? Should you go out of your way to impress on the children and remind yourself they have to endure grandma's tantrums or grandpa's surliness?

Neither solution is right. Both are hard on old and young alike. However, since the former have far less resilience, they are the ones who suffer most from family feuds. Since they generally have far more leisure than young people to dwell on their grievances, they are likely to nurse them longer, so it behooves you to ward them off.

Someone once said, "Every period of life has its peculiar torments. Babies often seem unhappy and are helpless to do anything about it; adolescence is full of despair and agony; maturity is a chain of worries and disillusions; while old age appears to be a cross between debility and isolation."

Notice, however, the word is "appears."

There is no natural law which requires old people to be set apart. Instead of saying, "Aunt Mehitabel and Uncle William are certainly not what they used to be!" give them a chance to get used to your new ideas. Remember the aging process in itself is a strain. In it the individual undergoes changes in his physical, mental, and emotional make-up, as many, and sometimes as violent as those in adolescence. And his behavior is likely to be as erratic. He may even use those defense weapons common to every age, from babyhood on. He may complain about ill-health or fatigue simply as a protest against his difficulty in a new environment, or as an unconscious attempt to draw attention to his need for tenderness and affection in a trying time.

Suppose, for instance, that Aunt Mehitabel invariably appears at family functions wearing a shabby dress *circa* 1900 when you know she has a half-dozen new ones you or some other relatives have given her. A psychologist might say Aunt Mehitabel is hoarding her possessions, as a squirrel hoards nuts, because she wants to make sure there will always be a supply, if not of the love she craves, at least of material goods. If you knew she wasn't taunting you with her poverty wouldn't you be more tolerant of her peccadilloes?

Or couldn't you look with a less jaundiced eye on Uncle William's attempts to flirt with every young girl who passes by if you realize he is only trying to comfort himself for his lost youth and present unimportance?

A good physician listens to old people's complaints about their backaches, their falling hair, their heart palpitations, or their indigestion. He is looking not only for a clue to their physical condition but to their state of mind and emotions. Then he tries to treat all three. It may be only a harmless tablet that sends mother away happy because someone at last has paid attention to her when she said she had daily headaches (which he realizes are born out of her unhappiness). Or it may be possible that she needs a cataract or a goiter operation, and he has to soothe her fears. In either case, he shows interest; he gives full attention to her outpouring of woes; he comprehends that the turmoil in the world which has torn security away from the young has played even more havoc with the lives of the old.

If you want to smooth rough places in your relationships you will have to assume the same attitude. From a practical point of view there is much you can do to help someone overcome disabilities or outwit frustrations. (There is an old proverb worth remembering: "Everybody knows the toughness of an old chicken.")

Something which most of us either ignore or forget is that many disabilities of old age are common also in other periods of life. They can be overcome by the same means. Accept the fact that all senses become less acute in an older person and do something about it, as you would if the same thing happened in a child's life. There is no reason why an old man should be left out of conversations or an old woman forego concerts as long as there are hearing aids which can be bought. If he needs spectacles or books with large print, get them and insist on his using them—act just as you would for a younger person you would keep mentally alert.

Doctors use the authority of their medical knowledge to enforce their advice. Your weapons have to be understanding, affection, even sternness if that is needed to make an old person learn to use a crutch or a brace. A shawl, an electric pad or a heater for an old body that feels the cold, or a skin lotion for old flesh that bruises easily, are very small attentions. But they mean the concern and sympathy which can help to keep even the closest of ties from wearing thin.

THE GOAL OF LIFE

The challenge of learning to live in amity with those the world labels "old" concerns us and our families now, and will concern us even more personally when we pass that artificial barrier, our own sixty-fifth birthday. For old age is no phenomenon from another world. It is we ourselves in the not very distant future.

There is no formula of the "how to make friends" variety which will provide you with a quick solution. But if there can be recognition on the part of members of the family that here indeed "charity begins at home" a genuine start will have been made toward relieving some tensions and difficulties which the old and the young alike frequently experience.

The effects of extreme old age cannot be warded off forever; the machine will eventually wear out. But with the right kind of help from family, physician and community, an older man or woman can postpone physical, mental and emotional decline for years.

When Cicero wrote his discourse on old age, one of the characters said to Cato, the protagonist: "You will do us a very great favor if . . . you would allow us to learn from you, in good time before it arrives, by what methods we may most easily acquire the strength to support the burden of advancing age."

Our goal must be to help those to whom our responsibility is greatest make that "burden of advancing age" less, for their sakes, and for our own.

NOTES TO CHAPTER 1

(1) U. S. Bureau of Census estimates, Nov. 1952. Also figures from Statistical Bureau, Metropolitan Life Insurance Company, based on computations from U. S. Bureau of Vital Statistics, July, 1953; "Some facts about Our Aging Population." Washington, D. C.; National Conference on Aging, Aug., 1950.

(2) Ackernecht, Erwin, M.D. Address at Northwestern University's Centennial Conference, June 7, 1951 on "Problems of an Aging Population."

(3) A paraphrase of Dr. George Lawton's chapter from *Aging Successfully,* published in its entirety, as "A Bill of Rights for Old Age," in the *Journal of Gerontology,* Jan. 1947.

(4) Cicero. *De Senectute.*

(5) "The Sponsored Neighborhood Village in Florida." Florida State Improvement Commission, 1951.

(6) Anderson, Elinor Murphy. "Existing and Preferred Housing of Aged Couples of Moderate Income in Manhattan, Kansas." An abstract of a thesis, Kansas State College of Agriculture & Applied Science, 1939.

(7) Cavan, Ruth S. "Family Life and Family Substitutes in Old Age." *American Sociology Review,* Feb. 1949. P. 83.

CHAPTER TWO

WHAT IS NORMAL OLD AGE?

Are deafness, failing vision, a slow gait, and a stoop the sure and certain signs of aging? Is the traditional picture of an elderly person as a forgetful, sometimes suspicious, often irritable, and frequently intolerant person (a portrait painted originally by Aristotle) a true one? Does the mind invariably fail and the personality disintegrate if a man or woman lives to extreme old age?

These are questions which can haunt any of us who see people we love show evidences of the wear and tear accumulated through decades of living.

What *is* normal in old age?

The answer is that aging is a period of life, just as distinct as the growth of the pre-school child or the development of the adolescent. Consequently people in the aging period, like the children, have certain similarities and characteristics which make a pattern. We need to get acquainted with it if we are to understand old people now and find out what is in store for ourselves. But generalizations in this field, as in any other, are fatal. "Normal" old age is like "normal" youth or maturity. That is to say, old age is not all decline and loss any more than all youth is necessarily growth and bloom. All old people don't fall ill, nor are all of them incapable of change, any more than all younger men and women are healthy or sick, progressive or conservative.

Your relative may be prematurely aged in contrast with his contemporaries. Or he may show none of the signs of enfeeblement you may have expected. He may act older than he is or be a good deal younger than he looks. Successful aging is a process of balancing assets against liabilities, as at any other time of life, and the range of individual variation is just as great then as earlier.

As former Federal Security Administrator, Oscar R. Ewing, remarked, "There is no scientific definition of old age, so far as the human body is concerned. What we are dealing with is not a group of people who are 'old' but a group of people who are merely labeled 'old' by others, even though their capacities differ widely."

OLD PEOPLE ARE INDIVIDUALS

The first thing to get firmly into your mind is that the old today are not going to resemble the pictures of your progenitors in the family album. In 1900, men and women in their early forties often looked and acted old, and a man in his sixties was considered a hoary ancient. Medical advances have made tremendous differences in our ability to withstand decrepitude. Such minor things as grooming, dress, cosmetics, and increased use of dentistry have also tremendously changed the appearance and the attitudes of "normal" old people of today compared with yesterday.

The second point to grasp once and for all is that sixty-five is still commonly accepted as the debut of old age, but it actually is an anachronism. An individual who is sixty-five may feel, even if he doesn't look, like forty-five, and his youthful outlook may match his body, or an eighty-five year old may be quite capable of activities his parent would have relinquished twenty years before, even if he looks his age.

This is one of the most difficult concepts for anyone under seventy—and sometimes over that—to accept as true and act on. Most of us lump all old people together. That is why so many of us are surprised when we marry—or are born—into a family which has a Miss Julia, when we find someone like Thomas Kubler (whom we secretly like a good deal better).

Every sunny morning, and often on stormy ones, Mr. Kubler goes to the butcher and the grocery store with his shopping bag on his arm. With his white hair floating like a nimbus around his hatless head, he looks like an old cherub. On his eighty-eighth birthday he invited the ladies on his block to tea. He spurned their offers of help and served as plentiful and as neat a repast in his spotless one-room-and-kitchenette apartment as a person half his age.

Miss Julia, on the other hand, leans heavily on her delicate condition. She is nearly always querulous, forever sh-h-ing her niece and nephew, with whom she lives. She complains incessantly about the noise their children make. Old and ill-tempered—and only sixty-eight.

Which of these two is aging normally?

The truth is each of them is "doing what comes naturally." And what comes naturally in old age is continuing to do what we have been doing in the past. Some people who have always taken care of their health, who have been making good adjustments to the realities which life has presented in youth and middle age, like Mr. Kubler, can slide easily into old age. Others, like Miss Julia, who have inherited or acquired a frail constitution, dwell on it. Perhaps because of it, they have always made demands or dominated people around them.

HOW OLD IS OLD?

Do you really know how old your relative is, and whether, as the children say, he is old "all over"?

Ask any person how he can tell when a person has aged and he'll probably say he thinks he knows it if a man or woman has a wrinkled, flabby skin, if he walks and thinks and speaks deliberately, if his voice has altered in pitch and quality. He will be sure of it if he finds someone is hard of hearing, forgets names of people he has been introduced to, and is "set" in his ways.

Scientists are not so dogmatic. They recommend that you think it over. Like the lady in the train, you may have a surprise. She looked at the little boy sitting next to his mother, and inquired, "How old is your son?" The answer she received was lengthier, and possibly more illuminating, than she had expected.

"Physically, he's ten years old. Emotionally, he's about seven. Intellectually, he is fifteen. Counting birthdays," the mother concluded, "he'll be nine years old next week."

The serious little boy who was seven, ten, fifteen, and nine years old is an illustration of the only two generalizations scientists say you can make about aging and be certain you are right:

1. *There are wide differences in the rate of aging of cells, tissues, and organs between individuals, even if they have the same heredity.*

2. *There are differences in the rate and amount of aging of cells, tissues, and organs within the same individual.*

In non-technical language, those two statements mean just this:

There is no one day or one year in which a person suddenly becomes old. By the time any individual has reached the age of sixty-five or seventy his whole personality, body, and brain, have seen years of service and begin to show it. Aging cannot be staved off forever. Everybody, regardless of vitamins, hormones, tissue culture, or cosmetics, eventually has depleted physical energies and accumulates damages to cells and tissues—but at an uneven rate.

One geriatrician compares the later years to a footrace. If the stop signal were given every participant would be at a different point. No one ages in exactly the same way as his neighbor, and not necessarily at the same time. Each person's skin, intestines, brain, muscles, arteries, and bones have their own ways of getting on with this business of growing old. And each continues to be an individual—physically, mentally, and emotionally—in the last year of his life as his first.

Dr. C. Ward Crampton, Chairman of the sub-Committee on Geriatrics of the Committee on Public Health of the New York County Medical Society, sums up the process in this epigram: "A sixty-year-old man may have a forty-year-old heart, an eighty-year-old liver, fifty-year-old kidneys, and may be trying to live a thirty-year-old life!"(1)

AGING TODAY VS. YESTERDAY

Will your relatives be old at sixty-five, seventy-five, or not until they are eighty-five or ninety?

The answer depends on many factors—heredity, environment, ability to resist disease, diet, way of life, etc. Also, you must realize that the concept of old age has altered with every period of history. Two thousand years ago at the height of the Roman Empire's triumphs, the average life expectancy at birth was only twenty-two. Fifty years ago in this country the new-born white male had a life expectancy of only forty-eight years, the average female, fifty-one. In the last half century, which added another twenty-one years to that record, old men and women have changed, and so have our ideas about them (that is, if we, too, have progressed with the times).

Whistler's famous portrait of his mother has inspired hundreds of sentimental advertisements and maudlin editorials since it was painted in the nineteenth century. Today it is as much outdated as a portrait of old age as the demure white cap which framed his mother's face. Men and women of our day who reach eighty or eighty-five or even ninety are more likely to resemble their own parents at sixty or seventy than any conventional idea of what octogenarians and nonagenarians ought to look like and be.

The key factors which have in fifty years increased the numbers of men and women in this country past sixty-five from three million to nearly thirteen million also have changed them mentally and physically. Unless you accept that fact you will find your relatives following Dr. George Lawton's definition of normal aging as "a combination of suitable quantities of rebellion and resignation."

These key factors need to be understood before we sit in judgment on our elders for not behaving as we think they should. They include:

A higher standard of living: This includes better balanced diets, more sensible clothing, more adequate housing, improved working conditions, and more recreation. It is true we need more of each, but the progress we have made has had its effect not only on babies but on their great-grandparents.

Tremendous advances in preventive medicine, and widespread public health measures: Pasteurized milk and abolition of the common drinking-cup from the little red schoolhouse are enough in themselves to account for many lengthened lives.

Great improvements in medical care and broad advances in medical therapy: Our century was the first in history to control the infectious diseases which used to sweep off babies and young people, and now is bringing great numbers of them into old age.

There were men and women at the turn of the last century, and in every other century, whose interests were constantly expanding and deepening and who always found life fresh and challenging. Nevertheless, the *average* elderly person today is considerably different in vigor and stamina from what his parents' or grandparents' physical and mental state was at the same age. You can prove it to yourself if you compare a woman like Mrs. Evans, aged ninety, with what her mother was.

The latter died at fifty-four of diabetes (in the *ante*-insulin days). Before she was twenty-nine she had been married and widowed, and was the mother of six children, two of whom died in their first year. Throughout the widowhood which lasted till her death, she wore nothing but black, violet, or white, and a "bonnet" tied under her chin. Although she had the strength to support herself and her children by running a boardinghouse for demanding railroad men, nevertheless, she thought of herself as "an old widow." She was a normal product of her nineteenth century day.

Mrs. Evans is a woman of another type. She has never learned to think of herself as "old." On her ninetieth birthday, last September, she was canning peaches. The day before she had canned cucumbers from her own garden, tended during a hot Tennessee summer. When the ladies' club invited her as their oldest member to talk about her early past, she snorted. "Past?" she said. "That's for young folks to study in school; I've got no time for anything but my present!"

Mrs. Evans is a good representative of the view taken by rehabilitation workers today. They say that age is not a handicap; if it is not an asset it is at least a state which need not be a liability.

THE SEVEN AGES OF MAN

The Seven Ages of Man have been defined for us, not by Shakespeare, but by gerontologists so we can understand why individuals show discrepancies. The first—chronological age—is the one we all think of first, but doctors think it the least important.

1. *Chronological Age:* How much older any person is than his years, or how much younger, depends on how he has aged in every other way. The net result of much research, particularly during the last half century, into the still-mysterious process of aging is this: Partial decline and partial degeneration start literally from the day of birth—some say conception. Partial growth and partial development do not stop with one's childhood, youth, or maturity. They can continue up to the last day man ever reaches.

How old your relatives and friends appear depends on who is looking at them. As the late Booth Tarkington remarked, "Youth classifies people as old people, young people and children; to youth it seems that the old always have been old, and are to be everlastingly in that condition. To a boy of twelve 'old' means anything beyond the twenties; sixty hasn't the advantage over thirty-five, both appearing to be pretty dismal."

2. *Hereditary Age:* Lafayette Lee Robbins explains old age in another way. This eighty-year-old former lumberjack remarks: "People get old quickly because they think they're old. I feel the same as I did when I was twenty-five and I'll feel the same when I'm a hundred. My mother is a hundred and seven and she feels as I do."

Mr. Robbins is presenting evidence in himself, if not his words, that a long-lived ancestry *tends* to make long-lived descendants. If your grandparents on both sides and their brothers and sisters lived to be ninety or a hundred, the genetic constitution your parents and you have inherited plays an important role in the life span. By itself, however, heredity cannot ward off the accidents and strains of living, or the changes in the machinery of the body which cause it to age, whether this is due to faulty diets, infections, or overwork.

As Dr. Crampton says, "The man of sixty whose forebears averaged ninety-five at death is potentially a far different man from one of sixty whose ancestors averaged forty-five years of age. . . . There is nothing that can be found in the medical examination of a man which has not been foreshadowed in the lives which produced the man. . . . The family is not only an organization, it is a living organism. . . ."

3. *Statistical Age:* Don't be confused by all the talk with which our ears are bombarded about the increasing length of life. What is important is the number of years the *average* man or woman may expect to live. This varies with sex, race, occupation, medical care, diet, and so on. It also changes from century to century, the great stride forward having been made in the years from 1900 to 1950. The remarkable leap of over two decades in increased life expectancy means that more and more babies, youths, and young adults are being pulled through diseases that used to be certain killers.

Whether or not this spurt will continue in the next fifty years there is considerable doubt, but at least we know the life span is not limited by Biblical edict. Today a white infant boy has at least sixty-six years to look forward to when he is born and his little sister over seventy-one. (3) (Non-white children lag a bit behind.)

In 1550 Lodovico Cornaro wrote a book on how to live to be one hundred and since that time many others have added prescriptions—or restrictions—that they believe will lengthen life. But even without giving up many pleasures, including smoking and drinking, the man or woman who lives to be sixty-five is a commonplace of our time. He has nearly fourteen more years ahead of him if he takes only normal care of himself, his wife even more. If chronic diseases can be conquered, if man himself will overcome his deficiencies in personal and public hygiene and work, then life expectancy ought to be increased certainly to eighty, perhaps to a hundred years. One theory is that the natural life span of living beings is five to six times the period of growth. In the animal world (of which man is a part, of course) dogs, for instance, are fully grown at one to two years and live to be twelve, fifteen, or even older. Cats mature at two and a half and have an average life expectancy of ten, and so on. Man, fully mature at twenty, is dying too soon, scientists say.

What matters now is that if your relatives have survived the knocks and pummeling of youth and maturity to reach sixty-five, it is for you and for them to realize that there is still a considerable period left for most people to use, not as a dead end but as the beginning of new, if different, growth.

There are plenty of still-alert old people to help educate oneself to the idea that old age does not necessarily spell decline, in everything. Henri Matisse at eighty-two ranked as France's greatest living painter. In the words of the *New Yorker,* he is "not only still alive but still expertly painting, with elderly, preserved ripeness. . . ."

You can find innumerable others who are not in the genius, or near-genius class. The octogenarian who continues to serve as a part-time worker for the New York Bible Society is one. Christian Sachtleben, a retired tailor is another. Neither would consider themselves out of the ordinary. Mr. Sachtleben gave Chicago photographers a field-day when he demonstrated he was in first-class condition on his hundreth birthday. When they came along with their cameras he was cleaning the snow, as he always does in winter, from the sidewalk in front of his home.

4. *Anatomical Age:* Just as the appearance of the first molar tooth marks an anatomical landmark in infancy, such changes as hardening of the connective tissue and shrinking of the thyroid mark an advance in anatomical age in senescence. During the whole of life, however, cells, tissues, and organs appear, grow, mature, decline, and atrophy. Therefore, even if we were all freed miraculously from the danger of disease, death would finally have to occur.

These changes in blood vessels, heart, kidneys, etc. are as inevitable as the changes in family structure, loss of friends, and a lessened capacity for work and play of a strenuous sort. Nevertheless, since each part of the body grows older at a different tempo, at varying rates in different persons, many people can accomplish a great deal even at ninety. (At that age Sir George Buckston Browne, a distinguished British surgeon, announced his intention of living to be a hundred, and renewed his lease on his Wimpole Street house for another ten years. When he died at ninety-four one of his colleagues said Sir George's death could only be attributed to "an arithmetical disappointment"!) (4)

The parts of the body with weak metabolism suffer the most

distinctive changes—cartilage, lens of the eye, cornea, eardrum, arteries. But when the body of some loved one shrinks, or he loses the ability to hear high sounds or read fine print, or walks cautiously because his joints have stiffened, there are two points which should keep you from over-sentimentalization:

The first is that such disabilities come gradually, are often painless, and are usually not fatal. The second point is that much can be done either to avoid damages, to treat them, or to overcome frustrations because of them. All senses become less acute with age, but they can be fortified. Better planned lighting will help poor vision, and higher temperatures will take care of increased sensitivity of old flesh to cold. There is much cheer latent in the proverb: "Everybody knows the toughness of an old chicken."

5. *Physiological Age:* This refers to functions which change, commonly declining in the last period of life. Nerve reaction time, muscular movement, or muscular coordination come to mind immediately because we mourn with "old" prize fighters and ballplayers who slow down when they are out of their twenties.

We still are ignorant of the basic physiological causes of aging. Scientists have not accumulated enough data to determine whether it is a normal process inherent in all cells and tissues or whether, as Dr. Nathan W. Shock of the U. S. Public Health Service says it may "result from successive and accumulated insults and injuries of living." What they do know has comfort in it. Though decline begins in the second or third decade and proceeds at a somewhat increasing rate to the end of life, Dr. Shock found some eighty year olds who had kidneys which were as good as the average in a forty-year-old group he studied. He also found what others have determined through various kinds of stress tests: The aged are not *necessarily* slow in reaction, and there are compensations the old can call on to make up for their lack of speed. (5)

This is a good thing to remind yourself of whenever you are tempted to curb an older person's lack of inhibitions. He may not be agile enough to be good at singles but he can still find a partner for doubles. After all, a Joe DiMaggio or a Joe Louis is an old athlete while he is still in his thirties. Defense factories long ago found that the notion of older workers as too slow and too inflexible is largely prejudice. If they don't have as much strength as young stalwarts on some operations, they make up for it in the slow grind and endurance jobs the young detest.

Follow the rule that Dr. Lillien Martin laid down in her Old Age Counselling Center, and you won't go wrong. She found that the best way to help older people overcome declining capacities was to induce them to make plans, set themselves a goal, and then work for it. She proved they could train a declining memory, overcome slowness of senile speech, and by doing practical exercises, such as taking brisk walks to explore new places, could conquer mental sluggishness and combat stiffness.

Dr. Martin's own experience in learning to drive a car at the age of seventy-six, and her reactions to her first failures and her later success, are worth quoting to any older person who needs encouragement.

Dr. Martin wrote down her experiences in order; she said, "To prove to some other old person the value to me of this experience. . . ." Her fears were legion, but her courage was high (which is the statement you can make about many other elderly experimenters unless their enthusiasm is dampened by too many "don'ts").

"I started to learn to drive," Dr. Martin writes, "when I was seventy-six years of age, and though I was prepared to find that to do the job well would take me a long time, I confess something like twenty-five lessons seemed to me about the limit of what I would require. I had more than fifty hours of driving instruction and practice, and was seventy-seven years old before I was entrusted with an operator's license. I look back now on my early beginnings and wonder how I could have lived through so discouraging and anxious a period. The shock of finding how slow my reactions had become, how worried I was when tackling a new activity, how hard it was to act as quickly as I could think, to coordinate the sensory and motor response, to learn to be relaxed under strain, brought me many hours of dejection. . . ."

She realized her fears were a protective measure; she was not master of her machine and because of her age was ineligible to carry insurance to cover any misadventure. So she "selected the most deserted streets and took my lessons at an early hour, practising to get experience in gear shifting, backing in, diagonal parking, turning in a narrow street, etc. As soon as I could do these things automatically my fears faded away and I began to find driving highly stimulating."(6)

Dr. Martin's experience can be anyone's, if not in automobiling, then in other aspirations. There is laboratory and practical evidence that our physical capacities generally reach their climax in our early twenties. But the physiological age is rarely, if ever, the same as chronological age. Most of us have our best period between forty and seventy, but it can be later. As Dr. Martin Gumpert, the geriatrician, says: "A man is old when he begins to act as though he were doing everything for the last time." In concrete terms this means that the individual who wants to learn can continue to learn at eighty, even though he doesn't have the ability to memorize by rote as quickly as he did at eight.

6. *Pathological Age:* A severe attack of influenza, chronic teeth infection, damage to the adrenal glands, bad sinuses or gall-bladder trouble—these, and a number of other illnesses—can age a man ten years or more. Physicians call this, aging through "an acute pathological incident." As long as he lives man ages by damage through his mode of living, accidents, or results of disease, more than by the mere passage of time.

Your goal, then, should be two-fold. Do the things with, and for, them that will bring your aging parents to a healthy old age. Or if pathological aging can't be prevented, then see that it is treated before it is irrevocable.

We think of arteriosclerosis, for example, as an old person's disease. (Strictly speaking, this is not correct.) But this change in the blood vessels has been developing over many decades. If the infections and intoxications to which the body is exposed can be prevented, or at least treated at an early stage, the organism has a chance to remain "young" however long man's calendar years are. Recognition of this has given medical men a lively hope they may yet succeed in making life long and happy by making us healthy.

Pathological conditions can be discovered by diagnostic search. Many of them can be removed before they create a drain on the body's resources. These two statements are reason enough to make sure that regular medical examinations start early in life and continue into old age. Unfortunately, few older people have this habit. If your elders are among them, it's not too late to begin the custom. Remember that a good many pathological conditions arise simply from bad life management. (One doctor defines it as "too many cathartics, sedatives, tonics, vitamins, and food fads, all self-administered in unscientific doses.") This, too, can be corrected, if the patient, and the patient's family, cooperate.

If your relative already has an impairment—heart or kidney disease, even an ugly ulcer—don't jump to the conclusion that he won't be able to function along normal lines. A social worker once read a medical record of a man whose list of afflictions covered a half page. When she saw his physician she said, "How sick this poor old man must be!"

"Sick?" he replied. "Why, he's getting along all right; he's not sick; he can live as good a life as you can!"

In spite of the presence of his diseases, the elderly gentleman's adjustment to them and tolerance for their symptoms were excellent. His palpitations, digestive disturbances, and arthritis didn't prevent him from being promoted to head an automobile agency at sixty-six. And he was still "growing"; he and his wife got along very well together, he was well liked by his associates. At sixty-four he had taken up painting as a hobby and was doing very well at it.

Don't fall into the trap of blaming "old age" for all the maladjustments and disturbances that might have come up at any age.

7. *Psychological Age:* Although they wax and wane more slowly than other phases of aging, mental and emotional life also begin, mature, grow old.

All cells in the body can multiply and reproduce with the exception of those of the nervous system. These are laid down in embryonic life and grow till, by the time we are adult, they stretch out into every organ and area of the body. When maturity of the organism is attained they no longer grow. Since they never reproduce themselves it follows that of all cells they are the most long lived. It also follows that they must necessarily alter with changing conditions in the entire organism. (7)

That is the scientific explanation of why old dogs can learn new tricks if they already know some tricks, if they are accustomed to learning, and if their teacher knows how to teach. This is the reason why Dr. Martin could learn to drive an automobile at the age of seventy-six—though it took her fifty lessons—and afterwards drive herself across the continent six times. It is also the reason that at the age of eighty-eight she could learn Spanish and typewriting.

It was Dr. Martin's belief that "normal human beings can grow mentally at any age, and reclaim life by re-animating mental processes that have become atrophied through disuse."

There is ample scientific evidence that Dr. Martin was right. The laboratory tests which Dr. David Wechsler used in three thousand cases, for instance, showed there is a relative loss of intellectual ability between the ages twenty-five and sixty which amounts to approximately twenty-five per cent. But intellectual ability is only part of what we know as intelligence. Its effective use depends on other factors—drive, persistence, and experience.

"A man," says Dr. Wechsler, "as he grows older may become wiser and hence in a broader sense more intelligent though he has less ability than he once had, just as a physician may become a better doctor with experience even though he has less scientific knowledge than his younger colleagues. But all this will depend on opportunities which he has had to acquire this experience. A doctor with no practice does not grow better with age, nor does a workman without a job become a better mechanic."

There is no critical age line beyond which intellectual production has to cease. Change in perception, activity, interest, and speed of learning are not serious handicaps. It is the individual personality and not age that sets the final limit. This is not only true in a Titian, who painted a great masterpiece when he was ninety-five, but for a Percy Gilkes. Mr. Gilkes is chief clerk of the Brooklyn (N. Y.) Federal Court where he recently completed his sixty-first year of employment. He observed his eighty-third birthday by working a full eight-hour shift.

It is the ability to remember isolated facts—proper names heard once, telephone numbers seldom used—that is almost universally lost. In the family circle, however, you will find that older people have little difficulty in hearing and remembering what they are interested in, and they can acquire new interests outside of it. Dr. Irving Lorge proved in some striking experiments at Columbia University that old people could learn. He found that those in the upper age brackets could acquire a totally new language—in this case, Russian—with as much facility as younger people.

Thomas Edison and Justice Oliver Wendell Holmes made brilliant contributions in their respective spheres when they were well past four score. Your older folk may not equal their ability. But they will be far more likely to prevent aging in the mental as well as the physical sphere from accelerating if they make continual use of experience. There are persons who have not grown since their schooldays; others are still developing at ninety. Whether your relative will be one of the latter depends on his background, the type of person he has always been, his will-power, and—to a degree not many of us are willing to recognize—the attitude of the younger people around him.

WHAT TO EXPECT OF THE OLD

At a University of Michigan conference on problems of housing the aged, one speaker shrugged his shoulders and said (as though it explained everything): "Well, you know how old folks are."

No, we do not know "how old folks are." Nor does anyone else. A doctor thinks of aged people very often—and mistakenly—as ill patients only. A young supervisor, impatient with an older worker's insistence on being careful and precise, thinks of all aged as fussy and slow-gaited, again a grievous error. All of us absorb the myths of our culture. Now our society is so geared that you must be wary of succumbing to what someone has called "our national worship of bratology." We are much more likely to think we are giving grandpa a compliment when we say, "He is a wonderful old man; you'd never know he was over fifty," than to remark, "He is a wonderful old man, full of wisdom."

What should you expect of the old?

A counter-question is to ask yourself if it is normal in old age to act as if one were adolescent, or even to imitate men and women in their forties. If you are one of those who tell older people they should "try to keep young," and think you are doing them a favor, you have your answer in this vigorous protest. It comes from one regular visitor at the Hodson day center for the elderly in New York.

"If our minds kept young," she says, "we should stagnate, never learn anything new and never improve. If a baby kept young its intelligence would never develop. . . . When we were young, we made mistakes because of ignorance and inexperience. Had we not grown older and wiser, we should be making similar mistakes now. If we tell our ages and someone says, 'I wouldn't think it!' we have not received a compliment. That remark is equivalent to saying that we do not appear to know enough to be older."(8)

You may also need to modify your conceptions and misconceptions about how much adjusting there has to be, even when reserves are depleted.

Climate: There is no doubt that when Old Sol is shining, the sick and the well, the young and the old, feel better. This suggests that many of the effects of climatic changes are purely psychological. The exact mechanism behind the way elements affect our bodily processes is unknown. What is known is that inclement weather causes more bronchitis and pneumonia. Also, that elderly people who spend much time indoors in bad weather need to be careful of the overcrowding, lack of ultraviolet light, and high humidity which encourage survival of germs. (But so do we all.)

The question may come up whether it is necessary for your parents or other old people to move. The best rule you can lay down is this: If it is possible to let them end their days where wind, humidity, and temperature are on an even keel, they'll probably feel better. The elderly and the infirm do not tolerate abrupt changes well. However, any aging person who is not abnormal, who wants to learn to adapt himself, can do it, if like the rest of us, he is compelled to make the effort.

Teeth: You may have to wean your elderly relatives (as well as yourself) from an old-fashioned notion. Teeth, unlike the leaves in autumn, do not have to fall out in old age. Many older persons take the fatalistic position that their teeth must come out. This psychological factor often causes neglect of conditions—lack of dental care, poor diet—that result in the breakdown of tooth supports, and so the teeth do come out.

Disposition: The best thing that can be said on that score was said by the late philosopher, George Santayana. He, who died at a great age, wrote in his last book:

"People do not grow better when they grow older; they remain the same, but later circumstances cause them to exhibit their character sometimes in a minor key with the soft pedal, so that they seem to us grown sweeter, and sometimes more harshly and disagreeably, when we think them sour and depraved."(9)

One could go on enumerating, step by step, all the things which affect or do not affect the different organs and the psyche. They can be summed up in this one sentence of Dr. Gumpert's: "Old age and senility are no more necessarily related than infancy and rickets."

The eighty year olds who are alive today are not a random sample of those who were fifty years old thirty years ago. We know that those who had long-lived ancestors, kept their weight down, their diet well balanced, and their mental and bodily processes under control, have survived in larger numbers than the rest. We also know that stagnant lives and age-dulled psyches can be aroused through such simple measures as regular exercise of the right kind, stimulating hobbies, or by correcting nutritional deficiencies through high protein diets, additional calcium or iron, or vitamin B-1.

FRUITS OF EXTREME OLD AGE

The concomitants of senescence—the wrinkles, the poor hearing and lessened vision, the lower capacity for sustained physical effort, the more deliberate thinking—are as indicative of maturity as they are of decline. It is not undignified to possess them. If you regard them as signs of a rich, full life, you will not be depressed by them or feel them abnormal.

Also, the picture is not uniformly dark. You need not steel yourself to endure old age, either in yourself, or in anyone else. A buoyant spirit can be retained till the end of life, provided the will is there. The capacity for love, for work, for intellectual enjoyment, for play—for a thousand other enjoyments—can endure, provided there is understanding and love to support them.

Some day science may be able to delay greatly this involution we call "aging." In the meanwhile we can ward off the worse aspects through better care of the living machine, and better understanding of the role the old body and the rich, ripe mind can play. There are four specific ways you can help older people make the prolongation of life more than an animal existence and give worth and quality to added years:

1. You can provide, as well as circumstances permit, for those special comforts that older people need and enjoy.

2. You can do your best to see that they keep their health.

3. You can take pains to see that they are kept in touch with life, literature, art and music, so their minds remain young and pliable.

4. Finally, you can help them give more than lip service to hobbies that will add interest and meaning to life, and give expression to the eternal values which are beyond the reach of time.

Take as your working philosophy this ideal which Dr. Robert Monroe set up when he talked to a convention of welfare workers, and you will never be at a loss to know what is "normal" in old age:

"We must abolish the attitude of defeat," he said, "if we are to do anything for, and with, old people. We must stop saying, 'At your age, what can you expect?' Old people are normal people, normal units in our social structure. Their defects stem from disease which requires treatment, and from social and economic disasters which require our cooperation as well as theirs to alleviate or adjust. They need guidance and motivation, not just sympathy. We must develop skills and resources to keep them as normal and as forward-looking as possible, for as long as possible. When their inevitable end comes, it should be our aim to see that it is as natural as being born, with little distress and in the midst of active life."

If you succeed in helping any older individual organize his life along these lines, he is not likely to succumb to the kind of bewilderment which seizes a good many more people than Edgar Rice Burroughs. When the creator of the youthful Tarzan was seventy-four he complained to a visitor, "I'm afraid I don't know how to grow old gracefully; you see I never expected to grow old!"

NOTES TO CHAPTER II

(1) Crampton, C. Ward, M.D. "What Geriatrics Means to the Medical Profession," *New York Medicine* Vol. 3, No. 10, May 20, 1947.

(2) Lawton, George. "Psychological Guidance to Older Persons," *Mental Health in Later Maturity*. Washington, D. C.: U. S. Government Printing Office, 1942. Supplement No. 168 to Public Health Reports.

(3) *Statistical Bulletin,* Metropolitan Life Insurance Company, Vol. 34, No. 1, Jan., 1953. Also letter to author from Louis I. Dublin, then Second Vice-President, Nov. 28, 1951.

(4) Cosin, Lionel Z., M.D., F.R.C.S. *The Need for Emotional Adjustments in the Elderly*. London: The National Council of Social Service, Inc., 1950. P. 14.

(5) Shock, Nathan W. "Biology of Aging," in *Problems of America's Aging Population*. Gainesville, Fla.: University of Florida Press, 1951.

(6) Quoted by Cosin, Lionel Z., M.D. *Op. cit.* P. 12-13.

(7) Wechsler, David M., M.D. "Intellectual Changes with Age," in *Mental Health in Later Maturity*. Washington, D. C.: U. S. Government Printing Office, 1942. Supplement No. 168 to Public Health Reports.

(8) *Newsletter,* William Hodson Center for the Elderly. New York: Department of Welfare, 1949. (Mimeographed.)

(9) Santayana, George. *My Host the World.* Volume III of *Persons and Places.* New York: Scribner's, 1953.

CHAPTER THREE

OLD AGE IS NOT A DISEASE

If someone in your family is in the last third of his life, there is no reason to conjure up a fearful picture of incapacity which cannot be evaded. This is the dread which hung over the generation just behind you, and is probably still nursed by your elderly relatives. It is a crippling idea, and ought to be dislodged as speedily as possible. For this fear—the gloomy anticipation of disabilities—can create the very climate which makes many an older individual succumb to minor illnesses and prevents him from recovering from severe ones.

Aging is *not* synonymous with disease. It is *not* a state of ill-health. A disabling, lengthy sickness is *not* an inevitable part of growing old.

These three statements are medical facts, long since proved. They ought to be committed to memory.

It is easy to paint a grim picture of the deficits of old age and the scars of diseases suffered earlier in life that drag on and work havoc. Yet the reverse side, the "grow old along with me, the best is yet to be" philosophy of Robert Browning, is just as misleading. Losses are inevitable (else we should all live forever) but they differ in degree for each of us. Furthermore, the diseases which are most at home in old age come on slowly. There is usually time to adjust to them, or at the worst, to ease pains so they are bearable.

THE AGING PROCESS: BASIC TRUTHS

The grave is not ready and waiting just around the corner even if your relative is in his seventies, eighties, or even nineties. He is at the time of life when bones are brittle, blood vessels less elastic, and circulatory trouble more likely. Nevertheless, he may still be a young old person, even in a nursing home, as Mrs. Mary Knipe is. Now a hundred and two, Mrs. Knipe is very much alive in Lincoln Manor. Her health is good and her mind is clear. She still likes to reminisce about her college days, and her diploma is her most cherished possession.

Not everyone can, or even wants to, be listed in the *Farmer's Guide of Centenarians,* as Mrs. Knipe is. But every one of us wants to know what can be done to make life easier and worries fewer when we get on in years. Your relative has the right to know these basic truths which have emerged from all the research into the aging process. To understand them will raise your morale, as well as his:

Many old people enjoy good health and die without any outward symptoms of fatal disease, in extreme old age.

Like Oliver Wendell Holmes's "One-Hoss Shay," all their competent parts are as strong as the others. When at last they do break down for all time, everything fails at once.

There is no disease or disability so peculiar to the aging as to be found only in the aged.

There are many disabilities which can afflict old mankind, to be sure, and certain diseases are more common in late life than in youth. Nevertheless, the chances that any older person will encounter more than a few are rare indeed. If he does, nature herself, as well as medical treatment, can sometimes "compensate" for the wounded member.

In the annals of the American Heart Association there is a story of an elderly gentleman who died peacefully in his sleep. In all his seventy-five years he had never suffered from a major ailment. Examination after his death, however, showed that his heart had half the larger arteries completely closed by clots—the medical term is "coronary thrombosis," something which strikes fear into us. Yet these clots, formed years before this man's death, had not troubled him or caused a heart attack. Neighboring arteries had come to the rescue; they had grown into a substitute network capable of handling the whole blood load.

This is one of the dramatic cases which enliven medical history. For most aged people the sensible course is to be aware of the chief foes that may strike in time to do something about them. For health in later years is not automatic. Usually it takes initiative, effort, and intelligence on the part of the older individual, and, if he has one, of his family.

CHIEF ENEMIES OF THE OLD

The diseases which affect the heart, blood vessels, and kidneys, are the greatest potential killers in middle and old age, with cancer not far behind. Three-fourths of the nation's deaths every year stem from them. Yet the important and comforting thing is this: Frequently a person with heart disease, high blood pressure, hardening of the arteries, or one of the allied conditions, can learn to live with it so he *can* enjoy life. Very often he *can* live to be very old if he stays within limitations the doctor sets. (In 1951, for example, forty per cent of the men and women who died from cardiovascular disease were more than seventy-five years old.) (1)

The cure or control of all the serious maladies that afflict us in the later years may come on any tomorrow. The medical profession is racing now in many research laboratories to find a way to whip hypertension, cerebral hemorrhages, and all the other deadly enemies of the old, just as they have already conquered the infections that mowed down childhood and youth yesterday.

Even now no older relative of yours should be fobbed off with the wisecrack: "At your age, what do you expect?" One of the most reassuring acts you can perform for him and yourself is to have a clear idea of the medical advances of the last few years that are taking the terror out of old age.

COMPENSATIONS IN OLD AGE

New diagnostic procedures, prevention, and treatment of even the most dreaded illnesses makes it possible for you to care for your old when they are sick much more easily and with much more favorable results than was possible twenty, ten, or even five years ago.

Tell your relative that. Let him know that *you* know age gives him protection against certain diseases. Assure him he no longer need fear others. Implant these encouraging facts while he is still well—and even more firmly, if he is not. Give him the statistical picture; let him know why he has immunity to some diseases and can resist others, and why the operation table is not something for him to shun. Here is a thumbnail sketch of what he ought to know:

The statistical picture: At least seven out of eight men and women past sixty-five are not so disabled that they cannot go about their daily tasks. Since 1940 their mortality rate has dropped by eight per cent. Life expectancy continues to rise. The average person who attains his seventy-fifth year can look forward to at least another eight, and many live much longer.(2)

These dry, factual reports emanating from the National Office of Vital Statistics come to life in the stories like Edward D. Blackwell's. In 1878 Mr. Blackwell failed to obtain insurance; he was considered a bad risk. Recently he celebrated his hundreth birthday in Goshen, Vermont. Mr. Blackwell is a living instance of the fact that older people's health future is growing brighter each year.

Immunity and resistance: Your relative doesn't need to fear the worst infections that beset children. He has already established immunity either because he had an attack of fever, measles, etc., or by repeated contacts with carriers of them. Some other evils, such as migraine or "sick headaches," are likely to disappear soon after the climacteric.

Pneumonia, only a few years ago termed by Sir William Osler, "Captain of the men of death," has been reduced to the rank of a private. Since 1934 the mortality rate from it in old age has sunk by over fifty per cent.(3)

Another conquest is the victory over diabetes, controlled, if not banished. As late as 1940 it was in the list of the first ten killers.(4) It is still more common among the elderly than the young, but it is not as serious. With the advent of insulin it is no longer a fatal menace threatening the old.

And the "misery" many older folk complain of is likely to be osteoarthritis, and is not the crippling type, but the stress-and-strain, wear-and-tear "rheumatism" which is seldom too disabling to permit an active life.

Successful surgery: If his doctor recommends surgery for any older person, get another opinion if you wish, but don't hesitate because a man or woman is old. Both aging and aged people *can* be operated on, and can get well. Surgery, even for an individual of ninety, is not the formidable obstacle it once was. The man or woman of eighty or more who rises up from a post-operative bed as soon as his neighbor of eighteen is a modern-day miracle. Doctors have developed improved methods of giving oxygen and anesthesia; they have learned more about using whole blood and plasma transfusions, and diets rich in proteins and vitamins to combat bone and body wastage. They have found out about the part sex hormones play in the metabolism of bone and have discovered new drugs to fight post-operative infections.

If you need to be convinced, ask your own physician to tell you where to find the numerous stories in the medical literature which parallel these typical samples:

1. At Mt. Sinai Hospital in New York City, a woman of eighty-three, plagued by an obstruction—diverticulum—in her esophagus, could not eat properly. She was told she was literally starving. She finally consented to an operation. Today she still is in good health, in her nineties, and relishes steak dinners.

2. At Oxford Hospital in England, a ninety-three-year-old man became a patient after vomiting for three months. He had been forced by his family and his physician to reconcile himself to cancer of the stomach. However, the discovery was made that he

had ulcers, bad enough, but not the disease he and his family dreaded most. This nonagenarian was operated on, recovered, and lived peacefully to be a centenarian.

3. At Johns Hopkins Hospital in Maryland, the vital pituitary gland was removed from a seventy-two-year-old bedridden patient. He had suffered great pain from a tumor in the gland which finally developed into cancer, and had spread. Three months after his operation, however, this man was walking around without trouble, had no more knotty pains, slept soundly, had a good appetite, and put on seventeen pounds.

SYMPTOMS OF DISEASE IN THE OLD

When should you take action?

The shortest answer is to say that any illness for which there is no obvious cause should be looked on with concern, especially if a person has had a lifetime, or almost that, of good health. He may seem to be suffering from vague symptoms. For any strain—an accident, a great sorrow—can suddenly bring out signs of one of those insidious chronic diseases—a smoldering cancer or narrowed arteries, for instance. As Dr. Frederic D. Zeman points out in this quip to hammer home the fact: "Disease in the aged is characterized by multiplicity, chronicity, and duplicity."

With older people, as with younger ones, there is always the question of how much of a deaf ear one ought to turn to plaints. Old people are commonly thought to have less sensitivity to pain than they had when they were years younger. Yet if you are fortunate enough to have relatives who keep silent about their aches it may mean only that they have had time to develop resignation. Sir Isaac Newton, at eighty-two, perspired silently during paroxysms of kidney colic, yet was able to discourse animatedly on philosophy between them. Your relative may be a Stoic, too. Or he may be a complainer. Both types of people have always existed. As Dr. Robert T. Monroe says, "The hundreth attack of gout can be borne with a different expression than the first." The way to be safe, not sorry, is to pay attention to symptoms that call for investigation by an able physician, but not necessarily for alarm.

Pains are one of them, if they are definite and severe. They may be caused by heart trouble, pleurisy, arthritis, rupture etc. Constant, indefinite aches that remain for weeks, months, or years, are not a cause for panic. They may be due to nervousness, fatigue, or worry. Certainly something needs to be done if that is the case. But at least you don't have to fear cancer or some other serious lesion because the patient would have become seriously ill long ago.

Apprehension and uneasiness is not the answer at any time. Palpitation is sometimes a sign the heart is being overworked but it is also common in nervous people, without such threatening overtones. Indigestion pains make many an excited person—and his family—think he is having a heart attack. The symptoms are often similar. Yet it is the physician's business, not the patient's, to find out the truth. Even a bad heart can usually be repaired with treatment and care. An over-anxious family attitude, however, may lead to chronic invalidism where there is no need for it.

When Mrs. Sarah Crayshaw fell several times in one year, her doctor diagnosed her condition as high blood pressure. Thereupon her family hastened to buy a wheel-chair, bundled her into it, and there she has sat ever since—but not because her physician recommended it.

Even if the sore that never heals or the bleeding from some body opening is finally diagnosed as symptom of a malignant tumor, you don't need to yield either to panic or despair. The reassurance you can have is two-fold. First, a cancer is always local at the beginning; if it is completely removed before it spreads to other parts, it does not return. Second, *every* cancer patient can be helped and many can be cured. Or the person who has that first little stroke may go another ten or fifteen years before he has another, and still more, before he has a crippling or fatal one.

The one clear course which will enable you to come to grips with a problem in time either to ward it off or to cope with it, is this:

You, or someone who sees your elderly relative at frequent intervals, should learn enough about the danger signals to recognize if there is serious trouble ahead. You need also to know common symptoms that do *not* mean danger. You must try to keep an older person from self-diagnosis, from dosing himself, from needless anxiety over every pain or ache, or its contrary—perhaps refusing to have a doctor even when he is steadily losing weight or strength or a sense of well-being.

There is no dearth of information you and your relative can get, even if you live in an almost deserted village. The cancer, heart, mental illness, and other foundations dealing with chronic diseases, the chief disablers of the old, all issue booklets. Much of the material is free. The major insurance companies, out of enlightened self-interest, will send you information on everything from the dangers of overweight to conserving a damaged liver or diseased kidney. There are regular health talks by officials of county and state medical societies in halls, and on radio and television; every popular magazine in the country either reprints them or publishes articles by reputable authors in the medical field. There are even syndicated columns by physicians which run in both large and small newspapers. And there is always the American Red Cross you can turn to. If you enroll in one of its home nursing courses, you can learn how to be on the lookout for diseases, and what to do if they come.

MEDICAL EXAMINATIONS A NECESSITY

It is the question of *time* which should concern you most. The chronic diseases—nephritis, arthritis, diabetes, cancer, *et al.*—usually start creeping up in early middle age. Most of them begin silently and may continue for a long time with no pain and little outward manifestation. But if these slight early symptoms are ignored, or dismissed as of no importance, or taken for granted as part of the process of getting old, the damage is likely to proceed to a "point of no return." All the best physician can do then is to try to relieve distress and bolster the courage of the sufferer.

But there is no need to let early troubles go undetected. If they are just starting, a good physician can not only bring relief but add years of life. Even if a person's disease is chronic, if it is checked he may have a long time ahead of him with something to look forward to besides pain. Dr. Malford Thewlis, one of the pioneers in geriatrics, tells of a sixty-year-old patient whom anyone would regard as hopelessly handicapped. He had heart disease, arterial hypertension, Bright's disease, diabetes, and pulmonary tuberculosis. Yet for eight more years he was able to work as a wool sorter, going about as if nothing were happening. Finally a lung hemorrhage ended a fight which had been gallant, and a life which even severe physical disturbances had not made unbearable, because he was told how to live it.

The best way to conserve anyone's health is to have regular physical examinations. In the case of an elderly person it should be a health consultation, at least once a year when he is well, and as often as the doctor recommends if he is not. It should be a time when the doctor and his older patient have a chance to sit down together long enough to talk over not only pains and aches, but any other complaints for which the patient needs a sympathetic ear. Detection of disease in the old is not hard; often it is only too easy, but old people need to be certain they are meeting with friendliness as well as medical skill before they will expose their real troubles.

HOW TO SELECT A PHYSICIAN

A good doctor, whether he is formally classified as a geriatrician or not, never gives up. Like Dr. Thewlis, he will work with an old patient, even one riddled with disease, to make the best possible use of his remaining assets. He will believe even small accomplishments are worth while, and that they may be coaxed into greater ones. His goal will be the restoration of mental and physical vigor in old people. He will instill confidence so that they will believe life is a *continuing* process and that they can gird themselves to play a good part in it as long as it lasts. You can judge him by these qualities, and by how gentle he is with his old patient. If he knows his business he will not place the accent on old age, and he will not say that nothing can be done for them.

If your relative already has a physician he trusts and he has gone to him regularly over the years he ought to continue with him if he can. A doctor needs to know a patient as an individual. The more he knows about his elderly patient's personal problems, what strains he lives or works under, what his reactions are in times of stress, the more easily he can solve health problems. The medical passport which physicians advocate for all of us is really an annual life record, begun when we are young.

If he has to make a change, see that the aged in your family goes to the kind of physician that Dr. Monroe describes as a "gerophilist—someone who likes old people well enough to work with and for them." This does not mean that all his patients must be old. It does mean he will take time to pay attention to their recital of troubles, real or imaginary. For many, this kind of a visit acts as a bracer which has benefits for the whole family.

When Mrs. Bartlett goes to see her physician for her annual check-up, she comes away with her head held high. For the next few days she tells anybody who will listen: "Dr. X. tells me I look ten to fifteen years younger than my age!" And she forgets to scold her son-in-law for his extravagance, and concedes that perhaps, after all, the daughter she lives with has some reason for her "new-fangled ways" with the children.

Like Mrs. Bartlett, your parent or grandparent ought to go to his doctor alone if he is physically able. If he is not, at least give him a chance to be with his doctor and do his own talking. If you, or someone else intimately acquainted with him is not around, he will be franker. Also the doctor will have a fairer chance to make his own deductions about his patient's physical and emotional health.

TESTS FOR A GOOD EXAMINATION

Measured in time, a good geriatric examination will mean several hour-long sessions, on the average; but if suspicious data turns up—too little blood sugar, too high blood pressure, etc.—with other puzzling symptoms, the doctor may want laboratory tests that take even longer.

Measured in dollars, such an examination is expensive (though the same type sometimes is obtained through a low-priced clinic).

Measured in returns, it is worth whatever it costs if there is a chance that an old man with a heart lesion, or an old woman with symptoms of glaucoma that, unchecked, will rob her of sight, can find out how to lead normal or near-normal lives for some years to come.

Here is the "real life" story to hold up to any doubting Thomas in your family who scoffs or balks. It is taken from the files of a New York geriatrician but it can be duplicated, or supplemented, by any physician who treats older people.

Mrs. T. was in her late sixties when the pain in her heart became so keen she complained she couldn't stoop and could no longer climb to the second story in her country house. When her physician made a detailed examination he uncovered other conditions Mrs. T. hadn't suspected, including long-standing infections of the gall bladder and sinuses. (Mrs. T. was one of those people who "don't believe in going to the doctor till you have to," or those conditions would have been noticed and treated long before.) When the doctor asked Mrs. T. about her eating habits she confessed she had cut down on meat because neighbors in her home town had told her it made old folks arthritic. So she was filling her stomach with starches and starving her tissues.

As a result of this and subsequent visits, the doctor cured Mrs. T.'s infections, put her on the diet she should have, outlined exercises she could take safely, and assured her life still could be good. Today, Mrs. T. has to take her stairs slowly but she can do it without whimpering. The sense of well-being and confidence she has is as important to her husband as it is to her. Instead of a chronic complainer, she is now a person interested in something besides her own aches and pains because she has stopped thinking she is "too old and too broken down" to lead a normal life.

Your own relative may not be so cooperative. He may "pooh-pooh" the idea that, like a baby, he needs regular medical supervision. Or he may resist going to a physician for fear of what he might learn about himself. The older generation regarded a visit to a physician as a portentous business. If you do have a tug-of-war with grandpa, you might convince him if you point out that it's better to find out whether the pain around his heart is angina pectoris or merely due to eating too fast, rather than to sit and sigh like a bellows with worry. Or if grandma discovers a slight growth on her breast, tell her it is wiser to find out if it is a simple cyst or a cancer, because neither in early stages is a cause of future trouble if properly treated.

Periodic visits to the doctor, of course, will remove some of your own doubts and worries about what to do. If an open case of tuberculosis turns up, it won't be pleasant to know it exists, but it will respond to rest and diet and nursing care, and you need to know the details of that. If you are worried about grandma's shortness of breath, take her to the doctor at the first signs. He might find a case of undetected heart failure or virus bronchitis—or he may decide her breathlessness is merely due to boredom, and tell you how you can cure that. In every case the "health inventory" will vary with the doctor and the patient's own needs, but it ought to include two essentials:

Medical history: An old person's body and mind are documentary histories of all that has happened to him, good and bad. His doctor will want to consider him as an entity, recording his present ills, past diseases, heredity, environment, social and psychological stresses.

"A person with a predisposition to ulcer," says Dr. Thewlis, "may withstand heavy financial hardships without symptoms until some social conflict causes anxiety. Then his sleep is disturbed, his appetite fails and he enters a vicious cycle."(5) In other words, the stress under which an older individual lives often determines the rapidity with which a disease soil becomes fertile.

Physical examination: The good geriatrician, like the good pediatrician, is interested in the future of his patient. Though, unlike a baby, the older caller at the doctor's office may have only five or ten more years to live, the physician will want a thorough examination of each important organ.

In his office, or at a clinic, the doctor can look at eyes and ears and test them; examine the skin, nose, throat, heart, and lungs, measure blood pressure, test reflexes, feel the abdomen to learn if organs in that area are the size they ought to be, make a rectal examination for signs of cancer or other trouble, and see what condition the pelvis or prostrate gland is in.

A physician today has a number of testing devices at his disposal, either in his own office, or through outside laboratories. And he uses them for the same reason which makes a mechanic examine an automobile engine to find out if it can manage to climb the hill ahead.

A doctor, for instance, will perhaps want chemical blood tests, for everything from suspected malnutrition to neuritis. He will certainly ask for a urinalysis, and if he thinks kidney disease is what is affecting your parent he may ask also for a special urological examination. If he thinks there might be trouble in the heart region or the gastro-intestinal tract, he will want x-rays, and so on. Finally, the geriatric examination, if it is a good one, will not be complete unless the physician asks about the conditions under which his patient lives and offers his advice. Living in an atomic age with all its accompanying fears and tensions is strenuous. It is natural and logical that the same set of conditions which are changing young people's lives have also affected older people's.

REHABILITATION OF THE OLD

Faced even with an incurable disease, a good doctor works on the theory: "If I cannot restore the crippled organ, then I must restore the man."

Dr. Stephen Smith made a surprise appearance at the fiftieth annual meeting of the American Public Health Association he had helped to found. He was then ninety-eight years old, but his voice was still loud and clear, and his message as cogent as ever.

"You all want to know the secret of my longevity," he told his audience. "It is very simple. Do as I did a half century ago. Get yourself a heart impairment—not too serious—and take care of it!"

That meeting was held a number of years ago. Dr. Smith was proving again he was well ahead of his times. Today, his recipe for a well-preserved life is the accepted practice among medical men.

Pulling your father through the first little stroke is not enough. He needs to be taught how to keep his weight down and his temper under control so he can keep going for another ten or fifteen years.

Physicians no longer label elderly patients "irremediable" or "incurable." Instead they bend their efforts toward getting the well organs to support the weak ones. Dr. C. Ward Crampton, head of New York County Medical Society's Geriatric Committee, calls this a "de-aging" process. If the heart condition is incurable, for example, all the other organs, the nutritional resources, and the patient's hygiene program will be brought to a state of highest efficiency to strengthen the laboring member. (Which is exactly the practice a good general follows when he disposes his strong forces so they will cover up the failures of the weak ones.) This enables the heart to give better service with less labor, and also may remove one or more of the original causes of the cardiac condition.

"Many a man," says Dr. Crampton, "has become more active, more vigorous after his first coronary attack by the use of this method than he was before."

An old man no longer has to wear a truss and bear his affliction; an old woman need not suffer the consequences of a collapsed uterus without hope. Fractures of old bones are no longer terrifying. A good example of the progress that has been made is outlined in this story of Mrs. V., a patient at Bellevue Hospital in New York City—though not for long. At eighty-one years of age she broke her hip and the bones did not grow together properly. Years ago that would have meant she would have been bedfast for whatever remained to her of life. But Mrs. V. has every expectation of walking again. The day she took her first steps she wore a broad smile. The physiotherapist helped her out of her wheel-chair, she shuffled up a small incline, and she started to learn to move her legs and feet again on a practice walk with hand-rails on each side.

There are about sixty so-called "rehabilitation centers" in the country now, not all of them connected with hospitals. (See pp. 396-400 for list.)

HELP FROM REHABILITATION CENTERS

Rehabilitation, in the formal use of that term, follows no set pattern. In one community the rehabilitation center may be a curative workshop; in another it may mean physical therapy clinics, sheltered workshops where handicapped people work at their own pace to earn money, or a complete department of physical medicine and rehabilitation in a hospital. No matter how much they vary, they all accept the point of view that age is not the prime factor to be considered. The guiding principle is expressed by Dr. Howard A. Rusk. He heads New York University Bellevue Medical Center's work with all types of disabled of all ages, from amputees to spastics. Dr. Rusk says, "It is not what a person has lost, but what he has *left* that's important."

No one is considered hopeless. Remind your relative of that if he is discouraged. Dr. Rusk taught a man with a broken back to walk and care for himself in only three months because he still had the use of his abdominal muscles.

A center may be sponsored by a hospital, a local Community Chest, the state, or it may operate on a fee basis as a private institution. Most of them provide medical services; a very few include vocational or pre-vocational training. The cost, like the work, varies with the auspices and the locality but the expense, if it is high, ought not to deter anyone. There are ways of grading fees to meet the income of the patient and his family, and there is state aid. Any aged man or woman who longs either to regain ability to care for himself and relieve others, or who is eager to be earning again, ought to have a chance, at least, to find out if something can be done for him. Before working out the details urge him to apply to the state Office of Vocational Rehabilitation at the capital to find out where and how he can find out about himself.

Rehabilitation means finding a life fit for a person, quite as much as making the patient fit for life. In old age the effect may be the end result of a long preparation. But this, too, ought not to discourage anyone to whom you can tell the following facts. At New York University Hospital there were a hundred hemiplegics, whose average age was sixty-three. Ninety of them were taught to ambulate and care for all their bodily needs. Over forty eventually were able to take up some occupation and earn money. Some returned to their old job, or got a new one based on the skills they had acquired. They worked on a full or part-time basis, at home, in an office, or in a factory.

A curious incident occurred when the House Appropriations Committee in 1953 cited in its report to the Congress certain cases. It questioned "payment for cataract operations and hospitalization for seventy-four- and eighty-year-old housewives who had been on public assistance for a number of years."

The truth of that story, Dr. Rusk points out, is this: The two instances of cataract removals made it possible for these old women to care for invalid relatives. Otherwise, both they and their kin would have had to go to a public, tax-supported institution.(6)

Who can doubt that the money was well spent in any of these cases which offer dramatic evidence that the current of life can flow as strong in the elderly as in the young? There is, however, one sour note. When Dr. Rusk and his associates at the Institute of Physical Medicine and Rehabilitation in New York studied four hundred and seventy-six cases, it was found that in terms of each individual (young and old) there was a high rate of success in functional rehabilitation. However, only fifty per cent of the cases studied were found to be "making full use of the abilities they had in a way satisfactory to them and the community." The best of training cannot help an individual if, when he is retrained, we give him no opportunity to gain a place in the community's life or to utilize the capacities he has developed. The old in many instances *can* be rehabilitated; the rest is our challenge.

SICKNESS: CHALLENGE TO FAMILY LIFE

Sickness of any kind is always a challenge to the family who has to bear it. Since older people are more prostrated by even a slight illness than the young and take a longer time to recover, the best place for them to get well is at home, if it is at all possible.

You may be the anxious type who feels that if grandfather

slips on a banana peel and fractures his shoulder his old bones will mend more quickly in a hospital or nursing home. But grandpa may have an entirely different view. He may think you are simply trying to get rid of him, or shrink from the trouble of taking care of him. Worse yet, he may think he is so seriously ill you are shipping him off to die. The "will to live" after the age of eighty-five or ninety, and sometimes long before, may be enfeebled, especially if the person has already had a good deal of pain and suffering.

Combatting pain is the physician's business but you can do a great deal to help any older person believe it is worth while recovering. Don't add to his troubles by pulling a long face. Otherwise he is quite likely to feel his death will be a relief not only to himself but to everyone else. It is common knowledge that once older people find themselves flat on their backs, they often give up hope too soon, even when a prognosis is favorable, accepting the fact that "this is the end."

Beware, however, of over-sentimentalizing. Many older people take delight in retelling their symptoms to every caller. This strong interest in their health may have its roots in an attempt to deny even to themselves their inescapable decline, and they ask for perpetual reassurance. It may also be a direct bid for attention, and a protest at being shelved. A hard-of-hearing person, for instance, is frequently accused in the family circle of being able to hear perfectly those things which touch on his own interests and being oblivious to anything else. He may be using his handicap to shut out difficult and painful experiences, it is true. On the other hand, the simplest remedy is to find out whether he actually can benefit by a hearing aid, and if he can, it will widen his horizon and give him the assurance that someone really cares deeply whether he knows what is going on, even if he is nearing the end of existence.

Beware, however, of yielding to the temptation to buy the latest in surgical belts or stockings or sun-lamps to show your devotion. Anyone who has observed old people knows how common it is for them to want appliances of one kind or another (to rejuvenate themselves, probably) and then, because they have difficulty in adjusting to them, never use them. (As one geriatrician puts it:

"Old people are suckers for patent medicines and gadgets.") They may be ashamed they need such help. One major company which sells hearing aids advises "oldsters" in its radio audience that they can have a booklet which describes the product "in a large white envelope with no printing on the outside."

Buy whatever an older person needs, but be certain before you do so that a physician has approved it. Otherwise you may be purchasing expensive equipment which an older man or woman lacks either the physical, mental, or emotional ability to use.

Old Age Assistance records in one city show a record which is far from unique. A lame, elderly woman had spent a long life dominating a meek husband. When he died, she had little money but plenty of energy. After she was accepted as an applicant for Old Age Assistance, she besieged the doctors for an expensive knee brace. Fortunately, perhaps, for her health, she never used it. Two years later a social worker was examining her case and found the record showed that she had demanded and recently been given another kind of knee brace. He interpreted this as quite a different kind of need—the impulse to deny her advancing age and enfeeblement, and a need for attention to replace the loss of affection which she had been unable to face.

This bears out Dr. Alexander Simon's contention. In his work at the Langley Porter Clinic, San Francisco, he says he found old people reacting to decreasing abilities "by retreating into a state of rationalizing disfunction with complaints of fatigue, weakness, digestive and bowel difficulties and physical illness."

You need to remember also that people in their old age may be cranky in direct proportion to the state of their health. This is the conclusion Professor Albert R. Chandler came to after studying more than five hundred reports on persons from fifty to eighty years of age. If this occurs, remember to be tender. It may only cost you the time to readjust a pillow or to place a bed at a different angle so the patient's gaze will not begin and end with a blank wall. It means creating a "will to live." Your business should be to make an older person think in terms of how well he may become rather than in terms of how ill he is. This is your challenge.

HOW TO TREAT THE SICK OLD

In Montefiore Hospital in New York City there is an aged man, condemned to bedfastness for the rest of his years, few or long. With the help of the social workers, he was able to start a small business which he conducts from his hospital bed. The record reads in part: "When Mr. Y. felt himself a participating, contributing individual to society once more, he was able to profit by medical treatment."

Not everyone has this kind of determination. Another person will want to be coddled, or will give up the struggle long before he needs to. The opposite number of the hospital businessman in Montefiore is the one in another institution. Although he had been greatly interested in music all his life, he insisted on having his room denuded of all pictures and books, his music scores, and his radio. He said these things made him too emotional and he feared they would disturb him to the point where he could not apply his full attention to his health problem!

Whether your own elderly patient is in a hospital or at home, your job, which may be a hard one, is not to intensify his feeling of helplessness. Don't be over-protective. Callousness to suffering is certainly not a desirable quality in anyone. On the other hand, an emotional backwash that takes control of one's wits, particularly at critical times, is decidedly out of place in a sick-room.

You must try to be optimistic, because it has a stimulating effect on the patient. You have to be understanding because it promotes his comfort and welfare. If you are going to live in the same house, or visit him frequently wherever he is, you need to cultivate toleration, especially if he has an illness of long duration, the kind that frequently occurs in the aged.

Illness can do strange things to any of us. Weeks, months, or years spent in alternating between chair and bed, or not even that much mobility, may destroy the last shred of self-confidence and self-respect. Anyone knows who has been hospitalized any length of time—even a few weeks—that the energies and thoughts that ordinarily are turned to objective pursuits become subjective so that matters of little consequence—a broken glass, a squeaking door, a shade raised too high or a room too dark—loom large. In the older person's case, especially, his symptoms, worries, and the knowledge that his age is a handicap in any situation that arises, may make him magnify, if not invent, causes of provocation.

If he does, you must realize that he is reacting to an abnormal situation in a normal way. "Just as anyone might," says Dr. Hyman Goldstein, "when restricted in activity, secluded from everyday life, and beset with the notion that life's junk heap is the next stop."(7)

Dr. Goldstein, and others, who follow the dictum that Aristotle laid down over two thousands years ago that "movement is life," offer this solution: If you really want to do something constructive for a sick older person, provide him with activities. Keep his mind occupied so he won't have time for self-examination and self-pity. Galen, a Greek physician, in the second century of the Christian era said that "employment is nature's best physician," and modern doctors have not been able to improve on this ancient's lore.

OCCUPATIONAL THERAPY IN SICK-ROOM

If your elderly relative is institutionalized he may have the benefit of occupational therapy which all good hospitals have, just as they have physical therapy in the form of whirlpool baths, exercise tanks, and oscillating beds. Essentially, the purpose of the two therapies is the same: to encourage use of afflicted parts and prevent complete invalidism. Even without the equipment and without any training at all you can achieve some excellent results at home. If you can discover a bent, hobby, interest, or latent talent, you will be doing considerably more for your relative than lowering the sick-room tension which often rises where there are empty hours. Active brain cells can carry on even where palsied hands leave off. Handicrafts in bed can give the thrill of achievement even if they involve no more than merely dropping one and purling one.

You can get hints from plenty of books, even in a small library, on how to keep convalescents happy. And you can get suggestions from the American Red Cross, or one or another of the several national groups interested in the handicapped. If you are not satisfied with this, visit any veterans' hospital and find out what the occupants are doing, especially those no longer young, who fill hospital beds they first occupied after World War I.

Elementary exercises (which your doctor will tell you about) can overcome the sluggish, half-sitting position most long-time bed-patients assume. And they will help overcome stiff joints, stimulate circulation and metabolism. If you want to prevent atrophy of the mind as well as the body, however, you must give sick old people some reason to think it's worth while to make an effort. It need not be anything big, or even a work on behalf of humanity, though an old lady will take more interest in knitting afghans, if you let her know her work is to cover someone else's crippled knees. Occupation has to be important to the *patient,* whatever it is, and not merely "busy work for idle hands." This older people are inclined to resent. They are not kindergartners, even when they are helpless, which is something a great many people forget.

If you look at these stories which emanated from Goldwater Memorial Hospital, a public institution for chronic disease sufferers in New York City, you'll see that will-power is as much a factor as the treatment, and incentive the best driver of all:

1. One old man exercises painfully crippled hands by weaving rag rugs. He keeps some and sells others. In either case he is limbering up afflicted extremities while at the same time he is giving his ego a boost.

2. Piano-playing was put behind one aging arthritic woman long before she came to the hospital, but revived there because her doctors considered it good exercise for her arthritic fingers. The day she gave a recital for other wheel-chair patients was a psychological, as well as a physical, landmark.

3. One seventy-three-year-old man was told he must exercise rheumatic legs. He protested, until he found he was going to do his exercises on the foot pedals of a jigsaw, and from then on happily made cut-out toys for his grandchildren.

EQUIPPING A SICK-ROOM

The sickness that can disrupt any household is unquestionably worse when it affects an older member, because his resistance is less, complications more likely, and recovery slower. Nevertheless, there is nothing to get tense over if you have to turn any ordinary bedroom into a sick-room, even for a long-time illness. There is just one major point to consider. A bed is the most important article in the room. Putting it where it belongs should be your first concern, even if you have to put your ancestors' heirlooms in the attic.

Place the bed so it can easily be reached from either side to lessen your own or someone else's work. Put it out of a direct draft, and, for the sake of the person it it, angle it so it won't face a direct light. An adjustable hospital bed which can be cranked up or down easily to fit a patient's posture is a great comfort if one has to be sick a long time. You can frequently rent one or buy it from a surgical supply house in any city. Later on you might want an "invalid's walker," folding service trays that make serving easier —the kind that won't let dishes slide off and won't upset if the patient rests his arms on it—pressure-point pads, and dozens of other labor-saving, and patient-saving devices. They can all be obtained from the same place. (If you don't know what to ask for, visit a local hospital, and make some inquiries of the social service department there.)

Any long-drawn out sickness is expensive, and you may want to cut costs if only to satisfy the older patient. Many old people fret, even if they have large bank accounts, if they think their, or the family's, money is being spent recklessly while they are helpless to prevent it. A simple handbook on nursing from the public library or the department of health will tell you some of the "make do" devices professional nurses don't scorn. If you don't want to buy a bed-rest, for instance, when it's time for your patient to sit up, make one. You can do it with five or six pillows, and a kitchen chair with its legs tied to the headboard. "Doughnuts" of rubber to fit an ankle or heel or some other pressure-point, to prevent bedsores can be bought, but you can make your own at less expense, if you like, out of cotton batting twisted and covered with a gauze bandage. With the same simplicity you can make a lap tray by knocking two sides from a shallow box, painting it a cheerful color, and letting the two ends rest on the bed on each side of the patient's knees.

The list of other equipment you might need—a thermometer, a hot-water bag or heating pad, and so on—is not so long as to prove a strain either on your temper or your pocketbook.

SICK-ROOM BEHAVIOR

What is more important than bedside tables is a thoughtful attitude. Home-nursing is not formidable if you don't make it so. One of the biggest barriers to getting well quickly for most older people is the fear their illness engenders, not only in them, but in their families.

Don't shut them off when they are sick from the normal activities in the home, unless your doctor insists on it. Familiar sounds, when they are not too loud, are reassuring. They mean to a person who is ill that no one is particularly disturbed about the condition he is in. If the children play about as usual in the yard, if no one lowers his voice or walks on tiptoe, the older man or woman will take it for granted everyone thinks he's going to be up and about soon. Even if that is an illusion, it is better for him and for you to preserve it.

On the other hand, if you whisper and he can't hear what you are saying to the doctor or the nurse, he will be sure to think he's badly off, and as a result, soon may be.

There are also those little matters of sick-room behavior such as taking away loose rugs, putting medicines out of reach of an impatient hand, or placing a guard in front of a low window-sill to protect a dizzy head. These are the acts which one professional nurse (who calls herself "a future octogenarian") (8) says are "the small acts of consideration towards older people which add up to a tremendous difference in their lives."

In her nursing lexicon they mean such trifles as a rose on a tray set with pretty china to tempt a capricious appetite, a luminous mat on a bed-table to give comfort at night to an invalid so he can see objects on it without fumbling, a hand-bell close at hand for emergencies when the lonely dark hours come, bright red or green eyeglass cases which old eyes can see clearly when they fall from trembling hands.

"Elementary," as Sherlock Holmes might have admonished Dr. Watson. Nevertheless, these are the actions a good nurse, without or with a diploma, performs automatically. They soothe and protect her patient, without the "fussing" so many anxious sons and daughters exhibit when they run for a hot-water bag to warm father's feet when it is unnecessary, or a shawl for mother's shoulders when she's perfectly comfortable without it.

These things may seem an extra burden, too detailed to matter, if you have to nurse your mother-in-law after a radical cancer operation and, as Mary Adams did, at the same time take care of three children, all under five. But any doctor will certify that such attentions have as much effect on the course of the illness, as formal bedside care. You can learn out of any book on practical nursing or in an American Red Cross course how to smooth out wrinkles and tuck a sheet tightly, without disturbing a patient, or how to protect a mattress, but it takes real understanding to realize that old age inflicts certain limitations which are neither an offense nor a great trial of your patience.

Your doctor will tell you what symptoms to watch out for, and it will help if your observations are written down. (A drugstore can supply the chart that trained nurses use.) He will take it for granted you know enough not to discuss a serious illness in front of the patient, or that the members of the family will cooperate in giving him privacy and quiet when they are needed. You should let his physician know if you notice any sudden changes, whether loss of appetite, loss of sleep, onset of a cold, coughing, or the more dramatic cases of bleeding from any source, or drastic lessening of mental coordination.

Beyond this, you need to spend all your energies left over from actual nursing in weaning old people from the bedfastness which one doctor terms "a medical suspension of the Act of Habeas Corpus."

THE CONVALESCENT OLD

All doctors try to get older patients out of bed as quickly as possible to avoid respiratory and circulatory complications which arise much more quickly in the sick old than the young. On your part, believe that an old man with pain in his back or knees can get out of bed even if he thinks—and probably is right—it is more comfortable and less mentally exhausting to stay there. Or that mother or grandmother who comes out of the hospital after a broken leg may be perfectly able eventually to leave her wheelchair with the aid, perhaps, of a leg brace or cane, and climb stairs again.

The day your mother asks for a mirror or face-powder, or your father looks around for his slippers or a razor, you can be sure their health is returning. But don't fret if you can't persuade them at first even to try a sitting position. They should, because it expands the chest and improves the posture of the spinal column. You may have to use wiles to back your physician's effort to overcome an older person's inertia and fears, but don't dictate. As one old man said to his worrisome daughter, "I may be dying and don't know it, but until I do expire, don't try to make up my mind for me!"

There are many elderly people, and your relatives will not be in the minority if they are among them, who are actually afraid of recovering. Psychiatrists call this "the will to fail." They are reluctant to get out of bed (though they won't realize the reasons) because to stay there guarantees they will receive attention which may be lacking when they are well. Or it may be a protective shield against burdens they are reluctant to take up again. One of the ways to combat this is to see that every older patient's slightest efforts give him some feeling of success, and that he has some *incentive* to get well, like the eighty-seven-year-old man Dr. Lionel Z. Cosin tells about.

This old gentleman's will-power was as effective as the treatment he received in the geriatric unit at Oxford Hospital, England. Under Dr. Cosin's supervision he was taken out of bed every day as one measure to prevent broncho-pneumonia. After three weeks, this man, who had a bad fracture, was astonishing the nurses by insisting that he do spring and sling exercises like other, younger patients he saw in the ward. Eventually, he recovered to the point of being able to hobble to a busy thoroughfare where he caught a bus three times a week to a near-by village. Curious at such activity, the nurses asked the reason for his journeys. It seemed he was courting a widow with a chicken farm and a "pub" in the hope of providing for his "old age"!

Your relative is not likely to have this particular form of rejuvenation on his mind, but he can overcome much which was accepted as inevitable in former years. Dr. Cosin lays down these suggestions for the staff in his geriatric unit which ought to be memorized by any member of the family who has to wait on a sick older man or woman:

1. Don't ask your patient to perform any activity beyond his capacity. (If your doctor doesn't tell you exactly and in detail what he can and cannot do, find out; most older people can do more than they realize.)
2. If it is necessary to help him do anything, explain why.
3. When he has performed some activity—as simple as sitting, standing, moving an arm or leg—display enthusiasm, no matter how unsteady or labored the action appeared.
4. Above everything, encourage him. Tell him what he will gain by standing and walking, and how it will affect his general health. While the end is inevitable there is much that can be done before that end is reached.

This is the word of the late Dr. Simon Baruch. He was one of those who believe that old age must not be depressing and that life should end as naturally as it began, with little distress, and in the midst of participation in society with no sitting on the side-line benches. "There are no incurable diseases," said Dr. Baruch, "there are only diseases for which no cure has yet been found."

NOTES TO CHAPTER III

(1) Statistics furnished by American Heart Association, May, 1953.

(2) Metropolitan Life Insurance Company; based on figures furnished by National Office of Vital Statistics, Washington, D. C., May, 1953.

(3) *Ibid.* Also, Monroe, Robert T., M.D. "The Medical Skills and the Services Needed by Old People," address to Welfare Federation of Cleveland, Ohio, Mar. 17, 1949.

(4) American Red Cross, *Instructor's Guide to Home Nursing of the Aged and Chronically Ill.* Washington, D. C., 1950.

(5) Thewlis, Malford, M.D. "Notes on Geriatrics." Paper read at Brooklyn Hebrew Home and Hospital, Mar. 17, 1952.

(6) Rusk, Howard A., M.D. *The New York Times* (Sunday), May 24, 1953.

(7) Goldstein, Hyman. "How to Nurse the Aged." *The Trainea Nurse and Hospital Review* (now *Nursing World*), Oct., 1941.

(8) Anonymous. "My Grandmother Is 80." *American Journal of Nursing* (Vol. 49, No. 5), May, 1949.

CHAPTER FOUR

GETTING ON IN YEARS —SAFELY

Your worries about the effect of aging on anyone—including yourself—will be considerably lightened if you accept the teaching of Dr. Lillien J. Martin. That believer in the potentialities of the old could write at seventy-eight, "I find life more interesting, more exciting, and more absorbing than ever before."(1) Dr. Martin believed everyone could feel the same way, if he worked at it. In the Old Age Center she founded (after she had reached so-called "retirement age") she told discouraged older men and women that youthfulness was largely a matter of mental stimulation, moderate exercise, and a healthy diet.

To most people this guide sounds too simple. They prefer, like Fannie Ward, the actress, to concentrate on ways to *look* youthful. Miss Ward's long-time act made press agents call her a "peppy young flapper" when she was a grandmother in her sixties. Her stories of manipulation of facial muscles and Siberian snow face-masks made columnists' tidbits until she died.

But there is a vast difference to adjusting sensibly to the aging process and making a career out of appearing youthful. No rigid muscle toning, heroic exercise, or Spartan diet is going to make up in a few weeks or months for damages which have been developing over many years.

Whether the individual is weak, miserable, and old at sixty, or young, vital, and vigorous at eighty depends to a considerable degree, nevertheless, on one factor. This is his past and current food program. For the older they grow the more your relatives' well-being will depend on undisturbed functioning of their digestive apparatus. This is axiomatic among geriatricians. As Dr. Edward J. Stieglitz once said, "We cannot stop aging but we can retard it. Aging is a problem of nutrition—cellular nutrition."(2)

GOOD FOOD HABITS POSTPONE AGING

Good food habits, like thrift, should start early in life. They postpone the physical, mental, and emotional deteriorations commonly associated with old age. But body building and repair work go on all during a lifetime—not merely when one is chronologically young. So that it always pays, and it is never too late, to make proper eating a regular part of any person's health routine.

This is reason enough to prod your relatives into changing their food habits, if they have bad ones. And it is quite likely they may have. If an old man shoves aside salad and fruit day after day and demands cakes and pies instead, it is probably because his nutritional pattern was set up years before talk of vitamins became fashionable. He comes of a generation which ate heavy meals such as we rarely put on the table today. If an older woman complains that food is tasteless or dishes served don't have the flavor they used to have, don't conclude she is simply being contrary. The very old suffer from a gradual loss of sense of taste and smell, a psychological factor which deadens appetite and lessens anticipation of a meal. Others may resort to a tea-and-toast regimen because a budget is small, or they haven't the energy or the desire to prepare anything else when there is no one to share it. Malnutrition is as common among the well-to-do as the poor.

FOOD FADS CAN BE DANGEROUS

To help any older person fight the abnormalities of senility, you need to know what, how, and when he eats. If he has food prejudices, help him overcome them. Often those who can least afford it are taken in by the promoter of a miracle food supplement, or a so-called "health food."

At the geriatric clinic of Peter Bent Brigham Hospital in Boston, Dr. Robert Monroe insists that old people be asked questions about each type of food they have daily. He says, "Of course, if you ask an oldster, 'Do you have a normal diet?' he says, 'Yes.' Any other reply would convict him of unintelligence."(3)

If you don't live in the same house or don't eat at the same table with your older folk, follow Dr. Monroe's method. Question them; find out if they are bolstering a haphazard diet with vitamin concentrates recommended, not by a physican, but by a book, or a radio or newspaper columnist. All authorities agree that the *best* way to get all the necessary nutrients needed by a normal, healthy person of any age is through an adequate diet. Older people are often taken in by nutrition quackery, a term that means just what it implies. In their search for the Fountain of Youth they are noted for self-prescribing. Pills are not the only source of vitamins by any means.

If grandpa complains of "indigestion" or nausea, or grandma has a poor appetite and says she is "nervous" or "weak" find out if either is relying on a bizarre diet or nutritional nostrums. Their ills are the type that are frequently traced to nutritional deficiencies caused by lack of essential foods. Your relatives may simply be victims of prejudice like many of Dr. Monroe's clinic patients. He found some were avoiding milk because of old wives' tales that it is constipating, or meat because many old people think it causes high blood pressure. Others were omitting fruits as "too acid," or were ignoring vegetables they found difficult to chew.

Without frightening your relatives, you can point out what scientific studies show. One investigation of elderly people's diets, for instance, indicated that three-fourths of those studied were suffering from lack of calcium and iron because they skipped milk and omitted the iron-rich leafy vegetables.(4) Dr. Monroe and his staff emphasize that snacks between meals are not good if they destroy appetite for "square meals." Breakfastless mornings are frowned on. Lack of desire for food when rising time comes is considered a fatigue hangover that ought to be looked into. Irregularity of meals at any time is regarded in medical circles as a symptom of a disordered, ineffectual life (and that needs something besides a better diet for correction).

WHAT OLDER PEOPLE SHOULD EAT

If enough, but not too much, food is one of the essential factors for a long and healthy life, what should older people eat? Do their meals have to be different or at different times than younger people's to ward off senility?

The briefest answer is the one the Department of Health of New York City gives in its food guide for older folks:

Every person, regardless of age, needs four groups of foods for health and well-being. Milk, cheese and eggs; meat, fish and poultry; vegetables and fruits; bread and cereals—these form the basis of good meals from infancy to retirement and beyond. (5)

If a man or woman is sixty, seventy, or eighty, still has average health and carries on his life much as usual, he doesn't need to be pampered at mealtimes or treated any differently at the table than any other normal adult. If you insist on his eating soft foods, or omitting this and that "because it is bad" for him, all you are doing is accelerating old age. If he is a bedridden invalid he will need his heavy meal at noontime and a light one at night so he'll sleep better. But if he is hale and accustomed to a heavy dinner then he will continue to enjoy it as much as anybody else. Too many older people suffer from insomnia in institutions and even in the bosom of their families because someone thinks they ought to eat lightly; they are actually hungry. Some older people fall into the category of those who rise late and get in their stride in late afternoon, while others are early risers and are tired out by suppertime. For the nighthawk, the evening dinner is preferable.

In other words, older people are still people. Unless they are under doctor's orders to eat otherwise, they should have these foods every day—the same as any other adult who is well and active:

MILK. *At least a pint, preferably a quart, a day.*

If he doesn't want to drink four glasses of milk or buttermilk, he should have some of it in soups, puddings, creamed dishes, or eat extra cheese. If he cries, "Too expensive!" tell him to try evaporated or dry skim milk.

MEAT, FISH, POULTRY, CHEESE, AND EGGS. *Two servings a day.*

Protein in one or another of these forms is important because all diseases are more likely to be increased in severity and frequency if protein is inadequate. Protein poverty causes three common conditions in aging people: anemia (low hemoglobin); asthenia (general weakness) and edema (collection of fluids in tissues of ankles, face, and abdomen).

FRUITS. *Two to three servings a day.*

Citrus fruits like orange, grapefruit, tomato, or their juices should be included, for vitamin C, the antiscorbutic vitamin.

VEGETABLES. *Three servings a day.*

A green, leafy or yellow vegetable and a potato contain the valuable vitamin B, and other substances important in maintaining good resistance to infection and in aiding digestion and elimination.

BREAD AND CEREAL. *One serving whole grain cereal plus three to six slices of bread each day.*

"Whole" or "enriched" breads or "restored" cereals should be used, for they furnish iron and the vitamins, thiamine, riboflavin, and niacin.

BUTTER OR MARGARINE. *Two to three tablespoons a day.*

This is necessary to complete the day's energy needs.

GOOD DIET FOR GOOD TEETH

A good diet is essential for good teeth—even false teeth. Diet affects gums and bone around the teeth as well as the teeth themselves. If there have already been many extractions, then properly fitted dentures are the best preventives to keep old people away from too much liquid, too much mush, and too much soft bread. They are common reliances of the old, not only because they find it hard to chew, but because a great many have lost incentive for living. They need someone to cook for them who doesn't take the attitude: "What does it matter? They're too old to care."

Regular tooth and mouth inspection by a good dentist is a much safer recipe for a comfortable old age than the hasty pudding which one hundred-year-old Philadelphian gave as his nutritional staff of life.

If your mother or father must eat mush because neither has good teeth or has false ones that don't fit, then see, at least, that it is the right kind. Elderly people who have to watch every penny often leave out meat, fish, and poultry because these are usually the costliest items on the market. But they wouldn't have to skip proteins which help maintain the tissues and energy, if they made mush or custards out of millet, sunflower meal, or its seeds. Less than a cup of either contains about thirty grams of good, inexpensive proteins. Use it plain or mixed with honey. This is the advice of Dr. Malford W. Thewlis. He is no chef, but he is Secretary of the American Geriatrics Society, and his book, *Care of the Aged*, is a physician's guide.

OBESITY: DANGER TO OLD

It is not enough to see that your aging relatives have enough of the right kinds of food to eat; it is equally important that they realize overweight is one of the most dangerous nutritional diseases. The folk saying: "Fat people dig their graves with their teeth," has ominous significance so far as the aging are concerned.

Scientists believe that the ideal weight at age twenty-five, in relation to height, is still the ideal weight at sixty-five or older. The common conception that it is "natural to get fatter as the years go by" is all wrong. Putting on too much weight is not a harmless, if annoying concomitant of "sitting around" too much as one's activities die down. Nor is it due simply to carelessness about appearance as one gets older. It is literally an illness, likely to be more harmful than many much-publicized "killers." Here is a partial roll-call of what is literally the vital impact of overweight, particularly on people past middle age.

It curtails life;
impairs vigor;
breaks down the liver;
affects cancer and other chronic diseases;
increases surgical risks;
increases likelihood of diabetes;
hastens onset of complications;
is associated with hypertension;

is associated with heart disease;	is associated with arterio-sclerosis

This list sounds formidable, and is. It would be more so if there were not plenty of books, pamphlets, and even lectures available for sound guidance, and physicians anxious to give advice if patients will only take it.

There is proof that even a ten to fifteen per cent addition of poundage above the normal means cutting life expectancy by approximately one-fifth. Ten pounds of flesh more than is needed adds approximately a half-mile of capillaries for the heart to feed, a strain it is bound to feel.

These are the types of facts to bring to the attention of those afflicted with overweight—and that is the proper way to describe it. Obesity is nothing more than taking in a greater number of calories per day than a person needs to expend as energy. The body is an engine, and its fuel is food. If more food is consumed than the body uses up, the extra fuel is stored up in the form of fat. Since metabolism slows down with the years, the old need fewer starches and sugars. Even if activity is the same when a person is sixty as it was when he was thirty, it is estimated that caloric requirements have diminished thirty-five per cent. (6)

WHY OLDER PEOPLE OVEREAT

The only way to reduce is to stop eating so much. But before you take your relative to the doctor to get a diet list for him, find out *why* he is overeating. Aunt May may look like a near-relative of the circus Fat Woman, continually munch on chocolates and pastry between meals, be a glutton at the dinner table—and it may be because she is anxious or discontented.

If this sounds like phantasy, listen to the words of two authorities:

Dr. Stieglitz says, "Eating may be an escape mechanism; it is a source of considerable physical pleasure and permits the individual to find calm because digestion and a full belly induce drowsiness and lessened awareness of annoyances."

Dr. Edward H. Rynearson of the Mayo Clinic also recognizes, along with many other physicians, that food can act as a sedative. Often it gives a temporary solace to those who cannot solve their personal difficulties. He says, "An overweight person is nearly always a compulsive eater who turns to his refrigerator like a compulsive drinker turns to the bottle."

When old Mrs. Turnbull's two grandsons were killed in Korea, her callers were surprised to see how she sat, hour after hour, listlessly looking out the window, stuffing herself with sweets. After her only son's death in World War I, she had taken his boys into her heart and home, since they were doubly orphaned within a year. When they, too, were gone, life seemed empty. Only her physician really understood why she had left a standing order for daily boxes of candy.

This is so-called "psychosomatic overeating."

Are your older relatives eating too much—*fressing* is the expressive German word, used only for animals—because they have too little to do? Is eating the one pleasure left to assuage life's losses, or a too-solitary life?

These, and other equally dismal reasons, have all been found to be the cause of over-indulgence in food. One might let it go at that if the victim were not apt to succumb much more readily to gall-bladder trouble, gout, or the foot, ankle, knee, back "miseries" so many old complain of.

The remedy for such psychological gluttony is simple. Substitute other satisfactions for food. Exert yourself to show acceptance of abilities and attitudes, and demonstrate your affection. Help older people cultivate outside interests, which is the occupational therapy which will take their minds off themselves—and food.

Of course psychosomatic overeating does not explain every case. There are those with gland trouble; there are also the "scavengers"—the mother or grandmother who hates to see anything go to waste and eats scraps all day; there are also the habitual overeaters, used to a bountiful table and unwilling to cut down on food out of pride or unwillingness to recognize that age has dulled appetite.

What are the alternatives? Changing the situations which bring about the evil is the best, but not always possible. The second alternative is to present food facts in such a way that your kinfolk may be impelled to change their eating ways. You can influence them, at least, not to follow the popular pastime of "living on a diet" without consulting a physician. Above everything else, preach to your relatives that to be too fat or too thin are both symptoms of disease. Do it with the usual proviso that if they are looked after in time through preventive health examinations the symptoms don't need to be disastrous; if they are ignored they may be.

MALNUTRITION: CAUSE AND EFFECT

The opposite of obesity is, of course, malnutrition. In our well-fed country we meet with it less often. It can come about as a result of having the wrong ideas about what to eat (a common misunderstanding of people reared in a less nutrition-conscious age) as well as inability to get enough food.

Malnutrition can arise through poor dentures, or none; it may just as easily be the result of psychological failures in life, sorrow or loneliness. The latter are far less recognizable in the family circle, but any good physician can and will take them into consideration.

If the condition is severe you will want to take your relative to a physician; in any case, find out what kind of food he is relying on. He may not be getting enough vitamin B or C, either because he is shying away from citrus foods—"too acid" is a favorite disclaimer—or thinks milk is just a baby food. Or he may lack certain food factors simply because his body is not absorbing properly what he does eat, which is a doctor's business to find out, not yours.

To get an older person to change his habits, especially food habits, late in life, is never easy. However, the results are usually worth all the patience, good humor, and even ingenuity, you may have to exercise. Components of vitamin B complex were all that was needed to help one old woman who complained of cramps in her legs at night, and the same thing, given to an old man with an unexplained depression, made what his relatives call his "gray moods" disappear.

GROUP LIFE AND NUTRITION

Few people are going to care about whether they have a balanced or an unbalanced diet if no one really takes their living habits and their dental conditions and appetites into consideration. It follows as a direct corollary that if you want your relative to be happy in any kind of boarding or nursing home or a home for the aged, you should look into the matter of meals. Before he goes there, find out how food is handled, prepared, and served. If meals are monotonous, if food is tasteless, if mastication is painful or tiring, if the post-dining period is marked by digestive discomfort, life becomes a succession of small trials. And if you are near enough, you will be made to feel them, too.

When Mrs. Oliphant visited her mother's friend, "Aunt Sally," in a home for descendants of Civil War veterans, that ancient lady spent all of the visiting time complaining of the meals. She was alternately fearfully expecting, or actually suffering from intestinal troubles. Talking about them at least brought her some attention. But when Mrs. Oliphant brought "Aunt Sally" to her home for a week's visit, her soda mints and aspirin tablets were forgotten. The old lady ate a hearty breakfast, served on a silver tray with dainty china, in her room; devoured her lunch with others at the table in the garden, and every night managed to stow away a good dinner. Though in the Home for the aged she insisted she never slept a wink if she ate after six o'clock—and then only milk and toast—she had no difficulty adapting herself to the Oliphants' seven-o'clock dinner hour, and as she said, slept "like a baby" when she went to bed around midnight.

You may not be able to find a nursing, convalescent, or boarding home which supplies silver trays and rose-bud china, but it is important *not* to take some things for granted. For instance, no matter how highly Mrs. ABC has recommended an old man's or woman's home (because someone she knows slightly, she *thinks* is happy there), find out how meals are served. Is there "tray service," or are meals all taken together in a dining-room, and if so, what kind of room? Is the institution so large that there is a cafeteria?

If so, how heavy are the dishes and trays, and is there anyone to help carry them?

Tray service makes for a solitary life; too often the dishes will be returned with food half-eaten, because of indifference or loneliness. Cafeterias are necessary in some large institutions, but may be difficult for a man or woman who has never used them, or who finds holding a tray impracticable. The family-service type of dining-room is generally the best. Older people like to sit with a few others at a small table set with linen, silver, and a vase of flowers. It gives a homey atmosphere which half conceals the hated "institutional" look—and thereby aids digestion.

Your relative will always have some compromises to make, but there are certain provisions of the sanitary code which you (or he) ought to make certain are being observed. A partial list of the points you ought to remember to check includes questions which may seem embarrassing to ask. If you don't pry into them, however, you will never know how much that passes for feebleness and fraility, or awkwardness and unsteadiness, is due to poor physical condition due to poor food conditions:

1. Inquire whether food-handlers have complete medical examinations before they are hired, and at least once a year after that.
2. Find out whether a physician removes them if diarrhea or any other illness occurs, or if this is left to the housekeeper.
3. Ask to see the kitchen and take the time to look for these things: floor drains; tiled or cement walls; separate refrigerators for meat, vegetable, and dairy products; and what garbage disposal is like.

As for food itself, don't hesitate to ask to see menus or be present at enough meals, before your relative takes up residence, to find out something about these items:

1. How many meals are served a day? Some nursing homes report two and an in-between snack. There is no excuse for that except economy, which is not sufficient reason.
2. How often do sweets, pastry, cake, and preserves appear? Some well-meaning hostess may think she is catering to poor appe-

tites by serving them often. But their excessive use tends to dull taste for essential foods and causes digestive upsets. Omitting them altogether means taking away satisfaction and some energy foods.

3. Is something hot served at *each* meal?
4. Is bread served as substitutes for other foods?
5. When meat or poultry or fish is not served, is some other protein always substituted? Poultry and meat *ought* to be served three or four times a week.
6. Is milk, or something made from it, on the daily menu?
7. How hearty is the breakfast?
8. Is there provision for in-between snacks, especially if the heartiest meal is at noon?

You can expand this list indefinitely, of course, but chiefly you must be concerned about the food that any hale adult, whether he is in his late maturity or not, ought to have. If an individual is a "picky," fastidious eater, all you can do is hope there will be someone around who won't be too unsympathetic if he makes a nuisance of himself.

FOOD FOR THE SICK AND OLD

If he is sick, however, the problem is different. Still, it is not insurmountable, even if an older person wants to keep on living by himself. If, for example, your relative is a person who has to live on a restricted diet, there is no reason why he can't learn what it is and have enough will-power to stick to it. Diabetic clinics, for example, give out lists, on the basis of size of serving and type of food to be eaten, which a child could follow. Your fears for an older person who has to live under food restrictions of any kind ought not to mean that you will put pressure on him to move from the environment he wants to stay in, for that reason alone. If you are too apprehensive, and force the issue, you may live to regret it.

It is true that many disease conditions call for diet adjustment which is often more important than the medicine bottle. A low-sodium diet, for instance, can bring down high blood pressure. A reducing diet may be recommended for both high blood pressure and heart disease—and so on.

If there is an elderly invalid in the house who needs special attention, it may take skill to cook and serve the food properly, but there are plenty of ways to find out how to do it, in addition to asking the physician and nurse. There are books and pamphlets of special recipes, and of advice on how to tempt flagging appetites or arouse sluggish digestive processes which afflict older patients. You can find them in practically any library or book-store, and the range is wide. Pages of the American Red Cross's *Home Nursing Textbook,* for instance, are devoted to such recipes, and so is *Food for Your Heart,* which the American Heart Association recommends. (See pp. 404-05 for list.)

In general, however, you could not do better than to follow the requirements laid down by the state department in New Jersey which licenses nursing homes:

"There shall be a sufficient supply of good food," this part of the regulations reads, "properly prepared with green vegetables and fruit emphasized in the dietary *unless otherwise prescribed by the physician.*" [The italics are ours.] "The foods served should be simple and easily digestible and should contain all the constituents required for good nutrition.

"It is best to begin a meal with something hot to stimulate gastric secretion and thus aid digestion, and to serve the heartiest meal in the middle of the day, supplemented by early supper and nourishment at bedtime. Quantities served at meals should be moderate in amount.

"Attention should be paid to a dietary for aged persons which will not tax their digestive powers. Consideration should be given to the texture of food served because of their difficulties of mastication.

"For tray service, a light weight, easily cleaned, smooth surface tray of ample size is recommended. Tray covers of paper, linen, or cotton are recommended. . . ."

DIET: ACCIDENT PREVENTIVE

Very often sickness cannot be warded off, but accidents can be prevented. That is the most optimistic note one can sound.

Since a large share of the long-term disabling or deforming injuries—fractures, sprains, dislocations of the hip, back, hand, etc.—that are common to the old are the direct results of falls, they are something to be concerned about without any apologies for apprehension. Make sure there are no stumble traps. They crop up in the best regulated homes. If you don't live with your parents, see to it a neighbor drops in often enough to be sure they aren't becoming careless. If they are going to live with strangers or in an institution, be certain the special hazards the old are susceptible to, are not ignored. This includes attention to their diet as an accident preventive.

Everybody knows older people are apt to be unsteady, and if they do fall, run more danger of breaking an arm or leg than when they were decades younger. Yet few know that what they eat and have eaten has something to do with the fact that old bones are brittle. If this sounds like something out of *Alice in Wonderland,* don't scoff. And don't let older people poke fun at the idea of drinking milk, eating milk puddings, and so on, to lessen the risk of falling. The scientific facts behind this truth are sound.

Dr. Henry C. Sherman, the well-known nutritional authority, says: "The ordinary mixed diet of Americans and Europeans, at least among dwellers in cities and towns, is probably more often deficient in calcium than in any other chemical agency."(7) And old bones become porous and lighter in weight and more fragile over the years because they are a chemical bank which is steadily being depleted. The calcium in them is being constantly called on to make up for the calcium loss in blood and tissues. This accounts for the fact that old people seem to—and actually do—"shrivel up." The skeleton has measurably shrunk because the calcium, the greatest insurance against falls, is being used up.

UNNECESSARY ACCIDENTS

If your parents have brittle bones—and that is the most likely assumption to make—do something about it. A man like Dr. David H. Bokhof who, at eighty-one, sent out challenges to all comers fifty years or older to meet him on the tennis court, probably knows how to take care of himself. But even he needs to use a sturdy step-ladder if he must climb, to throw away an unsteady bedside table, to use a nightlight unless he wants to risk a fractured femur—or neck. These are simple precautions anyone can take—and often doesn't. Mrs. Archibald won prizes for her roses for many happy years. When she was in her seventies she refused—quite rightly—to yield to her daughter's pleas to give up gardening altogether. Now the daughter is going around with a martyred air because for months she has had to nurse her mother. Mrs. Archibald broke her leg when she became dizzy and tumbled over a rake in her garden on the hottest day in the year, and the shock worked other damage. But she needn't have had the broken limb or the shock, the doctor says. All she should have done was to take things easy during the dog-days, and remember to put on her old straw hat when the sun was high.

Possibly your relatives have the same streak of stubbornness, or unwillingness to give way to the demands of age.

Proper shoes and low heels, for instance, are not as elegant as high-heeled pumps but for a tottery old woman to wear the latter is to court disaster. Falls account for more than one-half the fatal accidents that occur every year, and eighty-five per cent of them involve people past sixty-five. The chief reason is that as we grow older our sense of balance is not so good as it used to be. While there are hazards in a room full of old-fashioned, heavy furniture, sometimes its bulk provides a safeguard—something an old man or woman can hold on to as he moves about a room.

Older people don't want to be pampered and they don't want to be set apart; doing either one only means you are accelerating old age. But you can check on preventable hazards when you visit them—or get someone you trust to do it. Usually it will be enough to point them out; any handy old man or woman can do simple repairs around the house. If you find your relative isn't taking them seriously enough, don't hesitate to tell him what national statistics prove. That is, four out of five of the falls of elderly people occur in their own homes, and most of them in the bedroom. Yet of all the causes of disability in later years, they are probably the easiest to avoid.

Are there small, loose "scatter rugs" in the house? Or carpets with turned-up edges? Are the floors waxed and slippery? Is there a low chair or footstool in the way on the route to the bathroom? A door which hangs ajar? Poor lighting anywhere? A bed that is too high? Shaky stairs or rickety banisters? An unsteady bedside table? Obstructions on the floors or stairways?

The great majority of older people need to be reminded they are not as spry as they used to be. Without making an older person so fearful he will be afraid to lead a normal existence, you can call his attention to hazards and see that he corrects them. Your objective should be aimed at building his confidence as well as his physical security.

Older people's tendency is to prefer what they are familiar with, so avoid any of the streamlined gadgets, and stick to the sensible suggestions made by organizations like the National Safety Council. Here is the Council's advice to those who are getting on in years:

"*Bedroom:* Change the arrangement if you must, so you don't have to skitter around the furniture to get from bed to door. Tack down your 'throw rugs' if you must use them, and have a light near the bed so you can see where you are going at night.

Bathroom: Light the light when you go in; if you wear glasses be sure to put them on before you reach for a drug so you won't get another medicine by mistake. Put a grab-bar in the bathroom wall, a good stout one you can really hang on to when you're getting out of the tub.

Stairways: Light the light and hold the handrail before you go down.

Chores: Keep on doing them but be careful not to lift too much or carry loads that will strain you. If you garden, take it easy, especially on hot days, and wear an old straw hat.

Walks: Take them and enjoy them—but make sure you have a green light at the crossing. If you walk along a highway, walk against traffic. Put on something white—a muffler or a scarf will do—so you can be seen coming along the road."

Large, bulky pieces of furniture of a by-gone day are often cherished for sentimental or thrift reasons. Either have them pushed away so their sharp corners won't catch the unwary, or put lights where they can be easily seen when the old go from room to room —and insist on the lights being turned on.

Confidence that they can "see in the dark," or the excuse, "I can see just as well as I ever could," are some of the reasons people fall down stairs. Older people, especially, should hold on to handrails, and turn lights on at the top of the stairs before they start descending. If there is no switch there, have one put in, today.

Make sure there is a small nightlight, or a light switch, or failing that, at least a flashlight within easy reach at night, and be certain there are no trailing electric cords. Keep a nightlight on in the bathroom if you can't be sure an older person will always—not sometimes—turn on the regular light.

Floors that are highly polished are a concession to vanity; so are high heels. The old can afford neither. Pretty little Mrs. Judson was as proud of her size 2 shoes at seventy as she had been at seventeen. However, she invited disaster because she tottered on them. She shed more tears over the low-heeled, "sensible" shoes the doctor insisted on her wearing, than she did over the crutch she had to use for months after her fall. You can't do much when "all is vanity" like this.

But you can remember that deliberation comes naturally to the old and should be encouraged. Don't rush them when they are crossing streets, or doing anything else. If you walk with them, make sure the way is clear. Don't take it for granted they will look both ways before they cross the street; they may be afraid you are impatient, and will hurry to keep up with you. Slowness is something few can do anything about, except be careful—or perhaps ask for more understanding.

EXERCISE FOR THE ELDERLY

There is no reason why Everett Jones' daughter should nag him day after day because he wants to keep on doing her chores. She means well, but as he asserts, quite correctly, "Only vegetables rest all the time." Mr. Jones is in his eighties but he is still able to keep on shoveling coal for the furnace and snow off the sidewalk.

He'll be all right, provided he doesn't lift too much at a time, carry loads that will strain him—and does take his time.

This matter of how much exercise and how much rest older people ought to take is one of the vexing matters most young people aren't sure about, and the old are stubborn about.

Practically the only criterion anyone can set up is that too much rest is as bad as too little. Some people are like Walter Morrison, the Virginia ex-slave. When he was a hundred years old he gave this recipe for a long life: "When I works, I works; and when I relaxes, I just sits." Others are like Christian Klindt, who intends to keep on hunting. He began when he was twelve years old, and bagged his latest deer when he was eighty-five.

If you feel you ought to check an older person's desire to keep on playing golf, hiking, playing tennis, swimming, or some other activity, remember that all physicians agree on this: exercise at sixty-five is just as important as at sixteen. They even urge elderly bed-patients to take it. The body depends on muscular action to stimulate respiration, circulation, and digestion. A well man or woman is often able to play games and exercise long after his relatives and friends have relegated him to a back-seat—or a back-rest.

What should your relatives do to keep in physical trim? Dr. Martin long ago pointed out that an older person can get just as much benefit out of typewriting, polishing silver, or wiping dishes, as he could on expensive golf links, or in a swimming pool. Dr. George Frederick Miller, a seventy-two-year-old retired professor, can hike the full two thousand miles of the Appalachian Trail. George S. Groesbeck, an architectural engineer, at eighty-four still drives to and from work through New York City's worst traffic. He has played tennis for nearly seventy-five years.

Whether your relatives will want such strenuous play, or will have to be content with something like Dr. Martin's building-up exercises, ought to depend on one thing, and one thing only. What does the doctor say? If they are having thorough annual physical examinations, as they should, they'll find their answer (and probably your freedom from anxiety) from him.

Strenuous or light, a good exercise program should be *anatomical* (to keep structure of the body straight and strong); *physio-*

logical (to stimulate the internal organs); *psychological* (to release tension and help lift morale.)

These terms are more alarming than the exercises themselves. Dr. C. Ward Crampton, who uses them, cites the story of a sixty-four-year-old man whose chest was hollow, whose shoulders were bent, and whose head hung down. When he called on Dr. Crampton, his skin was muddy, and he complained of indigestion and frequent colds. He felt down and out, and looked it.

"In fact," says Dr. Crampton, " 'down and out' was his main trouble. His head was down, his chest was down, and his abdomen was bulging out. No wonder his health and spirits were down, too!"

What is the best exercise for such a person? Not thirty-six holes of golf every day nor a vigorous set of push-ups every morning. What Dr. Crampton prescribed was just one simple workout —standing up straight. Mr. "Down and Out" was anatomically distorted; his lungs and heart were cramped; his abdominal organs had slumped and all of his vital processes were stagnating. By lifting his head, raising his chest, straightening his spine, elevating his ribs, tightening his bulging abdomen, his heart and lungs had more room; his liver was lifted, and the blood was helped to rise from stagnant vessels to go coursing through his body.

Not every program can be as simple as that. The average individual, however, needs exercise as much as he needs recreation, and he can often get both at the same time. The degree differs only in proportion to how limber he has kept himself. If Aunt Maria has always loved to dance, she'll join in square dancing at the Old People's Club with a relish. If Uncle Joe has been a good bowler, bending over won't be likely to give him a backache (as it might if his wife asked him to bring up potatoes from the cellar). Most people at any age want their exercise in the form of play, and there is no reason why this should change with one's nonage. As one physician pointed out, "One *can* lead an orchestra in bed, and such playfulness is a good tonic."

There is one common, but false, idea that ought to be made clear to everybody. When the body is at rest it is true the heart works only about a tenth of its capacity. But it is a completely wrong idea, says the American Heart Association, that strenuous exercise damages the heart, by enlarging it, straining it, making it more susceptible to disease, or causing heart murmur. Enlargement comes only from a continuous added burden over long periods of time—far longer than any exercise can be kept up. Murmurs during and after exercise are a normal accompaniment of the heart's increased rate; permanent ones are not caused by exercise. And it is only when disease causes the heart to lose nine-tenths of its capacity that one need fear "heart failure." Even then many people, old people, too, live for years with the heart failing to perform its full function, and live fairly active lives, too.

All you need to reassure yourself and the family is this rule, also laid down by the American Heart Association. "Exercise that the individual is used to and that is reasonable *at his age* never harms a healthy heart. Only after the heart has been damaged need the question of cutting down on usual activities be considered. Of course, a man whose chief exercise has been walking from his desk to his car should not suddenly take up weight-lifting."

HOW TO LIVE

Almost everyone has some degree of degenerative joint changes by the time he has reached even forty, and sooner or later we all have to slow down. By the time a score or more of years have passed, the sixty year old should be taking his exercise, as a college athlete does: he uses a warming-up period at the beginning and an end spurt.

If there is any chance of altering the physical surroundings so that they can fit in with the necessity for equal periods of energy out-put and rest, older people will last longer at their own peaks. Eminent architects like Henry S. Churchill believe that this is not an unattainable aim, for as he pointed out at a conference on old age problems at the University of Florida, "all the so-called special facilities within dwellings for the aged are equally desirable for any good housing." The list of desirables he has compiled includes these:

"*One floor layout*. This is desirable at any age—for the creeper, the housewife, the sick, and cardiac.

If not a one-floor home, the stairs should be easy and the hand-rails solid; the stairs should be well lighted. Requirements for any good home.

Floors should be warm and resilient. I ask, for whom should they be cold and hard?

The possibility of reasonable privacy. Of course.

Convenient arrangement of space, such as easy access to the bathroom, kitchen, entrances, and minimum laundry facility. That is to say, good planning.

Sunlight, of course.

Good lighting, no dark halls, closets or corners; plenty of switches.

Safe cooking equipment, with automatic cut-offs in case the pilot light goes out. This should be mandatory. . . .

Non-slip bathtubs, strong grab-bars. Young people slip, too. . . .

No drafts—sensible and easy-opening windows, perhaps louvred sub-sill ventilation.

Reduction of transmitted noise wherever possible. This is a matter of cost and nothing else.

Outside sitting space, sunny and sheltered from the wind. Good for babies, too.

Well-planned and accessible closet and storage space.

Doors wide enough for wheel-chairs, that is, two inches wider than present standards, and with lever-handle hardware instead of the slippery round knob. This is the one item that might be at all unusual. . . ."

FITNESS IS ATTAINABLE

There is plenty of medical evidence that regular exercise *plus* play not only keeps limbs supple but has beneficial effects on those who have to combat both age and high blood pressure, arthritis, paralysis and other chronic diseases. As the head of Peter Bent Brigham Hospital's clinic for the old says, "Here is a field of rehabilitation as exciting and as rewarding as that with war casualties!"

The enthusiasm of Dr. Monroe is no denial that aging does impose limitations on strength. All the milk-baths, vitamin pills, injections, and exercise that can be devised will not overcome the eventual impact of time. Yet the four aims of a truly ripe old age —physical fitness, mental stability, good digestion, and social adaptability—are not unattainable. Something can be done to retard aging and aging is not synonymous with degeneration. You need to impress that on your older people and remember it yourself.

NOTES TO CHAPTER IV

(1) Quoted by Wingate M. Johnson, M.D. in *The Years After Fifty*. New York: Whittlesey House, 1947.

(2) Stieglitz, Edward J., M.D. "Aging as a Problem of Nutrition." Speech before American Dietetic Association Convention, Philadelphia, Oct. 15, 1947.

(3) Robert T. Monroe, M.D. "The Medical Skills and the Services Needed by Old People." Speech delivered at a meeting of the Welfare Federation of Cleveland, Ohio, Mar. 17, 1949. P. 6.

(4) "Eating for Health in Later Life." Division of Nutrition, Pennsylvania Dept. of Health. *Nutrition News,* Dec., 1947. (Leaflet.)

(5) "Food for Older Folks." Department of Health, City of New York, 1951. (Leaflet.)

(6) Division of Nutrition, Pennsylvania Department of Health, *Nutrition News, op. cit.*

(7) Henry C. Sherman, D.Sc. *Chemistry of Food and Nutrition.* New York: The Macmillan Company, 1952. Eighth edition.

CHAPTER FIVE

FINANCING OLD AGE

How much money do elderly people need to live in decency and with a measure of comfort?

The superficial answer is easy. No two individuals' requirements are the same because their backgrounds and standards differ. But this is practically equivalent to Marie Antionette's flippant remark. When she was told the people of France had no bread she is reputed to have said, "Let 'em eat cake!" This philosophy can apply only to that very small percentage of our senior citizens who can cut the loaf of living to suit their taste. If your relatives are like the majority of their contemporaries they have to trim financial corners. What they need to know is how other people do it with the least pain so they can follow suit.

If they fear joblessness, or fear losing what they have, or fear dependency on you or someone else, they have the wry consolation of being in good company. According to the 1950 census, one out of every two men and women past sixty-five has an income of under $1,000 a year. (1) Among those who were still heading their own households eighty-eight per cent were doing it on incomes which ranged from $500 to $1,500.

Even if your relatives have more than that, they belong to the generation, reared on Benjamin Franklin's thrift principles, that has seen the doctrine of "a penny saved, a penny earned," swept from under them. Most elderly people face a financial quandary they never anticipated when they set up housekeeping, took out a small insurance policy with each successive baby, and laid away something for "a rainy day" each week. They are still bearing not only the scars of the 1930's, that anxiety decade, but the effects of the inflationary period, which followed not one, but two world wars.

If your relatives fall into this category, or nearly so, you can help them best by knowing exactly how much they need to cover their rock-bottom needs. A study made by the U. S. Bureau of Labor Statistics of the requirements of an elderly couple will give you some useful hints. (This was at the half-century point. Make your own economic comparisons for this year's cost of living.)

A BUDGET FOR THE ELDERLY

This "budget family" consisted of a man and wife, living in their own two- or three-room apartment or house, independent, able to get about and care for themselves. They were sixty-five years old or older. The husband was assumed to be following the pattern of the average man of his age, retired, or taking only occasional employment.

The sum estimated by the Bureau to cover the essential needs of this hypothetical couple ranged between a low of $1,600 and a high of $1,900. In any one of thirty-four cities studied by the Bureau this married pair was expected to live "modestly" on that sum, not luxuriously—no automobile, for instance. But the budget was intended to give them enough to "maintain health and allow normal participation in community life according to American standards." This last qualification accounts for the fact that the estimates covered not only housing, food, clothing, housefurnishings, household operation, transportation, and medical care, but "personal care, reading, recreation, tobacco, and gifts and contributions."

You and your parents or grandparents may not wholly agree with the governmental idea of what constitutes a "modest budget" but you can use it as a starting point. (You will find budgeting manuals in any good library; or you can purchase them from the U. S. Superintendent of Documents, Washington, 25, D. C. for a few cents.)

If purse strings have to be tightened, there are a number of things an older individual can do without and suffer no hardship.

Almost all aging people have long ago seen the folly of keeping up with the Joneses, anyway. If they own a car they may want to continue using it, but not so much and with more care. They are far less addicted to expensive entertainments than in their earlier years and can give up country clubs as well as night clubs without regret. Most of them have wardrobes left from fatter years, and will lean on them, and take dress more casually than they did when they were younger.

One consolation the after-sixty-five-year-old group has is that federal income tax laws are kinder. Under present regulations they get a double exemption, and have the right to deduct all their medical expenses. If they receive any benefits under Social Security laws they are not taxable.

And so on, through a list you and they will find can be a long one, if it has to be. The very appraisal in written form has some comfort in it for the older person who has to pinch, and, like most of us, usually doesn't know where to begin.

The study made by the Bureau of Labor Statistics and some prior ones contain some general principles which are true whether the price of living is high or low. It was found, for example, that:

1. A two-person family's expenditures are approximately sixty-five per cent of those of a four-person family, when both families live on a comparable level. (This may or may not be an argument for older people to leave their own home and take up a domicile with others.)

2. The budgetary studies made of the elderly couple in 1950 showed that they could live on the smallest amount of money in New Orleans, Louisiana (for $1,602). The highest sum, $1,908, would have to be spent in Milwaukee, Wisconsin. The variation in expenditures in any of the thirty-four cities reported on was due to cost of comparable *housing*.

SHELTER: IMPORTANT ITEM IN BUDGET

This is the most important point of all. In any budget made for your relatives, shelter is going to be the main factor. It is major, not only from a financial, but an emotional point of view. (What kind of home they have and if it is their own, whether they can keep it, will be the thing which tips the emotional scales for most.) It determines whether they can stay where they are, or at less expense, move in with relatives, with strangers, or possibly seek their shelter in an institution.

If a relative of yours has a home, however humble, you will find that consciously or unconsciously he will regard it as his own personal social security. If you feel he ought to give it up because it is too expensive to keep up, or too run-down, or too hard to manage, you will probably find he will want to hold on to it, no matter what else he has to sacrifice. If you are skeptical about the meaning a home has for the old, all you have to do is glance at census reports. Over seven and a half million individuals in the group past sixty-five, out of a possible ten and a half million living in non-farm areas, owned their own homes in 1950. This was a proportion that exceeded all other age groups in the population. (2)

These figures would be heartening were it not for the corollary. Out of sentiment, inertia, or necessity, approximately 8.4 per cent of the aging lived in sub-standard housing. This, too, was a proportion that greatly exceeded others in the population. If your own relative lives in one of these dilapidated houses, or, especially, if he owns a better one, it is not a simple matter of insisting that he give it up because his strength or his income has diminished. There are definite questions that ought to be answered, and definite points to help him consider thoughtfully before he answers them.

SELLING A HOME: PROS AND CONS

If your relative owns his own home, does he know how much it is worth—now?

A great many older people count on the fact that in an emergency they can always sell their home—as a last resort. If the emergency does come most of them suffer a shock. Their beloved, old-fashioned, inconvenient house brings nothing, or next to nothing, because age, style, and ups and downs in the neighborhood have altered its value. The sober facts to consider are these:

If we are in a time of inflation, any dwelling is at a premium, and even an old house will be marketable at a good price. If your relatives must sell, they will not be able to choose; if they can wait, let it be for inflation. The Waring Gillespies' two-story home in Mount Kisco, New York, had been put together piecemeal through the years. Finally they spent $4,248 to modernize it. The kichen had not been altered drastically in forty years. It alone cost the Gillespies $1,064. The bathroom, with its clawfoot tub, no tile, no shower, worn flooring, and rusty pipes, was typical of the rest of the house. It cost $978 to re-do. However, when all the repairs were finished the Gillespies unexpectedly had to move because Mr. Gillespie got another job elsewhere. They sold their house, valued in 1950 at $9,000, for more than double that sum.

It was their great good luck that they faced a seller's market. Your relatives' home may not be worth repairing; or its location may not be favorable—too far out from Main Street, or too near. Or a hundred other factors may make it a poor man's white elephant.

HOW TO RETAIN OWNERSHIP

If he wants to hold on to a home for the rest of his life, should he stay in it, or rent it?

How much of a retirement income can be realized from a house depends in part on the age and strength of the owner, and partly on the price he is willing to pay—not in money. The possible solutions generally break down into three:

1. Renting anything from a room to a half house has proved for many older people a way of increasing income, and in fewer instances, a way of turning the tables on the young.

EXAMPLE: Mr. and Mrs. Lathrop had no desire to live with their married daughter but it seemed that they would have to—that is, it did until their grand-nephew came home from Korea. He was glad to rent their top floor, glad to pay cheap rent for his first home, and his bride, Della, was happy to have the chance to learn cooking and housekeeping from an expert. When they move into their own place the Lathrops intend to look around for another bride and groom. (A possible solution, as long as housing is "tight," for others than the Lathrops.)

2. A number of widows, widowers, and married pairs find it possible to escape Northern winters or Southern summers when they rent out their homes to someone else.

EXAMPLE: This may or may not be possible at a price which makes it worth while. The Boxers find it so because their home is located near the college campus where Professor Boxer used to teach. There is always a visiting instructor or professor glad to use his library and Mrs. Boxer's tasteful furnishings.

3. Some turn their house into a boarding home tailored to fit the strength, food habits, and inclination of the housewife-cook.

EXAMPLE. Mrs. Schwartz's solution may not appeal to everyone but it has the merit of suggesting similar possibilities even in a small town in the heart of nowhere.

When Mrs. Schwartz's husband died practically his whole estate was the big, white, two-story house he had almost beggared himself to buy. No one wanted to purchase the white elephant, but fortunately Mrs. Schwartz wanted to stay in the rambling old place. She managed to do it by letting it be known through her Lutheran pastor that she would take a few schoolteacher boarders. Since her sour-cream cakes and other delicacies were already wellknown through church bazaars, she soon had a waiting list. Now her niece, who helps her at the old-fashioned coal range, says she'll take over the boarders, the cook-stove, and eventually, the house, when her aunt can no longer stand the burden. But that, says Auntie, won't be for many years to come!

TO BUY OR NOT TO BUY

All the cautions that apply to selling a house operate in buying one—in reverse. Actually, many elderly people want to take on a big place like Mrs. Schwartz's, when they would be better off in a modest apartment where the janitor takes care of the chores and the depreciation is the worry of the landlord.

However, if your elders have the buying bee in their bonnet it will be uphill work to uproot it. At least make them understand these counsels, offered by Norman Strunk, Executive Vice-President of the U. S. Saving and Loan League, under the following points:

Mortgages: Mortgage lenders don't automatically reject applications from would-be home buyers because of their advanced age but it is considerably tougher for a man nearing sixty or sixty-five to float a home loan than it is for a family head in his thirties or forties. Lending institutions like Mr. Strunk's will finance home purchase by aging borrowers if they see reasonable prospects of the loan being paid off by (*a*) regular amortization out of income, (*b*) by a pledge of life insurance, or (*c*) if someone else—usually the old people's children—will co-sign the note.

Down-payments: Prospective home buyers in the aging group also have to put up bigger down payments than younger borrowers do. Lenders generally want the payment schedules worked out so the mortgage will be paid off by the time the borrower reaches the age of seventy—meaning a ten-year mortgage in most cases.

Price: This, of course, depends on general conditions, but, generally speaking, smaller cities and towns have a larger proportion of low-priced homes. Buying an old house instead of a new one is as risky as the stock market. An aging house, like an aging man, is constantly in danger of dilapidation. Repairs may be so expensive that they wipe out the bargain of a house bought in a period of deflation.

NEW LOCATION: ADVANTAGES AND DISADVANTAGES

The two sides of the holding or selling question are illustrated by these two stories:

Affirmative: Leroy L. Maxwell thinks he can continue to have his cake and eat it, too. At seventy-one, he alternates between living in a trailer in Florida during the winter, and in his Northern home in the summer. It costs him $110, including electricity, to park his trailer near a river five months a year, and $50 to store it in the seven months he's up north. He rents his house, furnished, collecting $500 while he is basking in the Southern sun. *Negative*: When the Jamesons retired they bought a home for $4,750 within view of the Gulf of Mexico, selling their old home and furniture in the Eastern city where they had lived for thirty-one years. They congratulated themselves. The town was small, the place to their liking, and living cheap. However, golden years were cut short when Mr. Jameson died less than two years after their move. Now Mrs. Jameson longs to be "back home" but her money is tied up in the house, and there are few buyers in this out-of-the-way spot. She is lonely for the city and city ways and is not likely to make new friends for her shyness keeps away her neighbors.

Good advice on the much discussed question of "to move or not to move" when retirement comes, emanates from Florida. Before your relatives join thousands of old couples in trailers, old people in automobiles or on the trains and buses, all hurrying some other place to live, restrain them long enough to consider the "yeas" and "nays" given by the Citizens Committee on Retirement in Florida:

"In general . . ." concludes their leaflet, "although it is often possible to reduce the cost of living somewhat by home gardening or by raising chickens, it is not safe to assume that less income will be required for comfortable living here than in your home city. It is helpful, also, if the new-comer has the funds needed for investment in a home in the locality where he decides to live."(3)

PROPER FINANCIAL COUNSELLING

The final precautions apply whether the question is buying, selling, or renting: "Do business only with people you know or who have been reliably recommended to you. Make sure you are dealing with a legally registered real estate broker. Don't buy property you haven't seen." There are reliable firms who give honest advice, everywhere, as well as Chambers of Commerce with sound people back of information desks.

Your relative may be stubborn enough, or wise enough to think he can manage his own affairs. It is just possible that he may be the financial wizard he thinks he is. The more common situation is that a man or woman doesn't know whom to call on, or thinks his affairs too inconsequential to bring to a financial counsellor.

Nothing could be more mistaken than this view. Every community has bankers, and bankers, whether in a city or a village, are excellent advisors. If they don't know all the ramifications of a particular problem, they can suggest reputable brokers, real estate firms, or investment counsellors who do. Older people, brought up to be self-reliant, sometimes have doubts and hesitations about applying even to such recommended sources. One way to reassure them, and also to check reliability, is to find out how long a firm or an individual has been in business. If they have been in the community a period of years they will not risk a good Dun and Bradstreet rating by sponsoring fly-by-night schemes, or make "suckers" out of elderly customers, no matter how financially naïve.

Nevertheless, even wise young amateurs often forget the basic facts of financial life. Never let older people ignore these essentials:

The higher the return, the riskier the investment. The old lady who prided herself on her acumen, when her husband died got nine per cent on her investment in an Oklahoma oil-drilling company. However, she crowed only a few years. After that she wept. The company failed and she lost all her meager capital. So did the good physician who had advised her to make the move. Note that he was a *friend,* not a professional counsellor.

Gambles like this are for young people; they can afford the time to repent—and accumulate more to reinvest. Few persons past sixty-five should think of capital gains; safety should be their goal. Widows and widowers who want to be happy should stay clear of stock promoters, invest-by-mail sharks, and big profit-making schemes which promise a high rate of interest.

Even an additional one fourth of one per cent over a long period will make a difference if the returns are plowed back into investments. They build on themselves. Nevertheless, from the standpoint of the later years, when a person may want his money —all of it—and want it in a hurry, savings accounts in banks, savings and loan shares paying a low rate of interest, and government or other bonds which do the same are best. They give little cause for insomina.

Inflation affects any kind of investment where there is a fixed return on the principal. About the only items not subject to this danger are common stocks and real estate. This advantage is counterbalanced by the fact that their values go up and down—rising with inflation and descending in deflation. Neither should be bought without special knowledge or, its equivalent, the advice of trained, safety-conscious advisors. It is true that investment-grade common stocks are frequently bought by trustees, who have to be responsible for other people's money. But they *know* which ones—like the American Telephone and Telegraph Company—are likely to make some profit under any circumstances short of total collapse of the country.

The pertinent interrogation is: Who is giving the advice and how much does he know?

A BUSINESS OF ONE'S OWN

Nowhere does this question become more important than in the attempts the old make to realize that common daydream—"a little business of my own."

If your relatives are average Americans, they will not be content with a small supplementary income, if they have been able to accumulate anything at all. They will want some useful activity when they retire. They would like it to yield a little money, along with interest and color for their later years.

This is the picture which emerges from more than one survey. When the Northwestern National Life Insurance Company asked three thousand of its male policyholders their future plans, three-fourths of those within hailing distance of retirement said they had no desire for complete leisure. (4) Many already had money-making plans, similar to those other average Americans seem to nurse. The most frequently mentioned were:

1. *Small farming.* (Enticing advertisements for years have been painting the joys of "five acres and contentment.")

2. *Small business:* the one most favored was a few tourist cabins. (Many elderly couples like to choose something toward which the Missis can also contribute her bit.)

If your relative has similar ideas, you may have to keep silent when you long to give advice. When you do speak, put your objections, if you have any, on a factual, not an emotional basis. Point out that organizations like the U. S. Women's Bureau presents this information to inquirers: A half million women were managers or proprietors of non-farm businesses when the last census was taken. Only eight per cent of them had an income of $5,000 or more, and fifty per cent realized less than $1,129 that year. There is no reason to believe men did any better.

But when you are inclined to damn what may seem to you a dubious venture, you have to remember that personal factors count as much after sixty-five as they did before. Some people do succeed. Clark Simmons, for example, is a retired sales manager who found his metier in a small bookshop in a summer resort. However, he had all the assets he needed—capital, contacts, knowledge of merchandising methods, and current market conditions. (Which is exactly what your kinfolk ought to have.) Furthermore, Mr. Simmons opened his shop in a resort he had been going to for many summers past; all the people he knew were glad to patronize him. The shop gives him exactly what he wants—continued contact with the public, part-time employment, and a little profit.

This yearning to carry out one's own ideas is not confined to the male breast by any means. When Esther Cameron retired from the electric light and gas company she had a hundred dollar pension to count on every month for the rest of her life. Her family did everything short of confining her, to prevent her from opening the flower shop she had dreamed about since her high school days. She sank into it every penny she had saved. It may or may not succeed. Miss Cameron's retort to all the misgivings of her family is: "I've earned the right to be an old fool, if I am one!" But also note this: she will always have her pension to fall back on.

If your own relative is determined to go ahead with some enterprise, don't crush his initiative by refusing to believe he can succeed. You can help him best by seeing to it he knows and investigates these resources:

Trade Associations. Practically every business field has one. Librarians will direct inquirers to trade papers covering an industry or a profession. The editor—or a business directory, available also in the library—will put an inquirer in touch with the proper officials. They give information, gratis, about business conditions, manufacturers of equipment, etc.

The United States Department of Commerce. This is a way to find out general business conditions, marketing trends, statistical information. Write the Department also for leaflets covering a particular interest, whether it is accounting methods or how to raise angora rabbits for fun and profit.

State Departments of Commerce. Many have set up special counselling departments to advise small businessmen and women on individual problems. A number issued booklets at the end of World War II, for the use of veterans who wanted to be "free and independent" in a business of their own, most of which are still available to citizens of the state. They give information on all types of retailing, from opening a tonsorial parlor to a diaper service.

Service Organizations. Each community has a Chamber of Commerce, Kiwanis, Rotarian, and other service clubs. These local organizations are invaluable for information about business conditions, and are in the best position to know which enterprises will be likely to flourish locally. Urge your relatives, when they make inquiries, to be candid both about their finances and their age.

HELP WHILE AT WORK

If your relative is still active, however, he can take precautions in several directions. Does he expect to have a pension? If so, is he certain about its provisions? These are some of the questions he ought to ask:

1. Will he be entitled to continue hospital insurance if he has it, after he retires? (If not, he ought to take immediate steps to enroll in some other form of medical insurance protection. See pp. 408-17.)

2. Does his pension plan cover permanent disability?

3. The average pension today is only $10 a week. How has he planned to supplement it?

4. Is his pension going to continue for his wife if she survives him? (Some pensions provide that only a percentage of what is due the worker comes to the spouse on his death; others expire with him. John Burton found his pension was of the latter kind; fortunately, he learned it early. He took out an annuity which will give both him and his wife an income while he is living. If he predeceases her, she will continue to have an income from that, something from his Social Security, as his dependent, though his pension would die with him.)

Pension plans alone, however, even with Social Security benefits to bolster them, at best can never equal a regular wage. What is your relative doing that will supplement either, or both?

If his financial problem is not immediate, try to get him to think of the future while he still has a chance to shape it.

RE-TRAINING: USING OLD SKILLS

Some few large companies pay for courses designed to help their workers prepare for retirement. If your relative is not in this favored class, he can still act on the same suggestion. In large cities, and small towns, there are vocational classes in everything from welding to flower-arranging. Anyone, at any age, can enter them. Usually they are held in the evening to accommodate workers. Or correspondence courses along practical lines are offered by an enormous number of colleges and universities. (See Chapter VII, *Active Leisure: New Ways for Old.*)

If your relative is lacking in ideas, or has no way of finding out locally what his old talents can be made to yield in dollars and cents, tell him to go to any large library. It will abound in books on hobbies, crafts of all kinds, part-time businesses in country and town, and how to develop them.

The story of Mr. Charles Mintor is one example, which could be followed with modifications to suit the local scene. His idea was first to determine the need for a certain product, and then secure the training and advice that would make it realize profit.

Mr. Mintor was an advertising executive whose health compelled him to retire long before he wanted to. He and his wife owned a summer cottage in the White Mountains and for years he had attended the annual craftsmen's fair there and formed a good idea of what would appeal most to summer vacationers. When he returned to the city, both Mr. and Mrs. Mintor entered a crafts school to learn to weave. In a year the Mintors had moved their looms and household goods to the New Hampshire cottage. Today, their customers are their summer neighbors, though they also take orders when they go South—with samples—in winter. The Mintors do not need the extra income, but it gratifies both of them to share a common interest, have no empty hours, and to be able to produce something creatively that the world will pay for because it is good.

Craft schools on the commercial basis, which is the type the Mintors attended, are common in big cities. They give courses in sculpting, weaving, ceramics, photography, and a score of allied arts. Other classes, usually much less expensive, are offered in many other schools, including the YWCA's and YMCA's and in vocational high schools. (If your relative is interested, and doesn't know where to go, suggest he get in touch with a local board of education. If it is not offering courses itself, the staff will know where the nearest ones are.)

Crafts as a way of earning money have an especial appeal to older people whose state of health and vigor is not what it used to be. A handcrafts business can be operated on part-time, at whatever pace is suited to physical well-being. (One elderly Vermont woman makes a living out of carving figurines resembling the original drawings for *Alice in Wonderland,* though she is bedridden most of the time.)

RE-EXAMINING INSURANCE

Not everyone, however, wants to work with his hands, or can. Nor is everyone covered by industrial pensions. Approximately three-fourths of our workers are still not covered by them.

Even when pensions offer some protection, and certainly when they do not, the question comes back to this: "Will my resources last if I live to extreme old age?" Or, even more urgently: "Will there be enough to cover long spells of sickness if they come, or permanent incapacitation?"

One answer seems reassuring. Most people in the upper age brackets have some insurance to fall back on. Your parents and grandparents were reared at a time when everyone believed that small premiums on insurance policies, paid in youth and during middle age, would bring their own rewards in a secure future, either because one was a beneficiary of a policy, or reaped his own policy harvests. That comfortable theory has been considerably watered down by the spiraling upward of the cost of living, but the older people still have the policies. The old ones they took out years ago can give them more benefits than you yourself could get today.

No matter how much your relatives are protected in other financial ways, urge them to get their insurance policies out of the safety deposit box and look at them carefully. Get them to read and re-read the fine print. Here are some good reasons:

Nearly any life insurance policy can be converted to yield a life income. Under the older ones the policyholder can obtain a so-called settlement income from the company. The rates will probably be less generous than the settlement options if the beneficiary were to cash the policy. However, if the need is no longer there, say for Mrs. Brown or one of the once-little Browns, why shouldn't old Fred Brown take the cash?

Many policies issued a number of years ago had a disability clause of the type which has been discontinued. The companies will still honor it if it appears in the old policy. For example: When Grandpa Jones was nearing sixty-five he fell and injured himself so that he could no longer work. He had a policy which assured him a disability income of $10 for each $1,000 of insurance. He now receives $100 a month on his $10,000 policy for the rest of his life, and all future premiums are waived.

Your elders may not be so fortunate in their policy, but whatever provision for disability it has, it is probably much more favorable than you could get now.

Find some insurance agent in whom your parents or other

older folk have confidence, and let *him* do the explaining. (If you don't know such an insurance agent, locate him as you would a doctor or lawyer in a strange community, through friends, or local business and trade organizations.)

ANNUITIES: SAFE INVESTMENT

There is one type of insurance which elderly people may find it to their advantage to take out, even at sixty-five. Annuities offer some advantageous aspects for a man or woman who has some money and doesn't want to lose it late in life.

1. Annuities mean that the person who has one will always be certain a sum of money will come to him regularly, for the rest of his life.

2. It is absolutely a safe method of investing. The capital will never increase, it is true, but one never loses what he puts in.

The Allens, for example, as your grandparents or parents might, considered the pros far outweighed the cons.

In his sixties Mr. Allen retired from his post as a bank teller. Both he and Mrs. Allen were in excellent health. The three Allen children were grown and able to provide for themselves. The Senior Allens had approximately $20,000 in savings, a wholly paid for home, and Mr. Allen's Social Security benefits. Their broker presented the annuity vs. investment picture to them in this fashion: (5)

Life Expectancy at sixty-five:

A woman: at least 17½ years; 41 per cent live twenty years longer

A man: at least 14½ years; 27 per cent live twenty years longer, or more

Cost of Annuity at sixty-five:

A woman: $18,500 for $100 a month, guaranteed for life

A man: $15,750 for $100 a month, guaranteed for life

Investment costs at varying rates of interest:

A woman: With $18,500 she would receive $100 a month if her money earned 6½ per cent for the rest of her life; with lower interest rates (which are likely) she could tap both interest and principal, and her money would last at 2 per cent, 18 years; 3 per cent, 21 years, 4 per cent, 24 years.

A man: With $15,750, would have a monthly income of $100 only if his money were earning 7½ per cent interest; with lower interest, using both interest and principal, his money would last, at 2 per cent, 15 years; at 3 per cent, 17 years; at 4 per cent, 18 years.(5)

The Allens wanted security without the worry of investment, or the care of their capital. They thought they could rely on their physician's word that it was probable they both would live beyond the average life-expectancy age for their years. So they were willing to take the gamble of enjoying life long enough to get the full use of their capital, though the annuity meant all payments would cease at their death and nothing would be left out of it to their children. Their two boys and daughter were more than willing to see their parents benefit from their own money. So the Allens bought a "straight life annuity" on the "immediate" basis. (Buying annuities on the installment plan is the young folks' way.) Their income began a month after the purchase date of the policy. It is the "joint and survivorship" type. When either spouse dies the other will continue to receive the income till he himself is no more.

FINANCING ILLNESS

If the Allens had only their $20,000 capital, or were in poor health when Mr. Allen retired, their budgeting might have been far different. What they should have looked for then, first of all, was some protection from the bugaboo of high costs of long-time illness.

If your own relatives have no medical insurance they still may be able to get some, even though they are sixty-five. The keyword is "haste." Long-time illness means tremendous financial burdens which fall, usually, on the entire family. For selfish reasons, even if your nearest older folk are in sound health, find out what kind of insurance, if any, they can get. The statistical risks of a person in his sixties, seventies, or eighties falling ill, or having an accident, are high. So that every month the older person delays means that it will be just that much harder to find a reputable company or a sound organization (the adjectives must be stressed) to enroll him. Here are the chief possibilities:

Commercial insurance companies: A limited, very limited number will insure men and women beyond sixty, and the premiums will be high. Mr. A.'s and Miss B.'s chances will be better if they are still working. Generally speaking, it is always easier to get insurance if an older individual is part of a group from the same business organization. The risks are spread, then, over men and women of varying ages, and computers of insurance tables will look more kindly on the hoary.

What will he get in benefits if he is accepted, either as an individual, or a member of a group?

The answer is complex because companies vary widely in their practices. When the Hospital Council of Greater New York surveyed the situation in 1951,(6) the most popular policy provided $6 a day toward hospital room and board for a limit of ninety days, and a lump sum for "extra services." This averaged $70. Before your elderly leap to reach an insurance agent, let them note this remark in the Council's report: "There has been a tendency to eliminate age limits for subscribers and cover more benefits. *However* the majority of *companies still have age limits of sixty-five or more and many have age limits of sixty-five for renewals.*" (The italics are ours.)

The report of the New York State Joint Legislative Committee on Problems of the Aging is even more definite. About half the companies selling insurance for illness and accidents would not issue it in New York to anyone past fifty-five. Applicants for hospital coverage were usually turned down if they were past sixty. Most companies would not sell accident policies to anyone over sixty-five.(7)

This is one more case, however, where a little half loaf is better than no bread at all. The only way to find out if your elderly folk are eligible, is to have them make inquiries in the proper places. If their own insurance agent doesn't know, write the state Insurance Department at the state capital for a list of companies in the accident and health field, and query each. (Or the Bureau of Accident and Health Underwriters, 60 John Street, New York 7; N. Y.; or the Health and Accident Underwriters Conference, 176 West Adams Street, Chicago 3, Ill. They are the central bodies for practical and technical guidance to medical associations and hospitals in the insurance field, and they can help you, too.)

WARNING: Newspapers all over the nation are filled with insurance advertisements of the mail-order variety. Some companies promise to enroll people up to eighty-five years old, and they do. Common sense should tell grandma and grandpa they cannot expect much for their money when they are in the age brackets which make them poor insurance risks. But reason is a poor substitute for hope at any age. Premiums are fairly low, and numbers of aging people do nibble at the bait. Many subsequently are surprised to find these "limited coverage" policies offer returns that are practically negligible except for the extreme cases—like leprosy—that rarely occur.

Non-commercial health insurance. Grandma and grandpa had no chance to enroll for any of the non-profit-making medical, surgical, and hospital insurance plans when they were young adults. These plans have burgeoned since World War II under the sponsorship of unions, co-operative societies, the medical profession and civic leaders. Whether or not they will be eligible now depends on the individual community. Each plan is autonomous, though membership in one may entitle the subscriber to benefits in another. For instance, both the Blue Cross Hospital Service Plan, and its sister organization, Blue Shield, covering surgical and/or medical expense, have provisions to cover the member who moves from one community to another. Or if he is hospitalized by accident or sudden illness when he is away from home, he usually can be admitted to a hospital in a similar Plan.

The only way to find out about older people's chances for eligibility, is to ask questions. Any local hospital or physician will know what non-profit-making plans are in force locally. The chief of them, Blue Cross and Blue Shield, now blanket the country and our territories. Since the bars are being let down, albeit somewhat reluctantly, to admit men and women beyond sixty-five, what may be true today of age limitations may be happily untrue tomorrow.

If grandpa is still working when he is past sixty-five (or grandma, if she's that enterprising), he may have a good chance of riding into membership on the coattails of his younger comrades. Group enrollment at the office or factory is usually less rigid than individual application. If your older relatives have this chance, urge them to take advantage of it and not put it off on the excuse that "I never get sick," or "I never have had to go to a hospital." This is a boast too many older people make—especially if they are still able to take their places in employment ranks. It is a kind of psychological reassurance they give themselves that they are "still young"—or young enough to ward off anything, even sickness.

The Blue Cross Commission, the co-ordinating body for both Blue Cross and Blue Shield, reported the outlook for the old in 1953. This gives a gauge (but only that) as to what you will find. (See pp. 408-17 for complete list, with addresses.)

The national picture currently looms up as this:

Fifty-one Blue Cross Plans have no age limit for eligibility if a person wants to enroll with a group.

The remaining thirty-six *do* have a fixed age limit beyond which they will not accept applicants, even when other prospective members in the group are much younger.

All Plans will permit a person who enrolls prior to his sixty-fifth birthday to remain as a member regardless of how long he lives.

Some Plans have different eligibility requirements for group and individual enrollees. (This is based on the sound actuarial principle of spreading risks among different age groups.)

Thirteen Blue Cross Plans—which should be starred in any lexicon—have no stated age limit for individuals who want to enroll; sixty-five is generally set as the barrier (sometimes seventy in rare cases) by sixty-six Blue Cross Plans. In other words, this is the general rule.

What are the advantages of enrollment which, under Blue Cross hospital insurance only, costs on the average $2.50 per person per month?

Your parent or grandparent may pay his dues year after year and never need hospitalization. But if he does, he'll have freedom from financial worry to this extent:

All Blue Cross Plans cover room and board in the hospital, varying from twenty-one to a hundred and twenty days a year. He will be entitled without extra charge to general nursing care, the operating room, laboratory service, medications, dressings. Most local Plans will allow him special diets, anesthesia, basal metabolism tests. A good many include oxygen therapy, X-ray, electrocardiograms, physical therapy, and pathology. He will not have to worry about having enough money in the bank to pay the hospital in advance; the Plan will do that for him. And he doesn't have to make a claim and wait for payment (as he does under most commercial insurance contracts).

Under Blue Shield, he will receive no bill from his surgeon (or regular physician). In most cases, he can sign up for this insurance at the same time he takes out his Blue Cross contract, and be certain it is under the same high medical sponsorship. Sometimes the fee covers only surgery, but in other communities it includes doctors' bills in an office or at home as well. Whatever he gets, it should be said bluntly, it is well worth the annual membership even if the family have to pitch in and help him pay for it. The problems and the satisfaction that arise are well illustrated in the stories of what happened to Thomas Senson and Henry Coyson, both residents of the same small Midwestern city.

When Mr. Coyson was seventy he was badly injured by a falling tree. Luckily he had joined the local Blue Cross Plan as a member of a group while he was working at the lumber company; under local rulings, he could retain his membership after he retired, which he did. He was in the hospital thirteen days, and had to have a cast. He was incapacitated for more than a year, from time to time returning for hospital treatment. Those benefits were life-savers to Henry Coyson; his company pension never could have covered his medical bills.

On the other hand, Mr. Senson was not so fortunate. When he was sixty he had to go to a tuberculosis sanitarium. Though he and his whole family were enrolled on an individual basis, the regulations of the Blue Cross specifically excluded the disease he had.

This was a blow, but he and his family had protection in case of other ills. This is the point of view you have to present to a person who resists the idea of insuring himself. Many a man has retorted, "I never expect to get sick," and lived to regret it. Or a great many older people take the attitude, "If I do get sick, what difference does it make? I'll never get well." (Actually they are much more likely to recover, or be long-time invalids, than to die quickly and inexpensively from one bout of illness.)

Even if there is only an outside chance that your relative will be accepted in any insurance plan which will lessen the stream of bills, it would be foolhardy to ignore it. Take your lesson from a survey made of beneficiaries of Old Age Assistance after World War II. Investigation made in two large cities disclosed that out of every dozen elderly couples who *needed* hospital care only one had some kind of insurance to pay for it.

WHAT SOCIAL SECURITY OFFERS

One major asset in a financial crisis is now available to a great many older people, though some have to be taught how to take full advantage of it.

What many loosely call "old age pensions"—a complete misnomer—is the result of legislation passed at the time when everybody's financial outlook was gloomy, in 1935. Now we all have a substantial stake in Old Age and Survivors Insurance, which was overhauled and extended first in 1939, and later in 1950. We who are young, it is true, pay in relatively large sums in contrast to the old who pay in little and get comparatively large returns. But we have two consolations for the bite presently taken out of our incomes. If we are no longer producers when we are aged, we, too, will benefit by this insurance program. In the meanwhile, we are paying today, in part, to support the current old.

If someone in your family has reached sixty-five, however,

don't let him take it for granted he is or is not entitled to a share. Even if he has never worked, or worked a long time ago, or is the survivor of a worker, he may be eligible. Like the Reverend Andrew Slabey of Mount Carmel, Pennsylvania, he may be pleasantly surprised. Mr. Slabey was a patriotic teacher who went into a war factory. "Naturally I knew taxes were deducted from my wages," he says, "and I had a Social Security card. But I thought I left all that behind me when I returned to the ministry after World War II." But in 1950, newspapers carried long columns about liberalized changes in the Social Security Act. Mr. Slabey read them. Then he wrote to Washington to find out if he had a right to expect anything from his war factory work, since he knew preaching didn't reward him under the Act! "Yes" was the answer! Because Mr. Slabey's work as foreman of a gang of fifteen men and women, and weighmaster, lasted several years, he is entitled to Social Security benefits on a minimal basis when he reaches the age sixty-five. "Not much," he says, "but to a poor preacher considerably important!"

Social Security was never intended, however, to be the sole reliance of anyone as a retirement income. There are many criticisms of the laws. Some feel the benefits are highly inadequate, that too many workers are excluded, that eligibility requirements are unduly restrictive, that the burden is oppressive on the young, that unlimited earnings ought to be allowed in all occupations, etc. But with all its faults, it represents a break in tradition, a break which gives many older people with slim resources a chance to be independent. Bring these points home to yourself and to them:

No automatic payments: All applicants must file claims, whether or not deductions have been made from their pay-checks. Any post office knows where the nearest Social Security Administration office is. If your relative is too feeble or too far away to call in person, he can get full information through the mails, or someone can do it for him, plus help in filing claims.

Social Security is a family plan: This program was envisaged as a way to aid both worker and his family. It may provide for certain of his dependents, even if the survivors are over sixty-five, and the deceased worker was not.

The striking case in the records of New York State which

brings out that point vividly is not likely to be repeated often, but it does illustrate one ramification of the law which is least understood.

One of the beneficiaries in New York is now a hundred and four years old. Her working days, if she had any, took place long before the Social Security Administration came into being. But her son—who died at a ripe old age himself—had been in "covered" employment. He was her sole support. On his death, therefore, she received the money which helps keep her in food, clothes, and shelter. She is still her son's dependent, though she has long outlived him.

Social Security is a right, not charity: Deductions are compulsory, not voluntary. This is true not only for wage and salaried workers but since 1951 for small business owners and certain other self-employed persons. Therefore when a person receives his payments, he is not enjoying philanthropy at governmental expense. It is his right. The whole Social Security structure is based on contributions, equal in nature, from both workers and employers.

Benefits are varied: Originally the Social Security Act provided for old-age benefits payable at age sixty-five to insured persons when they retired, and lump-sum death payments. Monthly payments for dependents and survivors were added by 1939 amendments to the law, and increased by amendments both in 1950 and 1952. There is every reason to hope that the benefits may be brought more in line with the cost of living. There is little point in trying to memorize current figures which may change with every Congress. The trend is indicated by what happened in Ida Fuller's case. This brisk, seventy-eight-year-old resident of Ludlow, Vermont, got her Social Security checks this year just as she has every year since the first check in the nation was mailed to her back in February, 1940. That first one was for $22.54; by 1952 it had climbed to $46.50.

When the time comes to find out what is due someone in your family, get in touch, or have him get in touch, with the nearest field office of the Social Security Administration, or its traveling representative.

To work or not to work: This is the problem which faces many older people who want to cultivate a side-line or make a hobby pay without forfeiting Social Security claims. You may or may not say the law is fantastic, but it is the law—at present. There is considerable pressure to change it, and that may come in your time. Currently, your relative has to decide whether the curative effects of continued work outweigh the money he receives under the law, or if he can earn enough to throw his Social Security rights out the window. If he ever stops working, or changes his mind, he can get the payments again. What Henry Trooper did may give your relative a hint.

Mr. Trooper for the time being is foregoing his Social Security check. He is applying the money—$75 a month—he gets as a pension from the automobile company where he used to work, toward his wife's doctor bills. She is crippled with arthritis. There are no strings on industrial pensions, so Mr. Trooper is taking another job. He always was a cracker-jack salesman, and on a commission basis he still can earn more than most of his juniors though he is in his seventy-second year. When Mrs. Trooper is able, they will move to the Southwest for her health. Maybe Henry will keep on working—maybe he won't. That Social Security check, he thinks, is a comfortable thing to have as a backlog.

PROVISION FOR THE HAVE-NOTS

But what if Henry had no company pension and no Social Security check? Or could no longer work? Or had no resources at all?

That bulwark of the society we live in, the family, might step in and carry the load. That would be an end to the matter—except for the probable strain on family relationships.

There is now another solution. As a nation we have finally realized that old people in want, whether through their own fault or society's, should be the whole country's concern, not merely their own, or their family's. The Old Age Assistance program, the second part of the Federal Social Security Act, gives them the right to decide for themselves whether they want to depend on relatives' hospitality, live alone, with strangers, or take refuge in some institution.

You owe it to any relative who has fallen on evil financial days to make him feel it no disgrace to take advantage of this forward stride in our thinking. He may even have a Social Security check, but one, like Sam Keyes', not large enough to pay his entire way. It would not be his choice, he said, to go to the "poor farm."

Mr. Keyes's story is a familiar American saga.

He had lived in the same Indiana town for sixty-seven of his seventy-two years. When he was discharged from the factory he was termed "too old," but he kept on working—at what he could get. He had no company pension but he did have a Social Security check of $25 coming in every month. For a couple of years he lived on that, dipping into his small savings when the odd jobs—lawn-mowing, snow-shoveling, canvassing from door-to-door—failed him. When his savings were completely gone, the bank manager suggested he could get Old Age Assistance. Today, Mr. Keyes still mows lawns and shovels snows and once in a while succeeds in selling some notions. His Social Security check comes regularly, and that amount is deducted (as it must be under the law) from the budget the county Welfare Department helped him work out. The County's check also is in the mails on the dot every month. He lives where he pleases, among the people he has known all his life, and they respect him.

It is no reflection on your relatives, any more than it is on Sam Keyes, if he has to apply for Old Age Assistance. And certainly it is no disgrace to the family. Let any older person know the facts and permit him to make his own decision, even if, out of family pride (which is more likely to be vanity) you prefer to hold out a helping hand. Perhaps he'd rather not have it.

What Old Age Assistance is: To be entitled to it, one must be needy, and sixty-five years old. This is the bare bones of the federal law. Everything else is left to the states and territories which share the cost of the program with the federal government. The only way to find out who is eligible, what the family members' legal responsibility toward them is, the amount of the possible monthly check, the right to retain property or bank account, is to apply at an official source. Usually this is the county or municipal Public Welfare Department.

General rules: Most states, but not all, require applicants to be residents; from one to five years is the usual rule. Many say he must be a citizen. In some he may own his own home and keep it during his lifetime. Generally he is required to give a lien on it so after his death it can be sold and partial or entire reimbursement to the state can be made.

Investigation: It is only just that anyone asking for financial aid give proof that he needs it. Someone has to decide what he has and what he has not, help him make a budget, and see that those legally obligated to support him contribute towards his income as much as they are able.

In these days of trained social workers, this kind of investigation works no hardship. In many cases, it means that an older person has found a friend who views his circumstances with sympathy and gives him sound counsel. Intimate questions will have to be asked but the client himself is accepted as the primary source of information. What is learned is put in a confidential file and neighbors and friends need never know anything about it. To anyone who looks on an official investigation of any sort as an ordeal, tell the story of the Indiana woman who said, "I'm ailing, my back hurts, and my heart bothers me, but I'm glad you came!"

Before Mrs. J. said that to the social worker she had been afraid of two things. The first was that she would have to give up her little home, and the second was that she would have to give up her telephone. When her husband died she left the small farm on which they had been tenants. He had made her promise she'd take the little insurance money and buy a cottage in town so she would always have a home. None of her four children were in a financial position to help her when her "bad spells" made it impossible to continue the housecleaning jobs she occasionally got. A son did send her money so she could have a telephone installed. She was afraid of falling ill in the night and needing someone quickly.

The friendly young worker was only too eager to reassure her. The county rules permitted her to live in her little home, and keep her telephone. It would be figured in the budget because a physician had certified she had a bad heart. If she needed him or medicine, this too, would be the "extras" in the budget, provided for in the monthly check if needed (as eventually it was).

Family responsibility: In the state where Mrs. J. lives no law compels an adult child to support his parents. Other states require close relatives to contribute when they are "able." But one of the most complicated and troubling questions any Bureau of Public Assistance faces is determining: "Who is able?" and: "If able, to what extent?" Here are two aspects of the same question.

Mr. Y. comes from a family which knew dire poverty in his childhood. He is determined to protect his own children from it at any cost. Now he earns about $6,000 a year. He says that it is too little to enable him to contribute to his father's support though the old gentleman is bankrupt. The law in his state cannot compel him to do it. The son's contention is that since he pays taxes, as his father did as long as he could, the old man should now be entitled to Old Age Assistance. What this modern Lear feels, the record does not state.

Mr. T., on the other hand, has no legal compulsion to aid his aged mother in this same state, but he sends her $5 to $10 monthly, though it is a genuine sacrifice. He has an ailing wife and three small, frail children continually on some doctor's doorstep. He gets a job only to lose it, it seems, for some good or bad reason. But he has a strong filial sense, matched only by his mother's fierce pride. When her varicose veins permit, she takes in laundry so her check from the county Welfare Department can be lowered, and her son's money returned.

YOUR RESPONSIBILITY

What is the financial responsibilty of the younger generation toward the old? Opinions differ as much as laws. One group feels sons and daughters have an obligation to lower their own standard of living, if need be, to take care of aged parents adequately. At the other extreme is the idea that the old have had their chance, and that young families should not deprive themselves, if it means a hardship.

Each one has to decide for himself where his own responsibility lies. The one thing that is absolutely certain is that the tremendous numbers of the aged in the future will be a financial burden on every one of us if we have not solved the problem before we ourselves are old. Old Age Assistance laws merely pick up the pieces of the old age problem that are not met in other ways.

Some of the experts would scrap Old Age Assistance altogether and substitute for it flat monthly benefits automatically payable to all persons over a specified age, financed on a pay-as-you-go basis from taxes levied on the whole population. Optimists point to this Canadian plan as our solution. In the Dominion across our northern border a pension is offered—though not always accepted—to every older man or woman who wants to claim it as a reward for seventy years of living. Others claim the best way to take the prospective tax load off all our backs is to let every older person continue to produce instead of merely to consume goods, as long as he wishes, or can.

If any of these, or some other plans come to fruition, or even if all the old who are willing and able to work, had jobs, there would still be a considerable group who would need help. Furthermore, any solution worth the name is something which will have to be worked out over a term of years. In the meanwhile, our road, if not clear, lies immediately ahead of us. What we need to think of is how we can do for the aging who are our individual responsibility what we should like our children to do for us.

NOTES TO CHAPTER V

(1) Bureau of the Census. *Current Population Reports,* Consumer Income, Series P-60, No. 6, table 12. See also "Some Facts About Our Aging Population." National Conference on Aging, Federal Security Administration, Washington, D. C., Aug., 1950.

(2) *Fact Book on Aging.* Federal Security Agency, Committee on Aging and Geriatrics, 1952. Also, "How Our Older Families Are Housed," by E. Everett Ashley. Fifth Annual Conference on Aging, University of Michigan, Ann Arbor, July 24, 1952.

(3) *Retirement in Florida.* Published by Citizens Committee on Retirement in Florida. Florida State Improvement Commission, Tallahassee, 1952.

(4) "Retirement to Idleness Not Aim of Most Americans." News-release,

Family Economics Bureau, Northwestern National Life Insurance Company, Minneapolis 3, Aug. 5, 1951.

(5) "How to Build a Retirement Income." *Lifetime Living,* July, 1952. Also "Annuities: What You Should Know," *The Kiplinger Magazine,* June, 1952.

(6) *Bulletin,* Hospital Council of Greater New York, Oct., 1951, Vol. 7, No. 10.

(7) *Young at Any Age.* Annual Report, New York State Joint Legislative Committee on Problems of the Aging, Leg. Document 12, 1950. P. 40.

CHAPTER SIX

TO WORK OR NOT TO WORK

Practically all of us take it for granted that when people grow old they ought not to be compelled to seek work in order to live. We pat ourselves on the back because the person who has not had the wisdom of the squirrel—or his opportunity—to lay up stores for his winter, can live without working, at least on a subsistence level, which aid we have legally provided.

But, as the great Dr. Samuel Johnson said, "Human experience, which is constantly contradicting theory, is the great test of truth."(1)

The sober truth is that many people look on work as play, or at least a habit, hard to break.

"Wouldn't it be terrible if every day were a holiday?"

This is what Mrs. Ruth O'Daniel answered when a reporter asked her why, at sixty-seven, she still wanted to head the stockroom at Endicott-Johnson's shoe factory.

No one can deny that retirement, well planned for, can be a good thing. For many it offers tremendous compensations. It brings freedom from competition of the merciless sort, and leisure for activities formerly crowded out. It is the forced retirement of a man or woman who is healthy, who *wants* to work, that is bad. It is evil for the individual and his family (who have to bear with his discontent, and perhaps a lessened income), and for the nation which should have the benefit of what he is willing to produce.

The questions which arise in most family circles are these:

Do the older people look on employment as a burdensome heritage from Adam? How important is it for them to have paying employment? If they belong to the small minority who can support themselves late in life, should they be encouraged to look for some kind of work for profit?

SHOULD OLDER PEOPLE WORK?

You will find part of the answers in this statement, based on many explorations into the lives of aging people: "For the vast majority, the chance to work—to have useful and gainful employment so long as health and strength permit—is the key to a happy and unfrustrated old age. It is the factor around which most other factors in this problem of the aging tend to revolve."(2)

That is the word of our federal Committee on Aging and Geriatrics. Dr. Edward J. Stieglitz, the geriatrician, puts it even more dramatically. "Premature retirement," he says, "while one is still vigorous, ambitious, and anxious to serve, can be a major disease." The truth that this is a deeply felt psychological need in older people—as strong as the desire to be loved and wanted is in them all—can best be learned out of the mouths of the old themselves. Test the reaction of your older relatives to the idea of work by everyday newspaper stories like these:

She called herself "One of the Over Sixties" in her letter to the New York *Times*. She wrote: "Why is a woman who has been a competent, successful teacher for twenty-five years no longer wanted in the teaching profession? Why is it that because she is over sixty she is no longer considered worth while? Is there nothing that can be done about this great injustice? We have to live but we do not want charity. . . ."

One man for years had looked forward to settling down in California sunshine. He wrote the author of a column titled "Golden Years" in this vein: "Maybe my experience will be of value to somebody. For what it's worth to people who think it is heaven to retire and go West, you might say I'd rather be back in the North, delivering mail in the snow, than sitting here in the sun twiddling my thumbs. Retiring to a big loaf is no good."

The point of view expressed by five thousand other men and women in nineteen cities is parallel. When interviewers from the

Bureau of Old Age and Survivors Insurance asked their opinions, it was found that few had quit work because they wanted to or had looked forward to retirement. About ninety-five per cent, in the language of the study, had retired "on the initiative of the employer." Of the five per cent of both sexes who had stopped work of their own accord ill health was given as the usual reason. Even then, at the time the survey was made one out of five had already returned to work. (3) Whether this was because they found they had too little to live on is not the chief point. The fact is they did want to go back to work, and succeeded when they were past retirement age.

You may believe that the elderly in your own family are entitled to leisure after a busy life, and want it. Or you may think their health would be undermined if they continued to work at the same pace. In either case you may be right. Yet there are thousands of people, like the actress Sarah Bernhardt, who prefer to die in harness. If this is another person's choice, consanguinity gives you no right to interfere with it.

There are people who, in Dr. George Morris Piersol's apt phrase, can, with no help from outsiders, "add not more years to life, but more life to years." An "Uncle John" White can serve farmers in Oklahoma at the age of seventy-four just as well as he did when he was a county agent. Hale and hearty, retirement only means to him a chance for another milestone. His *Farmer's Handbook,* based on many years of careful notetaking, has been hailed by admirers as just as important to the farmer as a cookbook is to his wife.

Similarly, when Alice Eastman, curator of botany at the California Academy of Sciences, formally gave up that post, she continued to spend much time in the laboratory. She worked there with her herbariums until she was past ninety.

It is the vastly larger number of Uncle Johns and Aunt Alices who have no work to carry on till the end of life who need help. Your share in their occupation-hunt primarily will be two-fold. You can help uncover assets that come with age and experience that older people don't always recognize. And you can look for places where these assets can be used and paid for.

Before you can do either one, however, you must realize exactly what changes have occurred in the working world's attitude toward the old since the turn of the century. You will probably need to interpret them also to the bewildered older person himself.

CHANGES IN LABOR MARKET

When your elders started to work there was no question that their parents or grandparents could continue at jobs if they wanted them. Most people lived and worked in the safe haven of the family or in a small town. There retirement was not fashionable.

The single fact that we are no longer a nation with half its population in rural areas is the chief factor in bringing about the great change which affects would-be elderly workers. The shift from a rural to a highly urbanized economy has taken away many opportunities. Youthful skills quickly become obsolete in an impersonal industrial economy; old-time apprenticeships are out of date. Slow, careful handworkers who used to be prized are shoved out by mass production methods which require speed and youth.

Social security provisions and industrial pensions which burgeoned before and after World War II have hindered as well as helped. They have given the older worker something to retire on, but they have also hurt his employment chances. When the Social Security Act was passed in 1935, it virtually made sixty-five the legal definition of old age. Private pension plans usually accept that date and buttress the myth that on a certain birthday a man or woman suddenly becomes unfit to do what he has been doing.

The net effects are summed up in the formal language used by the governmental Committee on Aging and Geriatrics.

"The decline over the past fifty years in opportunities for employment at the older ages has been paralleled by an increase in life expectancy. As a result the average number of years in retirement has lengthened . . . resulting [for the average man of sixty] in a net increase in retirement expectancy of 3.1 years."(4)

Translated into everyday terms, it means just this:

In 1900, two out of three men sixty-five years old or more were "gainfully employed." Today the proportion is less than one out of two. And that one is in a precarious position if he loses his job. He may find another, but it won't be easy. And, because he is living longer than his forebears, he has a correspondingly longer stretch of idleness before him once he is slated for retirement.

THE CURRENT OUTLOOK

Faced with this unfavorable national picture, can your older folk climb on the work-wagon if they have fallen off?

The heartening answer you can give is, of course, that many old people do, and stay there. The most remarkable employment fact to emerge from the 1950 census was the report that hundreds of thousands of men and women *past* seventy-five were still working, many self-employed. They are doing it—as others can—by figuratively turning the other cheek. They emphasize the assets they have. Very often these are the ones younger workers lack.

"The factors that are important to an employer," said an executive of Max Udell Sons & Company, "are competence, reliability, conscientiousness and stability, except for a few specific jobs which require a strong back and hearty constitution. The age factor must be taken into consideration with these other factors, but by itself is pretty meaningless—as meaningless as whether an employe has blue or brown eyes."(5)

The number of employers with this point of view is still infinitesimal, but it is increasing. You can expect some changes to occur, if only out of enlightened selfishness. The reason is a simple arithmetical fact. It has been estimated that unless we do something in the next few years so that old people can support themselves, every able-bodied person who is employed will have one individual aged sixty-five, in addition to his own dependents, as a burden on his back.(6) All economists declare that in a country where men and women sixty-five years of age and over are increasing at the rate of 400,000 a year we cannot long carry such a load.

Various plans to solve this complex question are in the talking, and occasionally in the experimental, stage. They range from retirement on a physiological rather than a chronological basis to tapered off work-weeks or work-months for everyone past his sixty-fifth birthday. The most hopeful thing is that the leaven has been at work for a long time. As early as 1929 Dr. Irving Clark wrote in the *Journal of Industrial Hygiene:* "Through medical supervision and careful placement, older workmen may be kept at work which is of value to them and to the company."(7)

NECESSITY FOR FAITH

The counterblasts against the current trend are still feeble but it is quite possible one of them may arise where your relative can take advantage of it. In the meanwhile, to meet an immediate problem, he may have to re-train for another occupation, accept demotion in a field in which he is still competent, or try to set himself up in some business, large or small. In either case the adjustment will not be easy. Guard against making it worse by letting your relative see that you are skeptical of his chances—if you are. The man or woman of sixty-five or over who can still do a first-class job deserves better from his family than the desolate thought that he is "all through."

Clarence E. Stone is an example of a man who succeeded because he had a relative who believed he still had potentialities. Until late in life Mr. Stone had been a railroad brakeman. When he was compelled to give it up he was restless. He confessed one day to a cousin that he had always had a hankering to be a hotel man but "guessed it was silly" at his time of life to think of that.

"Not at all," said the cousin promptly. "I can get you a porter's job in a fifty-room motel if you're not too proud to take it!"

Mr. Stone wasn't. It was literally a foot in the door of a motel; today, late in his seventies, he is managing one.

We can't all be cousins with jobs, even humble ones, in our pocket. But we can bolster an older person's faith in himself. We can remind him that whatever he may have to offer may be better or worse than some other applicant's assets, but they are better or worse in relation to *that* particular job, not his age. On that basis he can take his business chances with younger aspirants and hold his head up.

MYTH VS. FACT

It would be folly to disregard the plain truth that most employers are extremely reluctant to hire "mature" people. Many firms believe that older workers are less adaptable, slower to learn, have less stamina, increase pension costs, are absent more often, and so on. Some of these prejudices are valid and others are myths.

One of the best ways to help an individual cushion himself against resistance and prepare himself for it is to find out what is true or false in the arguments. The University of Chicago sponsored such a study and prophetically titled it "Pensions Are Not Enough."(8) These are some of its highlights:

Workmen's compensation rates go up when elderly workers are employed.

This statement is frequently made but is contrary to the real facts. Age does not enter into the determination of rates; they depend on the relative hazards of an industry and the accident experience of the individual company.

Older workers are presumed to have more accidents and endanger other workers as well as themselves.

This is another fallacy. For your own peace of mind it is good for you to know that accident frequency actually tends to decline with age. The reason is probably the same one which makes blind people good risks in working with machinery—they take more care than sighted ones.

What is true is that elderly people are likely to have more severe accidents, if they suffer any, and their healing process is slower than when they were young. However, Dr. Nathan W. Shock, Chief of the Section on Gerontology of the National Institute of Health, has this to say: "The diminished accident rate for older workers more than counterbalances this longer healing period . . ."(9)

Elderly workers are often supposed to be less profitable than younger ones because theoretically they cannot produce so much.

If he is still hale your grandfather will not be wrong if he tells you he can do as much—or almost as much—as he ever did. Dr. Shock says that a seventy year old can perform "moderate" work involving physical labor as well as a seventeen year old.

Speed and motor skills commonly level off as one ages, but even here the matter of individual differences enters. In a series of tests Dr. Shock discovered that ". . . a large proportion of older persons equal or even exceed the average performance of other individuals who are several decades younger."

Vision decreases and usually there is less sharp hearing as one ages. Both can be overcome through hearing aids and proper glasses so they assume minor importance as defects.

Research at Stanford and Columbia Universities reveals that up to seventy the chief mental decline is in reaction time—alertness of attention and speed of response. The loss may be relatively slight and it is often balanced by improvement in judgment and in the strategy of tackling problems, due to years of experience. This is borne out in many industries where reliability is important and age is measured by some other test than the calendar.

Older workers are unprofitable to train because of their short work-life expectancy.

This is true only where there is an artificial emphasis on sixty or sixty-five as the date of compulsory retirement. Doctors, lawyers, farmers, and other self-employed persons often work far beyond this age limit. Tests at the Harvard School of Business Administration and elsewhere prove that laboratory experiments are bearing out current history. A Winston Churchill, a Bertrand Russell, an Edouard Herriot illustrate the fact that what is too often thought of as the age of retirement may be instead the age of renaissance.

The old are presumed to be unable or unwilling to remain long on a job.

Countless war- and peace-time work records show the exact reverse. The stability of aging workers is one of their greatest assets in job-hunting. When the Joint Legislative Committee on Problems of the Aging in New York queried several hundred firms, the basic advantages of the old over the young worker were listed as these:

1. He is more conscientious. He needs work more and will work harder to keep a job once he secures it.

2. He appreciates work more and tries harder because he has more at stake than new, younger workers.

3. He is not so easily distracted by affairs outside his work; he is reliable.

4. He has more experience, therefore is better equipped in highly technical jobs; in lesser ones he wastes fewer motions.

Three out of four firms queried said they believed older workers could do as much work as younger ones; approximately seventeen per cent thought they were more loyal.

Older workers are believed to stay away from work more frequently than younger ones.

Doubting Thomases could be reassured by a survey made by the U. S. Bureau of Labor Statistics. Absenteeism rates for all reasons—illness and others—were lowest in the fifty-five to fifty-nine age group. While workers over sixty-five had a slightly higher rate, they lost much less working time than workers in their teens and twenties, and somewhat less than those in their thirties and forties. (No "grandmother's funeral" excuses for them!)

The public prefers younger workers in service jobs such as waitresses, clerks, office workers, saleswomen and men, according to popular opinion and most personnel departments.

There is no conclusive evidence to prove or disprove this assumption. Since this is the case, there is no reason why any man or woman of any age should not keep on trying to batter walls down.

Pension systems are presumed to make it difficult for even willing employers to hire older workers.

This is another misconception. Most pension plans do not mitigate against hiring men and women past sixty-five. First, many pension plans do not pay flat monthly benefits, but vary the amount due the beneficiary according to years of service. Second, some plans exclude short-service workers entirely, requiring a minimum number of years of work for eligibility. Third, some plans contain a provision that a worker older than the maximum age specified in the insurance contract is ineligible for inclusion so he is not a liability on the employer, and so on.

In other words, if an employer really wants to hire an older worker there are several ways a pension formula can be adjusted. One of them is an offer by the prospective applicant himself to forget the benefits—and get the job.

RIGHT STEPS TO EMPLOYMENT

Harry Howland, factory manager of the Ithaca Gun Company, says, "Gunmaking demands superb craftsmanship and patience which the average oldster has in abundance."

Mr. Howland himself is a good example of the fact that if an individual knows something that it takes years of apprenticeship to learn, he stands a good chance of holding on to a job as long as he likes. Mr. Howland has been with his company since he started there forty years ago as a toolmaker. His father worked for the same organization fifty-three years.

At Troy, New York, John F. Wiley, eighty-seven, still works for the Gurley Company. The company slogan is: "Keep a man as long as he produces" and the boast is that over twenty per cent of the employees are past sixty.

This is heartening evidence that the limits set for employment vary widely from occupation to occupation, and from one labor market to another. Also, that there is not a basic, unshakable conviction among all employers about the inherent limitations of age. Many found during the labor crises caused by World War I and II that they could use older men and women to advantage—because it was necessary.

Any older person who realizes this last fact is likely to be bitter about it. He will also be fully aware of the bitter truth that no employer is going to seek him out unless he has an outstanding talent. Most of us—young or old—are not outstanding and are not sought out. Just because he does know these things he will feel at a disadvantage. Don't let him give up too soon. Case record after case record shows that the older people who fail to land a job have been the ones who waste time, energy, and carfare in aimless hunting, then lose confidence in themselves, consider it useless to do anything more, and sit at home.

Without raising false hopes, you can help your relative over this hurdle, or prevent it from arising. The easiest way is to persuade him to use methods that have been tried out and found successful by the U. S. Employment Service. After World War II, an intensive, experimental effort in five different types of communities was carried on, to find out what where the most effective ways of placing older people. It was found that it requires more time, effort, and skill to obtain jobs for "the industrially old," but that it could be done. In some problem cases, skill had become dull through disuse, and morale was low because the period of idleness had been long. The answer sometimes was to refurbish ability, acquire new techniques—or bring knowledge of new techniques up to date. A wise man has more than one string to his bow.

For instance, when the law compelled Frank M. Eckerson, at seventy-two, to give up his job of village clerk in Spring Valley, New York, he was at no loss. He had never left off working as a blacksmith. When he retired, leaving a younger man to do the "heavy" job of wielding a pen, it was to work five and a half days a week. He is forging, tempering, and sharpening tools for his neighbors in the same shop where he started as a boy.

A great many job-hunters of any age believe they are doing all they can and never know why their efforts come to no good end. The plain, prosaic fact, which you may have to use much tact to get an older man or woman to accept (because they readily believe all the world is against them), is that there is no magic formula behind getting a job. The chief requisite is determined, continuous job-seeking of the right kind. The Federation Employment Service of New York City believes those five words—*job-seeking of the right kind*—are the keys to success. It has had a special unit for some years which is spectacularly successful in finding jobs for some elderly applicants. Its check-list for old job-hunters can be followed in a village just as well as in the largest city. The following section gives its salient points; bring them home to anyone who needs a more realistic view of himself and his local market.

CHECK-LIST FOR JOB-HUNTERS

POINT #1: *Know the objective.*

This is one of those simple statements which, as everyone recognizes, signifies an obvious first step. Often, just because it is so simple, people who have already worked for years and think they know what they can do and what they are after, ignore it.

If your relative has always been in one occupation, knows it thoroughly, and knows that people are being hired in it, he can continue to look for an opening. But if his occupation has outgrown him, or if opportunities have disappeared, either because he can't seize them any longer, or there have been changes which eliminate his type of work, he will have to do some self-analysis to find out what else to do.

There are several places he can find help.

In a large city there will be vocational guidance agencies. They are either non-profit-making or commercial. Sometimes they can uncover some half-forgotten salable talent, or point out how a known one can bring in an income. A commercial employment agency, or any welfare organization is likely to have vocational guidance counsellors or to know where they can be consulted.

Whether your relative lives in a metropolis or a small town, however, he ought to make full use of the state employment service or one of its branches. Here is one place he will not be discriminated against; on the contrary, he has a right to look to it for special attention. The range of aid he will receive is not the same in every area. The amount depends somewhat on the interest legislators take in making sufficient appropriations possible. For it has been proved that it takes more time—and so more money—to work for older clients than young ones. The staff has to use special persuasive powers to get most employers to consider older people. Also it takes time to encourage and counsel downhearted applicants on how to present themselves in the best light.

In general, the older applicant can count on this:

1. All states have the *Employment Security Manual,* prepared by the U. S. Bureau of Employment Security. It is the direct out-

come of study and experience in five states with solutions for employment problems of older workers. The *Manual* is intended to be used as a source of methods, procedures, techniques, and tools to give intensified, individualized employment counselling and job placement service to men and women in the upper age brackets.

2. Most states now provide formal training to their staffs to enable them to deal more specifically with the problems which confront older workers in their areas.

3. Many states are already operating a program which has substantially improved the chances of older workers, not only to obtain, but to retain employment.

4. All state employment offices and their applicants benefit by an almost continuous barrage of educational material which also reaches employers. The U. S. Department of Labor issues a monthly *Employment Security Review* which discusses problems and needs of older job-seekers. The Bureau of Labor Statistics and the Women's Bureau are both constantly engaged in researches. These make available facts on employment and economic trends which directly affect older people.

POINT #2: *Recognize limitations and take stock of abilities.*

Sometimes, in desperation, an old man or a tired-out old woman will tell a prospective employer, "I can do anything!" To the person he is talking to this means "nothing."

Before anyone goes out job-hunting he should sit down and do considerable thinking about what he has to offer. He should not delude himself, or, on the other hand, underestimate his possible strengths. If a man is no longer able to be an automobile mechanic he still could be a very good photographer. This is exactly what Bill Wilson decided when his firm "turned him out to pasture." A long-time hobby of taking pictures of his numerous grandchildren made him realize how much others might like photographs. He gave his services gratis to a series of baby-shops; every customer was entitled to one picture—free. But he seldom saw a doting aunt or grandma to whom he couldn't sell the other five or eleven prints he made.

The best way to determine what one can do, and at the same

time present it in a businesslike fashion, is to make a neat, succinct, one-page typewritten summary of qualifications. This is one of the indispensable items that every employment agency or personal director calls for. It is also a useful adjunct to have to distribute among friends, or as an enclosure in a letter-writing campaign for jobs.

There are professional agencies which charge a fee for digesting the information a client supplies. They then whip up what is called in the advertising world, "a presentation." They usually advertise their services on financial pages of large metropolitan papers. But anyone can prepare his own digest. Books on how to get a job flourish on public library shelves. Most of them contain samples of job-summaries that have proved winners for their makers.

For the elderly applicant the difficulty is selecting from his long and sometimes varied experience just those facts which will impress an employer. The suggestions counsellors offer are these:

1. He should not dodge the question of age, though the way he presents it depends on his own adroitness.

2. Along with name, address, and the telephone number at which he can be reached, he must include marital status (particularly important for a woman), his education and training. He may want to "play down" the date he graduated from high school or college, but he ought to indicate his background.

3. He should list the exact duties and level of responsibility of his *most recent* or *most important* employment. It is usually a good idea to omit all minor or early jobs. A man might have been considered a good machinist back in World War I but even wartime jobs that began in 1940 begin now to seem ancient.

4. If he has difficulty in making his job descriptions precise and exact, he may be helped by *Job Description Series,* and the *Dictionary of Occupational Titles,* Volume I, which can be found in any large library. They were prepared by the United States Employment Service. But he should put his descriptions in words a twelve year old could understand.

5. He should give only recent references. No one hiring a person in 1955 cares what he did in 1925, or who thought it good.

POINT #3: *Use every channel.*

In all the studies made of how people find work, friends, relatives, and personal contacts are noted as responsible for the highest number of placements. Urge your relative not to have false pride. At the same time you may be instrumental in jogging his memory about some possible contacts he may not remember he has.

1. Employment agencies are the first thing an out-of-work man or woman usually turns to. The state employment service will cost him nothing; the commercial type, which exacts a fee, may or may not be helpful. The owners face the unalterable fact that most of their clientele represents firms who put emphasis on youth. A few agencies make an effort to place older people; in any case, there is no harm, and sometimes good, in placing name, experience, and training on a register.

2. A recommendation from a past employer is always of value. It is weighty when carried to a trade association of other employers. Frequently it acts as a centralized information bureau on job openings in a particular industry, or operate placement services.

3. Trade association names and addresses, and other types of business information are listed in various business directories. A Chamber of Commerce or a public library will have the directories, or a list of them. Job-hunting plans, particularly letter campaigns, can be worked out through them according to industry or occupation.

4. If your relative has been a union member, he probably will know that union officials frequently know of job openings. If not, remind him, and see that he visits the headquarters of his union, his lodge, his club, or any other place where he will meet people he can tell his requirements to. Most organizations maintain bulletin boards for members; if he is too shy or too reluctant to talk about what he wants, help him write it out in the form of a notice, and see that it is posted.

POINT #4: *Use newspapers and trade journals.*

You won't have to remind anyone of "Help Wanted" or "Situations Wanted" sections of the newspaper, but you may have to call his attention to considerably more than that.

The financial pages, the business page, the real estate or woman's page, all ought to be scanned for job possibilities. New methods of doing business, new developments, additions, changes of ownership, and dozens of other news-stories each offer to a keen eye possible leads. One example is sufficient to point up the possibilities of using the entire newspaper (as few of the job-seeking fraternity, young or old, do):

Alice Burnett was forced to give up a secretarial post in a real estate firm because her arthritic fingers no longer were speedy on the typewriter. Since she had worked in the same office for more than twenty years, her "boss" offered her a clerical post at a fair salary. At sixty-seven Miss Burnett felt there was small likelihood of getting anything better—that is, until she saw an item in the Sunday paper. The reporter who described a new outlying suburban development said a woman's touch was badly needed to convince other women that the section had good living possibilities, even though the projected bus line was not yet running and the school was still in the blueprint stage. So far, not a single house was rented, and few sold.

Miss Burnett saw an opportunity. Her snow-white hair and neat figure made a good impression on the developer of the section. She knew the real estate business, she declared; who wouldn't after twenty years with a real estate firm? If he would furnish one of his new houses for her, she would give a series of luncheons and teas, inviting women from clubs and churches, take them around the division—and promised sales on a commission basis. The developer took the gamble. Four years later Miss Burnett won a scroll from the real estate board for civic enterprise in finding living quarters for moderate income families.

Not everyone can pick up and move as Miss Burnett did, or have her pluck. But everyone can take advantage of the other possibilities which lie in the printed word, which are off the beaten track.

Neighborhood newspapers: These flourish in cities. Because they are delivered to a prospective employer's home and contain local "gossip" they are likely to be read thoroughly when he is relaxed. Advertisements there cost less than in big-town papers, and stand out because classified columns are smaller.

Trade and professional magazines: These are literally read from cover to cover by their subscribers. The names and addresses of the thousands that exist in this country can be obtained through directories available at the library in any metropolis; a trade association, or a Chamber of Commerce will know the ones published locally. Advertisements here also cost less and can be geared, and should be, to meet the needs of the particular reading audience. In other words, if a man has experience with plastics, he should advertise in one of the several trade journals devoted to that growing field; if a woman wants to do free-lance editing for doctors, county medical journals are good media to make that fact known.

OFF-LOCATIONS AND OFF-HOURS

An older worker should not take less for his labor or work under substandard conditions merely to get a job—though many do. He can, however, recognize the practical fact that if he is willing to work where an employer has difficulty in finding young workers to take a late shift or climb stairs, he stands a better chance. If he's sensible, he will take advantage of this weakness in the young.

The Women's Bureau of the U. S. Department of Labor advises women over forty (women are "industrially old" younger than men) that the hard-to-fill job is easier to get. The Bureau offers the following check-list with the consoling thought that "conditions that girls and younger women dislike sometimes suit a more mature person very well." (That applies equally to men.)

Suggest to your relative that he make this self-analysis frankly. The oftener he can answer "Yes" the broader his chances are for finding employment.

Is He Willing and Able To:	Yes	No
1. Move to a region where more workers are needed?		
2. Take a job that requires living on the premises?		
3. Work (a) irregular hours?		
(b) a split shift?		
(c) weekends?		
4. Live where he cannot get to a department store, attend moving picture shows, or see television?		
5. Work where no smoking is allowed?		
6. Accept supervision from an experienced worker who may be younger than he is?		
7. Do work that may roughen the hands or break fingernails?		
8. Take a traveling job?		
9. Adapt himself to the pace and teamwork of a new job environment?		

Proof that being amenable helps get a job is in the files of agencies like that of the New York State Employment Service. These typical cases of men and women who were willing to compromise ought to be called to the attention of any older person. The jobs may not appeal to him but the techniques used to get them can be applied anywhere.

CASE #1: A sixty-year-old man secured a job as receptionist from five to eleven p.m. six nights a week at a club. He won over the competition of three much younger applicants because he made no objection to the unusual hours. He was lonely and the job meant "company."

Case # 2: A seventy-one-year-old man took two concurrent jobs. In spite of his white hair and dignified mien he was not too proud to work in one place as a file clerk and in the second as a messenger. Together they gave him an adequate, if modest, income. He was one of the unfortunates not eligible for provision under Social Security laws.

CASE #3: A housewife who had not worked for twenty-four

years had to supplement the small income her husband left her when he died. Her office skills were decidedly rusty but her personality wasn't. Her pleasing manner and calmness in the hectic atmosphere of a commercial art studio, and the fact that she made no objection when the artists asked her to make tea or run out and fetch them sandwiches, pleased them. A lively young predecessor resigned because she said she wasn't hired to be anybody's servant.

PLUG EXPERIENCE: DON'T APOLOGIZE FOR AGE

Possibly this is the most important, and least observed, rule of all.

Someone can always champion another person more effectively than he can speak for himself. An employment agency can "play up" the special abilities of an applicant, or a friend can recommend him in stronger terms than he would want to use about himself. But the major mistake to teach your aging friends to avoid is to stop apologizing for their looks or their age, and start emphasizing experience.

One young man tells the story of how he got his father a job; he confessed he was neither willing to support his parent nor have him live under the crowded roof which housed his own family. He set out to be his father's go-between to assure him a home of his own. The reason was this:

"After thirty years in banking and mortgages, reasonable health, reliability and dignity," the son said, "Dad couldn't bring himself to face the fact he was useless, yet he wouldn't ask for a job, and no one was waiting around to hand him one."

The young man was determined to be his father's "front man." He telephoned his own friends, wrote firms he did business with, and called on others that would be logical users of his father's expert knowledge. Each time he emphasized that his father had not ten, not twenty, but *thirty* years of experience. Without any "Please help my dear old father" routine, he presented a straightforward picture of a capable old man who still had a great deal to offer that the business world he knew could use.

"So I got him a job," says the son, "and a good one, too. And I could do it again, for someone else."

So perhaps could you.

TECHNIQUE OF THE INTERVIEW

But if the older man had been doing his own hunting, he probably would have had to undergo the wearing process of a number of interviews. This is a trial at any age.

"It seems clear that at best some of the unemployment of physically able older workers is due to their mental outlook, their habits, and the state of their emotions." This is what Commissioner Ewan Clague says; the words are born out of years of experience as director of the U. S. Bureau of Labor Statistics.

Employment agencies are practically unanimous in declaring that older applicants' ineptness in an interview—how they look, what they do and say—often disqualifies them at a crucial moment even when they have the exact experience and training that is wanted.

You cannot help anyone while he is being interviewed, but you can help the person realize some of the criticisms that are leveled against him. Show him how to prepare properly for the one talk that may land him the post he wants. Youth can "get away" with many things which are not acceptable later.

Appearance: If he tries to appear younger than he is—a common fault—he will deceive no one. If he is accustomed to wearing glasses or a hearing aid, he should use them, as a matter of course, and never apologize or refer to them.

"A young person never thinks of commenting on his spectacles," said one counsellor. "If he thinks about them at all, he assumes—and rightly most of the time—they enhance his appearance. If older people adopted the same attitude they would not seem, or be, so nervous."

The words of Lord Chesterfield are still applicable. "Take care always," he said, "to be dressed like the reasonable people of your own age . . . whose dress is never spoken of one way or another, as either too negligent or too much studied."

Timing: A man or woman ought to go to an interview only when he is at his best. A young one can tramp around all day and still look and feel as fresh as when he started. An older person ought to stop when he feels tired or discouraged. If he doesn't, his fatigue or his timidity will show in his walk or his face. If he feels a cup of coffee or tea will give him a "lift," or that he will take his mind off the last distasteful interview by dropping into a moving picture show, try to make him do it. He is not dodging or shirking if he takes time and money to prepare himself well for the next prospective boss.

It will save time, energy, and traveling expense, to sit down before he starts and jot down addresses. He should if possible see only those in the same general location on one day. He can be calm if he has to wait to see someone, if he will concentrate on the advantages he has as a mature worker—emotional poise, dependability, accuracy, good judgment, sensible habits, etc. Then he'll *know* when his time comes to be interviewed that he won't have to be apologetic for his age!

Actions: An older applicant too often is his own worst enemy. He is so eager to make a better impression than anyone else that he either over-emphasizes his importance or rambles on about his philosophy of work. Whether he is applying for a post as clerk, engineer, salesman, or vice-president, urge any man or woman beyond forty or fifty to let the interviewer take the driver's seat. Then stick to these rules:

1. *Be brief.* He should respond to questions with facts, not generalities, and avoid chitchat.

2. *Be specific.* He should explain, if he is asked, why he has qualifications for the job now open, not work in general, or not expatiate on a post he has held in the past, however important.

3. *Emphasize experience.* He should never, never try to gain sympathy or ask for employment because he needs it. The best thing he has to offer is that he is old enough to have had experience in meeting the world, adjusting to it, and acquiring skill.

4. *Talk little.* One employment agency hands this card to older applicants: "Allow the employer to satisfy himself about *you,*

and decide he is interested in *you,* before you talk about terms or working conditions. Don't try to tell him how *you* would run his business. Above all, *don't talk too much!*"

PROBLEMS OF THE DISABLED

Even if the older individual is both aged and disabled—enduring two handicaps—don't let him feel it is a completely hopeless task to find work. He needs, more than any other time in his life, to feel he is not on the scrap-heap, waiting to die.

Individual factors, of course, count as much after sixty-five as before. A person can be handicapped, start late in life to establish himself, and manage to be independent financially of his family and the nation—especially if he has a family who believe in him. Louis Mayerson was a barber; at seventy he had to quit. He had a fall which incapacitated his legs. After a year of idleness he decided to do something about it. He had a special wheelchair built whose seat can be raised or lowered so that he can work easily on either short or tall customers. Today, Mr. Mayerson smiles a welcome to customers in his own New Jersey barbershop.

In New York an eighty-three-year-old man, hard of hearing, secured a hearing aid, then went back to school to learn piano-tuning. He now has a job. In a large metal-working establishment there are two foreman; one is not handicapped in any way; the other has lost an arm. The one-armed man is ninety years old; his unimpaired colleague is only eighty-five.

These are the kinds of stories turned up by the U. S. Bureau of Labor Statistics when it studied the cases of ten thousand physically impaired workers.(10) They are the spectacular examples which will serve as inspiration to your disabled old folk. They also point up the important question raised by Dr. Michael M. Dacso, in charge of rehabilitation at New York's mammoth Goldwater Hospital.

"Who is fit for what?" he asks.(11) And he points out that an elderly man might fail in performance fitness tests for a factory job and still be good material for one in an office. When Arthur Davidson lost an arm, he secured an artificial one through a rehabilitation center, and although he is nearing his seventy-fifth birthday, is still capably holding down a bookkeeping job.

Mr. Davidson went to the state Office of Vocational Rehabilitation for advice and was referred to the right place for treatment and his prosthetic device and trained how to use his new arm. It was his right, not a charity. This is a source of aid guaranteed under our federal laws, open to anyone, regardless of age, if he is handicapped, and has "a reasonable chance of being made suitably employed."

This is the kind of help most older people don't know about, or if they do, think it is only for the young. Whether your relative will be found "eligible," and if so, whether he'll get the proper kind of re-training that will make him financially independent, involves many factors. But this is no reason to let him stand back. He is entitled to know that increasingly large numbers of disabled men and women of *all ages* are being helped. He may be one of them. These are the salient points of the program which operates in every state and all our territories:

1. It is a joint federal-state program. This means that work may be more thorough, more extensive and intensive in one place than another, simply because funds appropriated are larger. The only way to find out how much attention is given older people is to apply. The state Office of Vocational Rehabilitation is in the state capital.

2. Any individual can make an application, regardless of age or handicap and receive counselling, gratis. If he is not able to appear in person, a counsellor will be sent to his home, or wherever he is, to conduct the initial interview.

3. Whether he will be accepted depends on the decision made in his case. The law requires that he have a disability which is a substantial employment handicap. This is determined by a medical examination. The report of the physician, information obtained by the counsellor when he interviews the applicant, reports from psychological examinations, work history, and anything else which throws light on whether he can be helped sufficiently to overcome a physical or mental handicap, will determine his eligibility.

4. The state agency makes use of rehabilitation centers for medical services, physical therapy clinics, sheltered workshops, etc., depending on what is needed and what exists in the state. The situation varies from state to state, and so do costs. (See pp. 396-400 for list of major rehabilitation centers.)

5. The amount of interest in older people and time spent on them, the use of facilities, surgery, appliances, re-training, are variable from state to state. One of the great handicaps to a well-rounded program is the annually insufficient federal appropriation to match state funds. Nevertheless, there are a sufficient number of heartening instances of individuals who have been shown how to remake their own way late in life to make a trial by your relative worth while.

The following samples are taken from 3,042 cases handled by New York's Division of Vocational Rehabilitation in one year. Of that number 2.7 per cent—sixty-seven in all—were more than sixty years old. If your relative is downhearted, tell him about them. Or write the federal Office of Rehabilitation (Washington, D. C.) for a longer list of the over sixty-five year olds who have been "made over" physically (sometimes mentally) so they can work again.

Age 60: ninety-five per cent disabled right hand, some fingers amputated. Compensation case. Employed now as helper in nursery.

Age 61: Left leg amputated below knee, back injury. Compensation case. Assisted in securing the compensation adjustment to establish retail store. Earning $203 per week net.

Age 62: Cardiac, psychoneurosis and restricted vision. Formerly merchant seaman. Supplied with glasses and correspondence training. Re-employed as marine engineer in a higher grade than formerly.

Age 63: Emotional disturbances. Provided psychiatric treatment. Employed as bank teller.

Age 64: Back injury and osteoarthritis. Compensation case. Employed as assistant floor manager of cafeteria.

Holding on to a job in these cases and in every other instance where an elderly man or woman is concerned—whole or disabled—means more than merely making a living. It means social contacts, and the solace of knowing one is not a "has been."

CREATIVE OUTLETS

This kind of comfort, however, does not always depend on getting a full-time job under someone else's supervision, nor even staying on in a profession or business which has become too heavy a burden. The old workman who loses out to machine production will continue to find it difficult to get another similar post. But he may have enormous satisfaction at seventy—as at seventeen—in being able to produce something of his own design, or personalized so that it appeals to a public sick of mass production.

If all older people can't be like Grandma Moses, a good number of them can be like the ordinary, run-of-the-mill adult students who at advanced ages pursue arts and crafts in New York, with a view to making it give them a dollar-and-cents income.

Capitalizing on the tangible revolt against factory-made products, the New York State Educational Department set up a special program of arts and crafts to help older people explore potential talents. Its conclusions are enough to induce any elderly uncle or aunt of your own to try their hand.

Out of nearly 75,000 adult students, approximately one-half discovered they had a talent for making a unique bowl, a hand-carved coffee table, knitted gloves of a unique design, or a child's toy different from any on the market. As the report made to New York State's Joint Legislative Committee on the Aging, says: "Creative activity like this gives the maker a sense of belonging and contributing to the society in which he lives and works. Beyond dollars and cents, this is the appeal that craft occupations have for those who practice them. For the older person the craftsman's way of life may have therapeutic or rehabilitation values of the first order."

A man or woman who has worked a long time already has a definite advantage over young producers, though he may have to suit his pace to his state of health and vigor. Usually he has learned the value of good work habits, and has a wealth of personal experience, and the patience and persistence which working on one's own requires. Furthermore, there are trade schools in large cities, and evening high schools in both big and little towns, where crafts can be pursued, and marketing help through craft guilds. (See p. 134 for aids.) A modest income is possible even in this day of industrialization.

NO AGE LIMIT FOR RE-TRAINING

Don't let your kinfolk feel they "are not artistic enough" or are "too old to learn." If grandma has no desire to learn how to change her knitting ways she still can tutor foreigners in her native language, perhaps, or do a translating job. Grandpa may find his forte is restoring antique furniture or repairing fishing equipment. There are thousands of men and women who are doing just that at advanced ages—finding a new job. Mr. Erasmus Smith deals in old stamps and coins—a hobby he began as a boy, though he'll tell you his old business was selling shoes till arthritis made it too hard for him to stoop and fit the ladies. Miss Sophie Parsons is a doll-maker; she used to be a milliner and sewing comes naturally. That is, it does, as long as she doesn't have to work eight hours a day. Her costume dolls are "show-pieces" which society ladies rush to buy when the best gift-shop in town stocks them at Christmas.

One could increase the list by hundreds. Its lessons are bound up in the report on the first group of elderly women who came to the New York House and School of Industry to brush up on typing and shorthand skills. Many of them had not worked for years. Training classes, free of charge, are held daily for two months or until the trainee can be sent back to an employment agency, ready for placement.

"There is no serious problem in brushing up skills, even after a lapse of twenty to thirty years," says Dorothy Warren, the director.(12) "But that alone does not get the job, The paramount problem, the greatest problem is that of the trainees' own attitude toward age and its supposed handicaps. . . . This aspect of the problem necessitates the unceasing vigilance of the staff. Not for a moment can we relax our watchfulness for the negative, pre-defeated approach."

It is in combatting this hopelessness that you can be of the utmost help. This does not mean that you should encourage grandma to the point where she thinks she can make a fortune out of knitting her perfectly ordinary potholders; or overpraise grandpa till he forgets there's more marketing and design study in selling candy boxes or baby-cradles than in fashioning them. Yet innumerable older people can be re-trained for work; a large number have ability and lack confidence to use it. You can remind yourself (and them) that the trainees who have come to the House of Industry are almost all in this category, too.

But "After a week, two, or even three weeks," says Miss Warren, "they gain sufficient assurance to so present themselves to an employer that they *are* hired—and *do* keep the job."

The Canadian Employment Service offers even wider proof that what older people need is not more ability but more belief in themselves. Under their counselling plan every person over sixty who wants a job may come in and "talk himself out." His first interview with a sympathetic, trained counsellor lasts an hour. He is encouraged to tell everything about himself. That means not only his work history, but his problems and his hopes, and his desires for his future. For it is taken for granted that he will have one. This attitude in itself is enough to give confidence to the applicant. It provides many with the stimulus they don't get at home, and makes them conscious that they actually have a choice in what they want to do.

Of the first 1,138 applicants, some of whom had been out of work for more than two years, sixty per cent had been judged by less understanding employment agencies (and families) as "impossible to place." Yet over half of them did get jobs, four times out of six through their own efforts. Your elderly relatives, given enough encouragement, might be able to do the same.

NOTES TO CHAPTER VI

(1) Boswell's *Life of Johnson,* under the events narrated for July 26, 1763. Johnson himself is quoted.

(2) "Aging—A Community Problem." Washington, D. C.: Committee on Aging and Geriatrics, 1952. (Pamphlet.) P. 5.

(3) Stecker, Margaret L. "Beneficiaries Prefer to Work." *Social Security Bulletin,* Jan., 1951.

(4) "Fact Book on Aging." Washington, D. C.: Committee on Aging and Geriatrics, 1952. P. 26.

(5) Address by Adrian Udell, meeting on unemployment of aged, arranged by the Welfare Council of New York City, April 5, 1950.

(6) Rusk, Howard A., M.D. "Can Older Persons Be Rehabilitated for Work?" in *Never Too Old,* Annual Report, New York State Joint Legislative Committee on Problems of the Aging, 1949.

(7) Clark, Irving, M.D. *Journal of Industrial Hygiene,* January, 1929.

(8) "Pensions Are Not Enough." *Journal of Business.* University of Chicago, Vol. XXIV, No. 2, April, 1951.

(9) Shock, Nathan W. "Older People and Their Potentialities for Gainful Employment." *Journal of Gerontology,* April, 1947. Pp. 93-102.

(10) *Labor Information Bulletin,* Mar., 1947. P. 14.

(11) Dacso, Michael, M.D. In *Growing in the Older Years.* Ann Arbor: University of Michigan Press, 1951.

(12) Warren, Dorothy. "A Pilot Project in Vocational Training of the Older Worker." Presented at public hearing, New York State Joint Legislative Committee on Problems of the Aging, Dec. 11, 1952.

CHAPTER SEVEN

ACTIVE LEISURE: NEW WAYS FOR OLD

If you are worried because you don't know whether your parents can manage on your father's pension, or whether your grandparents should move in with you or live alone, what they do with their leisure may seem a trivial matter. But it is not. Older people whose lives are divided into just two tenses—an active past and a dull present—are headed for trouble. Unless they can find something more exhilarating to do than fill empty hours with vain wishes, they will be a burden to themselves and trouble to everyone who touches even the periphery of their lives.

Under the most favorable circumstances, retirement from work, whether that means a full-time job as a factory-worker, a banker, or a housewife, is a difficult experience. If the individual is to save himself from an abyss of loneliness he has to evolve a whole new pattern of living.

The question is, how can you help cushion what psychologists have named this "traumatic shock of separation" from an active life?

First of all, you must try to understand that it is serious. If you are still under fifty, you will probably have to make a considerable mental leap to comprehend the perils of retirement. For most of us, the prospect of throwing away the alarm clock and not having to do anything looks very alluring. The pleasures of continuous loafing, however, prove to be mirages which fade the closer one gets to them. The attitude of the average person is pretty much like the man in the cartoon. In the picture he stands looking sadly at a calendar. The caption underneath reads: "Thirty-nine days before I have to retire! I've looked forward to it all these years—till now!"

UNDERSTANDING RETIREMENT

Dread of retirement from life is not an occupational hazard of men only. Most women would agree with Mrs. Frances Pettingill, even if they are not so articulate. A witty woman, in her late sixties she began a career of lecturing to clubs because, she said, she wanted to be "a retired lady but not retiring." Mrs. Pettingill told her audiences she considered this to be the greatest penalty of old age: "To be lifted out of the sweep of life after having shared in it; no longer to be considered an integral part of life unless you fight your way into it."

Our own generation is bombarded on every side with strong hints that we would do well to prepare for long life ahead. We are urged to choose a second career before technological progress stalls the first. We hear that we must develop hobbies to have interests of our own when our children or our jobs leave us. We are warned to guard our health and our finances so that we shall have both when we need them most.

But all this is new. Most older people still would call it "pap"—or worse. They were born in an era when the common work-week was sixty, not forty hours. And they were reared on the theory that if a man and woman worked hard, were thrifty, reared their children decently, and were good citizens themselves, their old age—if they ever had any, which was doubtful—would take care of itself. The majority of the old in our time still hold this view. They need to learn, sometimes painfully, that those men and women whose interests are constantly expanding and deepening, who find life always fresh and challenging, remain young, whatever their years.

What you have to combat is the idea that play and old age are incompatible concepts. The truth is that old people *need* to play, and recreation is not merely something for children.

PREPARING FOR RETIREMENT

The late Dr. Alexis Carrel, one of the great biologists of our era, believed that misuse of leisure was more dangerous for older people than for the young. In common with other scientists, he felt that inaction impoverishes the mind. In his own case, he worked as hard, for perhaps longer hours in the laboratory after he was officially retired from Rockefeller Institute, than before. It is true that there are only a few people who have the stimulus of genius like his, but almost as few ordinary mortals are ready to meet old age when it comes.

Anna Robertson Moses, commonly known as "Grandma Moses," is one of these. She made a fantastic success in the art world late in life, but she would have been a successful human being anyway. Looking back on her long life, she once said:

"If I hadn't started painting, I would have raised chickens. I would never sit back in a rocking chair, waiting for someone to help me. I have often said, before I would call for help from outsiders, I would rent a room in the city some place and give pancake suppers."

If an older person in your family has this healthy attitude, you have nothing to be anxious about. If he is like the majority of human beings, however, he will need help. If you have a petulant older woman (or a discontented older man) to contend with the chances are she is suffering from a common affliction of the old. She is probably drifting into the last phase of life without any idea how to make it either satisfying or interesting.

What you have to do is to help prepare for retirement, not from life but from one activity into another. How serious a problem this is you can see from the survey made of needs and problems of members of the International Ladies' Garment Workers Union.(1) In interviewing approximately nine hundred employees, or retired employees, one of the questions asked was this:

Are you doing or did you do anything to prepare for retirement?

The findings showed that only about one-third had. "Interviews indicated," the report said, "that the members desired greater consultation and advice prior to retirement" not only on pension payments, medical expenses, and other expenses, but on many other problems.

But the next question is even more pertinent:

Since you retired have you had too much time on your hands?

The answers indicated that forty-nine per cent of the retired members who said they *liked* retirement, nonetheless, confessed "they had too much spare time on their hands." But "sixty-seven per cent of the retired members who had expressed their dislike for retirement said the same."

PLAY AS THERAPY

You can be certain that any older person would prefer to be respected for productivity, rather than antiquity. But if your relative is with the vast majority, like the retired workers of the International Ladies' Garment Workers Union, he will need someone to tell him where to go. He will need help to find out what he can do in the community where he lives, votes, and languishes.

If your elders seem to concentrate wholly on themselves, their ailments, unjust treatment by others or by life itself, ask this question: What else have they to do?

That grand old lady, the late Dr. Lillien J. Martin, discovered the right answer for thousands of downcast old people. When she founded in San Francisco the first Old Age Counselling Center in this country she did it because she was convinced that "old dogs" could and should learn new tricks.

Old Age Counselling Centers are rare, and so are psychologists of Dr. Martin's calibre. Nevertheless, her ideas can be applied by anyone. If play is to be genuine therapy that will make the leisure time of the old steer them out of a rut, it must embody these objectives:

1. It must be more than "fun." It should invigorate the whole personality.
2. It must meet the physiological needs of the aging body.
3. It must satisfy the psychological need for continued expansion of the horizon of the individual at any age.
4. It must answer the need every person has to use all the energy he generates till the end of his life, however long.
5. It must help every person feel useful and keep or rebuild social relationships.

If you are only on reasonably good terms with any older person, you still ought to be able to sit down and discuss these objectives with him in terms of his own likes and dislikes. It is rare to find a human being who has reached the age of sixty-five or seventy without some buried desire he would like to have realized. You may have to dig hard to find out what it is. And perhaps work harder still, once you do find out, to help him fulfill an ambition he has put behind him. You may even have to batter down his resistance to the idea that he is young enough to acquire new interests; or you may need to convince a person who scorns whittling or costume dolls that all avocations are worth while. Not everybody can, or wants to be like Adeline de Walt Reynolds, heroine of a Hollywood success story. After rearing and supporting her family, "Grandma Reynolds" at last found time to realize two ambitions. She went to college and has a degree, and she applied for and has a chance to act. In her eighties she fulfilled her youthful ambition of going on the stage, playing important supporting roles to such stars as Charles Laughton and James Stewart.

Mrs. Reynolds, you will say, is an exception, and so she is. But her career does illustrate the fact that old people, too, have legitimate desires and that given the chance, they can see them fulfilled if they act on the *credo* which that wise woman, Dr. Martin, laid down. She said to the discouraged: "There is some activity for the least gifted to the very end of life."

Financial security is not the sole preparation for retirement; old people must have something to live for as well as to live on. If you can help your relative find a constructive outlet for his energies it will lessen the strain on family life and better his relationships with everyone. Neurasthenia, or fatigue state, in the aged is no more to be met by old-fashioned rest cure and isolation than it is earlier in life. The best medicine for any aging person is to have some activity which grows out of his past experiences. It may be a paying job, on part- or full-time, or one which brings in no money at all.

Remember that for many people hypochondria is simply a method for filling empty time. If you have consulted a physician after your relative complains and if there is nothing radically wrong, the most humane thing you can do is to help him cultivate a new hobby or resurrect an old one.

An Elmer Trent can think it "fun" to grow Spanish onions after forty-four years in the utility business. Perry W. Berner had a burning ambition to make violins as a boy. He had to wait till he was a retired railroad man to gratify it. He will never be another Stradivarius, but he gets a great deal of satisfaction out of the many instruments he has fashioned since he was seventy. Your own relatives may be stimulated by seeing people fashion copper trays or by watching people their own age weave fine fabrics or raise roses or Persian cats—and again they may not. For in the business of making leisure become something more than rest, there is no pattern anyone can lay down.

NO NORM TO FOLLOW

This is one of the many instances in which the *Don'ts* for you are as important as the *Do's* for the old.

Don't try to foist your own ideas of recreation on any older person, no matter how much you think something may "do him good."

This sage advice of Dr. Irving Lorge, of Columbia University's Institute of Psychological Research, is a good guide.

"Older people," says Dr. Lorge, "must have outlets to interest them and keep them happy. It doesn't matter whether the outlet is making model trains, airplanes, keeping a diary, collecting things, caring for the younger generation, or cooking, as long as the person derives satisfaction from it."

They tell this story at one of the city-wide recreation centers for older people in Philadelphia. One day gales of feminine laughter issued from behind the closed doors of a large room. Finally, the director of the center stepped inside to see what the mysterious thumps and the laughter meant. She saw five or six elderly, usually demure, ladies, vying with each other in trying to turn somersaults.

In Salem, Oregon, two of the most active volunteer fire-fighters have been Louis Barnett, seventy-two, and Louis Smith, seventy-five.

If your own cousins or your uncles or your aunts find something equally exciting or absorbing to do, whether or not you think it suitable for their strength or decorous for their years, forget your misgivings. Be thankful they have ideas of their own and grit enough to carry them out.

Don't crush an older person's attempts to solve his own problems by a misguided effort to protect him.

Winston Churchill, that elderly statesman who relaxes from world crises through painting and raising race-horses, says this:

"To be really happy and really safe, one ought to have at least two or three hobbies, and they must all be real. . . . It is no use doing what you like; you have got to like what you do."

Whether or not anyone tried to prevent William E. Bailey from bicycling from Burlington, Vermont, to Chicago, Illinois, the record does not state. Considering that he was eighty-six at the time, it is conceivable that someone might have. The late King of Sweden was a monarch with a strong will so probably no one dared challenge his right to play tennis at the age of ninety.

It is safe to remark that neither the King nor Mr. Bailey would have been able to do so much if their confidence had been undermined by an over-anxious family. A timid soul who ventures to try a new path and is made to feel it is ridiculous for him to compete with his juniors may be so much harmed, however heartfelt the reasons given him, that he will shrink into a shell and never try anything again.

Don't expect any older person to acquire fresh interests or a new hobby overnight.

Instead of ebullience that leads them to assert a right to "play" as they please, you may encounter the more usual attitude of passivity. Most aging people need to be aroused to a belief in their ability to learn something new, or encouraged to hold on to something they learned early in life.

A failure is more serious to an older person than a young one. Use the same tactics when he begins that you would use with a child. Praise, and praise again. But don't expect Uncle John and Aunt Susie who were never fond of a social life to be enthusiastic when you announce a taffy-pulling at the village church. They may think it childish. Or they might be the type who feels that all leisure-time activity has to have a practical end. They may get pleasure out of raising radishes for the orphanage or packing boxes for soldiers.

Similarly, if people have never been gregarious they may not enjoy the idea of being segregated with a group their own age no matter how good the auspices. They might be induced to visit a "Golden Age" club, however, or take time to find out about adult education classes. Or they might prefer to stay at home and collect buttons or stamps instead. Most hobbies can and often do include contact with others, though like the button and stamp collectors, they often can get it through the mails.

KNOW YOUR COMMUNITY RESOURCES

In short, like old horses, old people can be led to water but no one can make them drink. Your obligation is to help them find out what choices are open to them locally, and spur them on to take advantage of everything that will keep them alert mentally and physically.

Researches have shown that one major reason old people fail to participate in community life is that they are unaware, first, of what is going on, and second, they are uncertain where they are welcome.

In 1952, a special, intensive campaign to interest older people to help themselves and others was held in Grand Rapids, Michigan. The University of Michigan had already in the past three years held courses for the older population in "Living in the Later Years." It also sponsored the 1952 effort. Grand Rapids had a city-wide, active Committee on Aging, an "Over Sixty" club which had regular weekly meetings, and a library and a museum which had special activities catering to the elderly. Nevertheless, during the campaign the working committees, composed in part of old people, thought it necessary to issue a directory. Its title was, "Interesting People Are Doing Things." Its purpose was to call the attention of the older population to the varied assortment of interests open to them. The list included everything from special tickets to the radio and television studios to special tours arranged by manufacturing plants.

Similar directories are not likely to be available to you. However, there is ferment all over the country in communities that have at last begun to recognize that older people should do something more than "enjoy" rest. As you do your local exploring (with or without the older person at your side) keep these questions before you:

If an aging man or woman has a hobby but no place to exercise it, or insufficient means to carry it on, is there any opportunity in the community for him to hold on to it?

If he wants to study, or simply find a place he can use for a club to be less lonely, what is his town doing for him?

If the word "hobby" rings distastefully in his ears, how else can he prevent himself from going to seed?

Some older people, of course, will ask these questions for themselves, and find the answers. Alfred A. Spalding retired from an industrial plant. Since he lived in an area where there was a river and lakes he saw an opportunity. He began making rowboats to rent and sell to fishermen and hunters. He wouldn't have been happy in a rocking chair. Nor would Joseph Geffen of Philadelphia. He retired as president of a hospital supply house and then began working an eight-hour day—free—for the Allied Jewish Appeal. "It keeps me young," he said.

You may have to help your own older relatives or friends to make their choice. You may even have to find other interested citizens and with them call on religious, civic, and welfare organizations to help launch a local enterprise. But there are an increasing number of activities which are already open to the old in both large and small communities. Each one of them is designed to keep an older person from shriveling up—or worse.

CLUBS FOR THE OLD

"Golden Age" clubs now have mushroomed, partly because they can be started with small funds anywhere.

"Happy Hour Club," the "It's Not Too Late Group," "The

Three Quarters Century Club" are the picturesque titles indicative of the purpose of these organizations. They are designed to give people in the upper-age brackets a meeting-place and activities of their own. Are they enjoyed? The answer is in this anecdote.

The oldest member of a recreation club for the aged in Philadelphia is a hundred-and-three-year-old man. He walks two miles to the meeting-place every week, and two miles back to his home, and never misses a session.

If you think your relative would welcome an opportunity to meet with his fellows for sociability or to exercise old skills or uncover new ones, look for "Golden Rule" clubs under these auspices:

In cities and large towns: Senior citizens' groups are formed by public welfare or city recreation departments; social welfare agencies; boards of education; social settlements; YM or YWCA's; and by churches. If you can't locate one, call on the Council of Social Agencies or the Community Chest.

In small towns and rural areas: The churches play the leading role here though you may also find the county welfare department, the Grange, or one or another of the service clubs—Rotary, Kiwanis, Altrusa, Lions, etc.—taking older people under their wing. The size of the community is no barrier. In one little Iowa town of less than a thousand people, a group of young women make the birthdays of every eighty year old memorable.

CLUBS' ACCOMPLISHMENTS

What a club can accomplish, and how it may arise is illustrated in this Philadelphia story.

A few years ago an elderly woman in the City of Brotherly Love committed suicide out of desperate loneliness. A neighborhood minister was so troubled by a situation which he knew affected many others that he resolved to do something about it. The result was a recreation center, financed by his church and administered under the leadership of the Health and Welfare Council (which now sponsors similar recreation centers on a city-wide basis).

Programs of this club are typical of those you will find elsewhere, no matter what the sponsorship is. Postcards which announce events to come are often the only mail some members receive. Weekly activities include lectures on everything from current politics to current art. There is music by members or by professionals brought in to give special performances, and there is a place where hobbies can be carried on with adequate instruction and equipment. In the summer there are excursions, sometimes with other clubs, to historical points, picnics, boat-rides. And always there are refreshments, usually prepared by the members themselves.

Do the members like such activities? One little old lady can speak for all. The day her club went to the zoo she exclaimed, "Why I believe I never had any more fun as a youngster than I'm having right now!"

There are many instances where older people, under the spur of instructors' interest and the warmth of their comrades, uncover unsuspected talents. This gives an aged spirit, as it would a young one, a tremendous lift. One man of eighty-four, a former sea captain, said: "I suppose I should feel like Rip van Winkle come back to life, but heck, just look at this ship's model I made!" (The sequel to that story is that Captain Morrison was petitioned by fellow-members to teach them; today he has a class in woodworking.)

Caution: Any organization whose objective is to reduce the devastating effects of isolation and boredom has to cater to individual needs. You can't just hunt up the nearest equivalent to a "Golden Age" club and dump your mother's oldest sister or your father's uncle there, and bask in your own approval of a duty well done. They may not fit in it at all.

If there are no clubs you think your relatives would like, organize one. It is not difficult. Rules have been worked out which are easy to follow. (See pp. 424-28 for plan of organization.) All you need, in essence, is the conviction that a well-adjusted older person is one interested in one or more activities, and that his community should provide an opportunity for him to have them.

ALL DAY, EVERY DAY CLUBS

Day-centers are an extension of the "Golden Age club" idea. As yet they are limited to a few large cities. However, the principle which underlies their organization is simple, and there is no reason why they cannot be formed anywhere if sufficient support can be found to launch them.

Harry A. Levine, who originated the idea for New York's Department of Welfare, is administrator of a dozen day-centers. He outlines their objective in these words:

"We believe that recreation should be used as a means, not an end. The Day Center program is concerned with the free time of the individual, not his leisure time. We think deterioration sets in much more rapidly during the nine to five hours of the day when everyone else is busy and has no time for older people, and when they may be, or think they are, in the way."

Instead of weekly meetings the day-centers have a daily morning and afternoon program. Sometimes there are evening meetings as well, and special weekend and holiday activities. The Department of Welfare in New York, and other social agencies elsewhere, staff the centers. They are financed by individuals and organizations who believe that older people no longer busy at work or at home need a daily, not a once-in-a-while substitute.

The William Hodson day center, first in the country, has nearly a thousand members on its rolls. Their average age is seventy-four, though many are in their eighties and nineties. About one-fourth of the members come daily to the old Borough Hall Building in the Bronx which hums with activity.

At William Hodson and at other day-centers the accent is on *participation.* Passivity is not encouraged, and democracy is the keynote. Members elect their own officers, appoint their own committees, join to do everything from staging birthday parties to visiting sick comrades. They prepare lunch and tea, and serve both, and take care of the dishwashing. The men chatter just as animatedly over the teacups and washing up as the women do.

On a typical day at William Hodson orchestra practice will be going on in one part of the building, while in another the choral society may be preparing music for Saturday afternoon dances or musicales. Out of several hundred women and men, some will be weaving fabrics, sewing, or doing tailoring for each other. Another group will be busily carving or painting. All the murals on the walls are their work, and they also prepare the sketches and drawings which ornament the monthly magazine, written, edited, and mimeographed by members. One man who never had formal schooling is now writing poetry for the magazine. There are classes in English and current events, and plays written, produced, and costumed by the people who act in them.

What Mrs. S. said one day is a clue to what a day-center can mean in the life of any older person whose family take him for granted.

Mrs. S. was born in Germany. In her own eyes and her grandchildren's, she is still a newcomer though she has been a proud citizen for several years. She never held a palette in her hands till she came to the day-center when she was in her seventies. She is amazed that art critics take her work seriously. Asked what she thought of the acclaim given her one-man show at the Center, Mrs. S. said, "Of course I'm happy about it. But the best thing of all is that now my relatives show me respect!"

LIBRARIES: NEW RESOURCE FOR OLD

Recreation is often the starting point for a fuller life, but it is not necessarily of the type which expresses itself in hobby-shows or handicrafts.

Libraries have always been a solace to old people, but today they are forging ahead in a new role you should investigate.

The librarian's profession is one which makes him a public-minded citizen. Usually he has or can get information on what is available in any community for adults in their late life, particularly along cultural lines. Also the majority of library boards are always open to suggestions about how to introduce some services as a link between books and their readers.

For an invalid, for instance, many libraries have installed specific facilities. If there is an older "shut-in" in your family ask if the service you need on the following list is available, and if not, see what can be done to institute it. Any one of these will bring some light and life into a sick person's day.

Pick-up and delivery service: In most large cities and some smaller places volunteers, either adults, or adolescents from organizations like the Boy or Girl Scouts will take books to an invalid who has no one to bring them to him, and later return them to the library. The "callers" also make a welcome break in lonely hours.

Books on the ceiling: Many a feeble old man or woman, who hates to ask favors, blesses the inventor. It is the device in the form of a reflector which permits reading by those unable to hold a book in their hands. It is not common, however.

Bookmobile: This is a well-established activity in rural communities. It is particularly valuable when an older man or woman lives in remote districts because it brings human contacts as well as reading matter. A good place to inquire about bookmobile service is at the county public library.

This traveling truck is either fitted with outside shelves, or is the walk-in type, capable of carrying two thousand volumes. It may complete its rounds in charge of a trained librarian two to three times a month, or as seldom as once in six weeks in outlying districts. Usually the bookmobile stops at a designated point. It is an event in remote spots, so the schedule will be announced over the radio or television, or printed in the local paper. The occasion of its appearance at the central spot—the post office, the American Legion headquarters, some general store—is the occasion of a community gathering. This, in itself, is of value to the isolated.

In large cities the bookmobile is used to reach, as in New York, the areas where branch libraries are few and far between. If your relative is a bed or wheel-chair patient there is usually someone, perhaps the librarian herself, who will carry in an armload of books so he can make his own selection. Or if he wishes a particular work he can drop a postal to the nearest public library branch and be assured that it can be sent out the next time this traveling truck makes its rounds.

OPPORTUNITY FOR LIFE-LONG LEARNING

Book "larnin' " in another form is making tremendous inroads on the somewhat restricted lives of adults who never had a chance to complete their education. When the census of 1950 was taken, it was found that the average man or woman past sixty-five had had no more than an elementary school training. If education has passed your elders by, or if they want to go back to school in search of a more abundant life, to become more familiar with this strange world, or to learn a new trade or a profession, there is every reason why they should, and can.

Yet the flocking back of grandfathers and grandmothers to the classroom is so recent that your own elderly folk may not know about it. Or if they do, they may dismiss the idea of becoming potential "pupils" again on the old-time theory that learning belongs to youth.

Nothing could be more fallacious. "After the critical age between fifty and sixty has been passed," observes Dr. Martin Gumpert, "there often seems to be a new flowering of gifts and talents, colored by all the splendor of the setting sun. . . . Greater longevity demands new, almost life-long education."

He caps his observation by citing some of the indisputable evidence that men and women who wanted to continue educating themselves always have done so, and he fires the dormant minds of his elderly patients with accounts of achievements of some notable senescents. Titian, for instance, well past ninety-five when he painted "The Allegory of the Battle of Lepanto," Michelangelo who was almost sixty when he took up poetry and wrote sonnets; Darwin who was a septuagenarian when he wrote *The Power of Movement in Plants.*

You don't need to go to antiquity to give your parents or grandparents inspiration. Watch for stories like that of Frida Beckman and John Ely to make them feel that they, too, can have a good time in school again.

In hundreds of communities from Florida to Oregon men and women in their sixties, seventies, and eighties are studying everything from Bach to biology, from how to make slip-covers to semantics. Frida Beckman was one of those whose fellow-students said of her, "She was never late, never absent, homework always done, teacher's pet."

At seventy-nine Mrs. Beckman, the oldest student ever enrolled in a New York high school, received her diploma there.

"In my youth in Fuerth, Bavaria," Mrs. Beckman says, "I had a good education, as good as any young lady could have had in the last century. But I was only sixteen when I left school in 1889. I was expected to plunge into society and get married. I did. But now I know that isn't enough!"

It wasn't enough, either, for John B. Ely to see the world though he left school forty-five years ago to do it. Then he went back to class and didn't consider himself unusual at all. When Mr. Ely was eighty-three he was one of the "boys" who graduated from John Muir College in California. His goal is a Ph. D. if he lives long enough.

People with this much initiative won't need to be prodded but the average person may think wistfully of lost opportunities and still do nothing about them. Do your part by seeing to it that every notice of special classes or re-training opportunities is brought to the attention of every older adult in your household, or wherever he lives. Give him reassurance by telling him these facts:

Psychologists' and educators' tests prove anyone can learn till the very end of life if he hasn't fallen into a mental rut.

"If a man or woman in the upper sixties or seventies says he can't learn anything new or shows no ability to study Italian or refuses to go to China when the trip is offered him, it isn't because old age has overcome him; it is because he has already stopped learning before he started thinking."

The words are Dr. Gumpert's; he was speaking to doctors at the Montefiore Home for the Aged in Cleveland. What he told them is what you should tell all the protesters in their own sixties or seventies. Most people stop learning, Dr. Gumpert pointed out, at the age of sixteen or seventeen when their mental faculties are still undeveloped and immature. By the time they are sixty and see time beginning to whiz by they may feel an urge to learn new things. By then the effort involved may be bewildering and frustrating. But if grandpa and grandma want to know what their grandchildren are talking about when they casually discuss radioactive elements or electronics and leave them out of the conversation, they must be urged to conquer their mental inertia.

As Dr. Gumpert pointedly told his physicians, "If I had

stopped practicing twenty-five years ago I would be so rusty today I wouldn't trust myself to treat a cold let alone be able to comprehend sulfas, dietetic innovations and hormone therapy."

There are special classes intended to help an aging person meet the facts of old life.

In Los Angeles, for example, twenty thousand persons (aged from sixty-five to a hundred and four years old!) are enrolled in courses specially designed for senior citizens, and sponsored by the local Board of Education. Unlike boby-soxers, these eager students are so unwilling to take a vacation the school board has to operate a six-weeks summer session.

Other communities do not have such an elaborate program but they do have classes in high schools and in colleges that any older person is free to attend on a non-degree basis if he cannot qualify as a matriculated student. In many cases the fees are modest; in others the classes are free. When Russell Sage College announced in 1952, for example, that henceforth its adult extension courses at Troy and Albany would be free to all persons who had passed their sixty-fifth birthday, hundreds took advantage of the offer. They came to study business administration, mental hygiene, retail buying, home furnishings, and a dozen other courses to keep their minds alert so they could take better care of themselves and cope more effectively with senescence.

If no such courses are open where your own relatives live, one way to establish them is to ask others to join in a petition to the high school or college boards. If enough people want a course, it is almost certain that they can have it.

An older woman or man can feel perfectly at home in any class whether or not he is segregated with his own generation.

If a man or woman wants an academic course, there is nothing in the law or the *mores* of our time which hinders him from entering high school or college. Even if he wants elementary school no one will look at him askance. The number of older people who like the infectious gaiety which comes when they study with young classmates is proof of the fact that they are both acceptable and accepting. At sixty-two, Mrs. Alice Hickman took a business course; Mable Hoffman, at the same age, finished a regular four-year course at Cunningham High School in Kansas right by the side of her own grandchildren! Retired Major Peter Rodyenko travels four nights a week to Long Island University to study philosophy and history. His reason is that "people sacrifice their whole lives to make money and suddenly find themselves unable to enjoy it." But he, with thousands of others, does enjoy school.

What do older people like? The anxious query that younger people make is unnecessary because older people like exactly what younger ones do—that is, they differ from each other. In Wisconsin, C. L. Grieber, Director of the state Board for Vocational and Adult Education, says that "older people take to school work like they would a job." (Note his significant comparison.) He finds that men flock to courses in woodworking, art metalwork and current events courses. Their wives listed as their favorites knitting, weaving and rug-hooking.

In other states there are courses in ceramics, painting, leatherwork, pre-retirement counselling, health in later maturity—and everything else likely to interest someone who wants to fill in gaps. New York, the first state to appoint a special supervisor for education of the aged (an experiment likely to be followed elsewhere) finds that old folks take themselves seriously. In Hewlitt, Long Island, the local school board gave them a permanent studio for their successful crafts classes. One seventy-year-old member—an amputee—said, "All this means joy, real friendship. It restores my faith in man."

VOCATIONAL CLASSES

Even without this intensive state-wide effort, it is possible to find vocational high schools which also restore man's faith in man and offer companionship at the same time.

Many schools offer evening classes which appeal to the old because the enrollment is a mixed one, and age is no hindrance. (If such courses are not well publicized make an inquiry at the office of the local Board of Education.)

The experience of Walter Green, who describes himself not untruthfully as a man of average capabilites, can be duplicated in hundreds of places. It is indicative of the almost accidental way in which a person can find himself late in life through the stimulation of fellow-students.

Mr. Green, a printer for nearly fifty years, is one of those many men who retired too soon. Because time hung heavily one day, he went with his grandson to the local town high school on "open house day." His purpose, he said, was to see what "new-fangled education these youngsters are getting." He remained to admire the woodwork shop, especially the fascinating potentialities of the jigsaw. The instructor found him hanging over it.

"Why don't you come around to our evening class?" he asked. "You'll find other men in it. You're already so interested you have a head start on the boys!"

Possibly the psychology the teacher used won Mr. Green over. In any case, he did enroll. When he began, his idea, a vague one, was to make furniture for his granddaughter's doll-house. "Why not?" said the instructor. Later he stimulated Mr. Green to haunt libraries, museums, and antique shops for ideas. Today, Mr. Green is well known in collectors' circles for his exact miniature reproductions of antique furniture. Quite often they bring fancy prices.

The point, however, is not that Mr. Green and countless others are making money out of a latent talent discovered years after they stopped formal schooling. This is important, of course. But more so is the self-respect that goes with it, the feeling that they can compete on anyone's level, not only with their contemporaries, and that they are having fun. This is a rejuvenating process even for a centenarian.

This kind of learning is not shut off from the old even if they have to live in a home for the aged. The best of the homes recognize the value of activity programs in maintaining physical and mental health, and go farther. They recognize the fact that the sale of an article made by the creator brings satisfaction and the activity takes on added meaning. The Federation of Protestant Welfare Agencies in New York arranged "come-see" visits to its homes so that its board and staff and community members could see the programs. The residents staged "demonstrations" in how they made stuffed toys from scrap material, made jewelry and trays, and showed that good style, design and workmanship were used even for articles sold in a Home bazaar.

SERVING THE COMMUNITY

Old persons who can make some returns to the community for services they once received become less self-centered and happier, whether they are in the "world" or housed in an old people's home or confined to a nursing home. The skills of an older citizen often can be converted to civic uses and social ends. In the process of taking themselves out of a narrow circle and into the lives of others, older people can regain any self-respect they might have lost by being made to feel "unwanted" whether this occurred through being pensioned or shelved at home.

If your relatives have always given generously of themselves to philanthropic and civic organizations, they will probably keep on doing it without any prompting on your part. But if they feel that they are being pushed out by a younger generation, make them realize there is a dearth of laborers in the welfare vineyard and that there never can be too many hands. Because they do have more leisure than younger people, they can do volunteering for many more hours per week or month. Even at a very late age their ability in helping mould the structure of the society they live in is unlimited.

If a man has been busy all his life with his own affairs, or a woman has been too occupied with rearing her family to have gone into the community, you may have to show him or her that there are dozens of simple, useful tasks that need doing, and that require little energy. There is no chance of any person feeling sorry for himself if he is like the seventy-three-year-old woman who was given well-deserved recognition by the Volunteer Bureau in Lansing, Michigan. In one year she was active in twelve social agencies. She now divides her time between the county infirmary where she is a craft instructor, and the Cancer Detection Center where she is a dressing-maker. In addition, she is an office worker for the Community Chest in its annual drive for funds.

Many communities now maintain "Volunteer Bureaus." (See

pp. 428-32 for list.) Anyone who has the desire to serve his community can go for an interview and find out what he is equipped to do. He may be asked to enter a training class before he can be a hospital aid or a helper in a laboratory, or he may merely be given a list of jobs that are open and the names of the organizations that will extend a cordial welcome to any worker willing to set his talents at their disposal.

If there is no established Volunteer Bureau, ask any welfare agency, a minister, a hospital, or even the Chamber of Commerce, what help is needed. Even a disabled elderly person has a wide choice open to him to make something of his limited abilities.

Stanley Hardwick has to work from his wheel-chair but his handicap has never kept him from gathering newspapers. His calls on his neighbors net huge bales of old papers which he himself packs, stores in his basement, and eventually sells to junk dealers. He donates all the proceeds to a philanthropic agency of his choice, changing the organization annually. One of his pleasures is to take time to become acquainted with each community activity, and the staff of each one has a big smile for him and his genuinely useful contribution to town life.

Mr. Hardwick's chief rival is his friend, Mrs. Marjorie Norris. She is blind, past seventy, and has one shriveled leg. None of these handicaps stop her from being one of the town's most industrious producers of knitted garments. She delivers them herself to the storage warehouses for overseas orphans.

In brief, all older people need as many forms of self-expression as the young. They need things to do indoors and out-of-doors, with people, and alone, that will use all their senses and bring out all their latent abilities. These are not *desiderata;* they are necessities if deterioration is to be kept down.

Bottled-up energy is just as devastating at eighty as it is at eighteen. For one person expression may be in square dancing; for another old person it may be improving his mind, or making someone else's life less miserable. In all events, he is looking *forward.* It is this sense of a future that we must preserve. There are enough instances of dour old people who have become cheerful human beings when they know something more than passive rest lies ahead of them to make it worth while for any of us to help our own relatives live fully.

NOTE TO CHAPTER VII

(1) O'Connor, Joseph B. "Survey of Needs and Problems of the Members of the International Ladies' Garment Workers Union Prior to Retirement and After Retirement." Address delivered at the New York State Welfare Association meeting, Nov. 11, 1951.

CHAPTER EIGHT

LEAVING THE WELL-ENOUGH ALONE

At what point should an older person give up fending for himself?

This is the almost inevitable question which arises at some time if a man or woman lives beyond four score and ten. It is especially acute if he lives alone, or is left to himself when a spouse dies.

Nearly always it puts most of us in a delicate dilemma. Have we the right to foist on older people our ideas of what may seem to us an easier way of life? This is a difficult decision for which there can be no blanket answer. There are, nonetheless, certain principles you can and should abide by, no matter what are the circumstances in a specific situation.

First of all, in these days of Social Security laws and industrial pensions, no one actually needs to give up his own rooftree for lack of money, though he may have to alter it. Hospitalization may be a necessary matter temporarily, even if you have to insist on it. But the mere tie of blood relationship gives no younger person the right to condemn an older one permanently to someone else's rocking-chair or bed, when what he wants is a spade or a broom of his own.

In your eyes parents or grandparents may be too old or too feeble to keep on putting out the cat, winding the clock, or banking the home fires. But how do *they* feel about it?

Before you call a family conclave to decide in whose house mother and father should make their first long visit, or where Aunt Mary or Uncle James should apply for succor, be certain you understand how powerful the craving is in old people to preserve a familiar address.

MEANING OF "HOME"

As we age, the hulls of existence, its external setting, good or bad, become of prime concern. Psychologists say that to many older persons the breakup of their homes symbolizes a breakdown of their personalities and importance. (1) Mrs. Elizabeth Breckinridge put it in these words when she was directing Chicago's project for the aged: "One way to define old age is to say that people show signs of it when they lose hope in the thing that is really important to them." And what is important to practically every person over seventy is to live so that he will not have to adjust to new surroundings, new people, and new ways.

That is why, if your relative has a will like Bridget O'Daly's, you will have difficulty uprooting her even when all the circumstances seem to require it.

For nearly eighty years Bridget has been a familiar figure on York's Lower East Side. For seven of them she struggled on alone, after her peddler husband died, in a damp basement. In winter she warmed her rheumatic bones by an old kerosene stove. It took the combined efforts of the case worker and the physician sent by the Department of Welfare, the visiting nurse and the parish priest, over a period of many months, to convince Bridget that high blood pressure and varicose veins were reason enough to seek a sheltered nook in an old people's home.

This deep-seated love of "a little place called home" is not confined to women. The mere suggestion by one daughter to her father brought a frantic appeal from Mr. Harrison to his physician. The daughter felt that since her father had already suffered one heart attack, he ought not to live alone when her mother died. But Mr. Harrison had no such fears. "Tell her," he urged the doctor dramatically, "my heart is where it was meant to be—at home."

Don't make the mistake of believing this threat to home-ties is a blow only to those in the low-income class. All the evidence seems to point to the fact that the majority of men and women in the upper age brackets, regardless of social strata, prefer to live by themselves. Most of them choose it—if society and their relatives permit—even if it means living on a miniscule budget, eating inadequate meals when they might have luxuries at someone else's table. (The simplest way to test this attitude is to ask some member of the older generation in your own family how he feels about it.)

HOW OLD PEOPLE WANT TO LIVE

When you begin to have qualms about letting a relative continue to live by himself, consider what these surveys brought out:

Several years ago the Benjamin Rose Institute in Cleveland made a study of nearly three hundred men and women who were living on very small monthly pensions.(2) The findings showed most of them preferred to be "beholden" to no one. These are the actual figures:

200 lived in their own homes or small apartments
37 lived with relatives
27 resided with friends or in boarding homes
34 were in nursing homes

What is equally significant is this statement in the report. Those who lived alone did so because they were physically and mentally capable of doing so; those with relatives lived there, not because it was forced on them, but because it was the happiest arrangement for them all.

The Cleveland cases are not an isolated phenomenon. Many national surveys show the same persistent desire of the old to remain independent as long as they possibly can. One survey of 438 beneficiaries of Old Age and Survivors Insurance, on the rolls from three to four years, showed this:

One half of the men who chose to live by themselves had children with whom they might have resided.

Two-thirds of the aged couples who stayed together in their homes had adult children who lived elsewhere.

Those in better economic circumstances have a better chance, possibly, to make a choice, but the result seems to be the same. At the Second International Gerontological Congress in 1951, a speaker reported that retired Cincinnati teachers paid about $65 a month for a place of their own. "And," said the expert, "they don't want to live with other people, not even members of their own families."

This parallels the story of the old gentleman who said he lived on canned soup for three days in his walk-up apartment in a Chicago blizzard. When he went out, the corner grocer asked why Mr. Burkhardt hadn't called a taxi to take him to his son's hotel in the Loop. His answer was: "Because I might have had to stay there!"

In psychiatric terms this fear is sometimes called "loss of personal recognition." If you think this is a high-flown expression, born out of the strains of our time, you are mistaken. The same fears have always existed, and the same kind of understanding has always been necessary. When Benjamin Franklin's elder sister, Elizabeth Douse, was eighty, she was living in a run-down house, with a companion to take care of her. A relative who knew Ben was supporting Elizabeth, wrote to inquire if it wouldn't be better if the latter sold her house and furniture and went somewhere to board. Franklin's reply tells us how deeply he understood old people and their wants, and it is as just as good a guide to conduct today as it was then.

"When they have long lived in a house," he wrote, "it becomes natural to them; they are almost as closely connected with it as a tortoise with his shell. . . ." So, by adding exquisite consideration to his charity, Ben allowed his eldest sister to remain in her own house among her own things to the end.

THE CONVENTIONAL ANSWER

If the question is yours to solve, tradition presents you with a ready answer. If a man or woman loses a spouse, or an elderly couple no longer have the agility they once had, society still says the best place for them is in the home of a relative, preferably that of an adult child. It is no reflection on your filial piety, if, in the words of Ira Gershwin, you feel "It ain't necessarily so." If offering a place with you or another member of the family seems to be no real solution, don't be afraid to flout convention. We are far from the stage where we can say that if an elderly individual wants to preserve his independence he will have no difficulty in doing it, but at least we have arrived at the point where we see that he ought to have the chance.

Keep a watchful eye open for development of some of the housing ideas for the elderly, but don't count on them too much. Only a start has been made in public housing which gives attention to the requirements of older people, and private capital thus far has virtually overlooked this investment opportunity. Nevertheless, there are pilot projects which are "boring from within" and many of them are bringing the best that institutions have to offer directly to the older person in his own home. Others give him props if he is neither completely self-sufficient nor so dependent as to need residence in an institution. (See Chapter XIV, *Where to Turn for Help.*)

OVER-SOLICITUDE, A HINDRANCE

If your relative is hale, or nearly so, the resolution to let well enough alone may be easier than you think. That is, it will be if you avoid the danger of over-anxiety. (Dr. Walter C. Alvarez, a consultant for the Mayo Clinic, says he has given "serious thought" to founding a society for the prevention of cruelty to aged parents by their over-solicitous children.)

Every one of us would agree that all old people should live out their declining years in decency and comfort. Nonetheless, these two words may mean one thing to a young person and something entirely different to someone in the seventies or eighties.

One pyschologist, who counsels many older people faced with pressure to change their way of life, says he always thinks, "Will they ask for what they want? Or for what their families think they *should* want?"

He, and everyone else who deals with problems that rise in older people's lives, feels that relatives are often unnecessarily fearful. In their anxiety to have peace of mind themselves, they remember only that a man or woman is old, and disregard the fact that he is a person with desires, hopes, and very frequently a belief that he ought and can do things for himself. A woman of seventy-five or eighty may be perfectly able to direct her household, or if she wants to do her own work, putter about the kitchen, make her bed, do the marketing, call on her friends, and be active in church and clubs. A man of the same age may feel—and in countless cases proved it in wartime—that he is not only able to work and travel long distances in crowded buses or cars, but return home to sweep and dust, even to get his own dinner.

Possibly your own relative wants to undertake more than seems wise in view of limitations on his strength. He may even run the risk of finding himself in a hazardous position occasionally, especially if he falls ill and is alone. If he has a strong desire for independence, however, the sobering question you should ask yourself is this: *How much pressure have I a right to bring to make him change his mind?*

One decision can be clear cut, at least. If you accept the fact that he is going to continue to live by himself, don't make him—and yourself—miserable by conjuring up possibilities of disasters which may never happen. If you are over-anxious, you may find yourself in the locked-out position of the granddaughters of one doughty lady. When she was ninety-five she finally had to take to her bed in what proved to be her last illness. But her doctor reports Mrs. B. as saying at the outset, with vigor, "Don't let those women come near me! They have worried me into my grave before my time!"

The prime disadvantage of living alone carries with it the burden of wondering if anyone will be at hand in case of an accident. This is the fear which haunts the young and drives a good many of the old into living with relatives or going into a home for the aged. Yet a great deal of this anxiety need not occur. Careful planning and sensible precautions are the right answer whether an elderly person lives with another family, alone, or in an institution. For the tragedy is not only that fatal home accidents are the ninth leading cause of death year after year, but that almost all of them, particularly those the old suffer, could have been prevented.(3)

ACCIDENTS ARE PREVENTABLE

If change of circumstance in the life of an individual gives him a chance to move into a new house, or build one, certain measures can be incorporated which will add considerably to his convenience and health, and prevent accidents. The features which will be included in five per cent of the apartments reserved for the elderly, in New York public housing projects, for example, can be copied anywhere.(4) Be sure your relative knows them. They include

Bathrooms with non-slip floors.
Square bathtubs with hand-grips in the wall to facilitate getting in and out.
The elimination of thresholds to lessen dangers of tripping.
Electric instead of gas stoves to prevent utility gas escaping from defective heating equipment.
Shelves and cabinets which don't require neck-breaking ladders to reach.
Mechanically operated casement windows to avoid strains.
Exposures which will face the sunny side only, not only for the sake of cheerfulness for the housebound, but to assure more daylight to counteract the gradual impairment of vision which is common in senescence.

Your relative may not be fortunate enough to avail himself of everything housing experts recommend, but no matter how old the place he lives in, there are simple improvements which can be made, and even simpler matters of dress and habits which ought to be altered.

Other factors, like having a telephone connection near his bed so he can call someone easily in an emergency, are simple enough to attain, even in a furnished room. Others are harder. For example, he ought to live in a neighborhood where he'll feel safe when he goes out at night; preferably one near a hospital, and his shopping. He should also be accessible to good friends, if not his own family, who can drop in now and then to see that all is well. There are also a few developments in community service which offer protection and at the same time preserve independence. The most important is the so-called "Homemaker Service."

HOMEMAKER SERVICE, NEW TREND

A "Homemaker" is a visiting housekeeper employed and supervised by a social agency. So far she can be obtained chiefly in large cities, but the service is expanding. Your local Department of Welfare will know whether it exists, or is contemplated. In the meanwhile it is worth while finding out what standards and work-patterns social agencies use, so that if need be, they can be adapted. For even in communities where Homemaker Service is offered, the need is tremendous, staffs small, and waiting lists often long.

WHAT HOMEMAKER SERVICE IS

To be able to adapt Homemaker Service for old people you must understand it is an offshoot of society's earlier concern about children. For some years past visiting housekeepers have been sent by agencies into motherless households to serve as substitutes for the real mother during her illness or absence, but in any case the home is kept together till her return.

Recently, the idea has been extended to helping the aged. But a Homemaker who comes into an old person's home to aid him keep his independence is in a more delicate position than one who "mothers" children.

The National Committee on Homemaker Service, composed of representatives of welfare agencies, believes the outstanding quality of a person coming into a household of elderly people should be "the ability to understand and to accept the idiosyncrasies of aged people. She must help them in a way that neither makes too heavy demands in direction or supervision from them, nor takes away their feeling of independence." (5)

This is asking a good deal. Yet this model of behavior can be found, if you do what any agency has to do—interview enough people till you secure what you want. To do that you must have clearly in mind—as they do—what to look for.

It is quite possible that your relative will never be able to benefit by a professionally trained Homemaker and the caseworker service of an agency. Yet it is possible to find women of good-will and competence to do somewhat similar work, even in a hamlet.

THE RIGHT QUALIFICATIONS

Here is a word of advice from an organization which has successfully employed Homemakers for a period of years:

"Long experience has shown that a meticulous, conscientious housekeeper is apt to be less easily accepted by the elderly than an easy-going, not too fastidious person who has a real liking for old people. The most successful seem to be gay, breezy individuals who laugh often, love a good time, have big hearts and strong maternal instincts. Older people can adjust more easily to someone who is comfortable inside herself, even though she may be boisterous."

Specifically, visiting housekeepers are generally selected on this basis:

1. The applicant must be willing to adapt to older people's ways, and not expect them to give up long-established habits. For instance, if some eighty-year-old woman has always boiled clothes in her wash-boiler and wants to keep on doing it, the Homemaker should not argue about the virtues of an electric washing-machine, even if a good-hearted relative has installed one.

2. She must have patience and enough tact to accept so-called "eccentricities" in behavior which may be normal for that individual.

3. She should be a cheerful, not too talkative, middle-aged woman, preferably one who has, or who has had, her own home.

4. She should prefer part-time jobs, which will either enable her to continue to care for her family or to help aged people living in different households.

WHERE HOMEMAKERS ARE MOST USEFUL

How can this type of help best be used?

Here again guide yourself by the experience of those who have employed Homemakers longest. Agencies over a period of years find them invaluable in these situations:

1. To relieve a husband or wife when one spouse is ill and medical authorities agree hospitalization is not necessary.
2. To prepare the way for changes in living, such as sorting out household effects for disposal or storage when an elderly person expects to enter a home for the aged, a nursing or boarding home.
3. To care for a partially disabled person for an indefinite period.
4. To help out temporarily when a younger member of the family who normally cares for the older ones, is incapacitated.
5. To aid someone who is on a long waiting list till the time comes when he can enter an institution.
6. To help the person who has an aversion to institutional life of any kind, has a strong desire to be independent, yet cannot manage to do everything for himself.

If you need to bolster your own feeling that someone can live well enough alone, if only he has the right person to help him out, consider these actual situations. They occurred in the group served in a special "Old Age Project" in Hartford, Conn.(6) It was designed to find out just how far trained housekeeping service could alleviate problems older men and women often have to face. These are typical:

The chronically sick: Mr. and Mrs. A. were a couple in their early eighties. Each suffered from severe cardiac conditions. Tensions and strains arose between them and their relatives. They were considerably lessened when a capable visiting housekeeper put their home in order. She then established a regular routine by which these infirm old people learned to live more comfortably.

The ailing individual: Miss B. was a retired professional woman with a spinal and cardiac condition. She was too infirm to keep her attractive apartment in what to her was acceptable condition, and had no close relatives to lend a helping hand. Much against her desire, she was considering applying to a home for the aged. Several hours' cleaning service weekly, not by a domestic, but by someone trained to accept the conservative, sometimes querulous, desires of the ailing old, were all that were necessary to restore Miss B.'s poise and interest in life.

Relief for young and old: Miss C. was a woman who had to give up her work to care for a chronically ill mother; her father was living, and at home, but too infirm to help care for the invalid. The part-time housekeeper who came enabled the daughter to resume vocational training and eventually take over the support of the household again. When she did, she hired a regular domestic worker through commercial employment channels, and released the Homemaker for other jobs, where her more skilled service was needed.

WHAT TO EXPECT: COSTS, DUTIES

What you will have to pay depends on several factors. If your relative is able to secure a Homemaker through a social agency, the sum he pays will be calculated, usually, in relation to his income, whether that means contributions from relatives, or his own resources.

If you or he have to rely on regular domestic workers, or secure some other type of person, whatever market rate prevails in the vicinity will be the base, plus a little more. (For example, in 1952 the Jewish Community Service of Long Island paid its "Family Aides" $50 weekly, slightly above the local fee for domestic service.) In either case, a good understanding of the responsibilities the worker is to undertake is vital. Members of the regular staff of an agency know exactly what they are expected to do, and specifically what they are not to do. This is a rule which will work under any circumstances.

It is important to find a person who will do only as much as an older person needs—no more. This is not to save the worker's strength, but to be sure she doesn't undermine her employer's struggles to avoid complete dependence.

Even when older men and women are completely housebound, a well-qualified Homemaker needs to work only part-time. If she comes half-days, or several hours a day, two or three times a week, for example, the Jewish Family Service of New York City finds she can market, prepare food for the week, and organize the home so that it will run satisfactory in her absence.

This is the list of responsibilities a trained Homemaker is expected to assume, which you can use as a score-card.

Light cleaning: Heavy work, such as window-cleaning, does not come within her scope. Her time should be more profitably spent in household management problems. But she should mop, dust, wash kitchen and bathroom floors, keep closets and drawers in order.

Laundry: Personal laundry comes within her province; she is supposed also to see that some plan is made and carried out which takes family laundry out of the problem category.

Food: Many older women, and some men, resent having anyone else in the kitchen. A good deal of what the Homemaker does in regard to marketing, meal-planning, preparation and serving of food, depends on this, and on the health of the household. The Homemaker is expected to surmount the sometimes difficult task of seeing that acceptable nutrition standards are maintained without upsetting too much the normal food habits.

Personal service: The amount varies. Some people need to have assistance with dressing or bathing, or both; others need sewing or shopping done. A number of people can manage very well if someone regularly does the outside chores for them.

Bedside care: A Homemaker might serve meals in bed to a temporarily ill person, or give an alcoholic rub or a bath, but she should not be asked to do nursing. Where agencies find professional skills are required, usually a Visiting Nurse Service is asked to supplement what the Homemaker does.

HOW TO SECURE A HOMEMAKER

If no agency in the urban area is offering this aid to the aged, it is sometimes possible to obtain it indirectly if your friends or relatives are members of a family group in which there are children for whom Homemaker Service is rendered. It is also possible that visiting housekeepers for motherless homes may be supplied by a county Department of Welfare in a rural area. Occasionally they have applicants on their list more suited to work with older people and can refer you to them.

If you have to rely on recommendations or cull applicants from newspaper advertisements you place, have clearly in mind the essential qualifications welfare agencies look for.

PREPARE FOR RESISTANCE

Whether you secure a paragon or not, be sure to prepare yourself and the stranger-to-the-house for this not uncommon fact: Older people who actually want to stay at home but desperately need aid, often resist it just as desperately. When, for example, the New York Department of Welfare introduced its housekeeping service, it had, in many instances, to do battle to secure acceptance of it; in spite of circumstances which would have meant dreaded institutionalization the old people feared almost equally the changes a new person in their homes would bring. (7)

An extreme example of this is the story of twin brothers of eighty and their eighty-eight-year-old sister. They had been able to manage satisfactorily by themselves until one of the brothers, the leader of the group, had a leg amputated. In spite of his handicap, he continued to manage the household. Finally his sister, worried about their future, persuaded him to ask the Jewish Family Service of New York for help. Each of them fiercely repudiated the idea of entering a home for the aged. After much discussion, they did allow their names to be entered as applicants for one—but only after they were assured it would be several years before their names would be reached!

Something had to be done in the interim. The solution was a Homemaker. Fortunately, she had excellent supervision and was herself a well-balanced person. For several weeks the triumvirate refused to call her by name, permit her to cook, or even plan housework with them. They attempted to get it done before she arrived, or if they didn't, criticized every task she undertook. The caseworker—an important element in every case—advised the Homemaker to fit in wherever the three aged clients would permit—and have patience. This attitude gradually bore fruit. After a number of weeks, they accepted the Homemaker as someone who could give them what was needed so they could continue to stay together, at home.(8)

This extreme may not be one you have to face, or you may not be able to have the services of a social work agency to help iron out the problem. But you can realize what such grudging acceptance of aid means, and not be impatient at this instinctive, temporary reaction if it does arise. It bears no relation to the sound principle that you should let the well-enough alone.

As Dora Goldfarb pointed out when she was chairman of the National Committee on Homemaker Service: "When the elderly person is confronted with the necessity for changing his way of life, his anomalous feelings of dependence, in conflict with his struggle to hold on to his 'self-determination,' often underlie his strong resistance to the Homemaker, even when the facts of his situation clearly indicate his helplessness."

Though Homemaker Service is not new—a few agencies have included it in their programs for a quarter-century—it is very small in proportion to the need. An even newer service, still limited to a few cities, is worth knowing about because there is some indication it fills such a gap that it may spread even to rural areas in all parts of the country. This is help you can often obtain from many homes for the aged.

AID FROM HOMES FOR THE AGED

Some homes for old people have taken a long step forward in making part of their services available to those who may never be residents. As every admission committee realizes, many people who apply for admission—or whose relatives ask for them—would much rather remain at home. Many of them have no need for institutional care but must have some kind of assistance, whether it is moral support or financial aid or help in keeping house or finding a part-time job.

To meet this need, extra-mural services have sprung up in some urban communities. It may take a long time before this program penetrates to all parts of the country, but there is more than one thing in its favor to make it acceptable. It conforms to the present feeling everywhere that the longer old people can stay out of any type of institution the better it is for them. Also it costs considerably less to help applicants lead their own lives outside an old people's home than it does to give them the intensive and expensive supervision they would have in it.

To find out whether "non-resident aid" (the term used by Peabody Home for aged women in New York City) exists, inquire at any welfare agency in a city. In the country, the county Department of Welfare is the place to ask. The title of the service will vary, but the form usually followed by homes whose directors introduce it, is this:

A trained social worker investigates both the home conditions and the physical, mental, and emotional condition of the applicant. If she feels he will be happier and better off in his own home, she helps him meet current difficulties.

Her aid may be in the form of arranging for visits to a doctor or a hospital, or bringing a visiting nurse or a visiting housekeeper into the picture temporarily. Or it may be restoring morale by helping an elderly man (or woman) find a job, or assist him to plan his budget so that he stays within his means, or having the home supplement his income so he can stay where he is.

The most important feature of this type of help is that the social worker and the institution are always in regular touch with the individual. So that if the time ever comes when an institutional life is the *best* way of life for him, he will have it. Or, what is equally likely, he can avail himself of its recreational or therapy facilities—and stay out of it.

Here are typical instances where such aid has helped normal adults for whom "protective living" of any kind is an unnatural way of life.

Mr. Abernathy saw his wife die of cancer and developed a morbid fear that this would be his own fate. His sons, tired of reasoning with and reassuring him, told him to apply to a home for aged men. Mr. Abernathy was willing because he thought if cancer developed it would be recognized and treated sooner there. The social worker who interviewed him listened, investigated, and acted. He was told to come to the institution's infirmary weekly for an examination. Nurses were instructed to hear his complaints without comment, examine him, and give him assurance that he was still free of the disease he dreaded. Gradually his confidence came back and his visits decreased in frequency. Within a year the social worker had helped him not only to go back to his old trade as tailor, but found another lone elderly man with whom he set up housekeeping.

Today, his mind at ease, Mr. Abernathy comes periodically for physical examinations, but more that that, to pour out his problems and his small triumphs where he is sure he will have an understanding, sympathetic hearing. At seventy-eight, spry, dapper, and content if he can work till the end comes, and that in his own bed, Mr. Abernathy has fully proved the worth of "non-resident aid."

Mrs. Berk, on the other hand, applied for help to an old people's home largely because she was convinced her son no longer loved her. The monthly allowance he was accustomed to send her had ceased; she had not heard from him for months. Contact with the Red Cross in the city where he was last heard from eventually revealed that Mr. Berk was in a hospital for the chronically ill. He had assumed his mother would get in touch with other relatives when she did not hear from him. This the authorities did. A grant from the home tided her over to the time when her son was able to work again, and a visit from an elderly sister soothed her in the intervening months.

The report of a two-year study of the program Peabody Home inaugurated in 1943 states: "The health of the non-residents is

better, even though they are two years older. Also they seem to be happier and more vitally interested in life than the women admitted directly into the home who *might* have continued to live in the community." (The italics are ours.)

WHEN SICKNESS COMES

Illness, or the possibility of it, is a terror which hangs over distant families as much as over the old person himself. (He may be philosophical about it, or like V. Sackville-West's heroine, his ailments, and the routine of his life may be "the only reality," things for which he "feels quite an affection.")

You may unconsciously vent your own feelings of anxiety by trying to force an older ailing person out of a home he often need not leave. A man and his anemia, for instance, can get along very well, provided he follows his doctor's orders. So can a diabetic. He can keep to his diet, and learn to administer insulin himself if he has to have it, or a neighbor can be taught to give it to him.

Physicians declare that from seventy per cent to eighty per cent of the old can safely stay in their own homes if they are chronically ill, provided they have the proper auxiliary clinical and medical services. (9)

There are times that enemas, injections, or special types of bathing or medication are needed. If an elderly individual can be assured he will have this help till he is able to care for himself again there is often little reason to insist that he leave his home for someone else's—or for a hospital. His own physician will be the best judge—not his family—whether it is safe for him to be alone. Possibly he will need a full-time nurse for a while, or a part-time visiting one. In addition, substitutes can frequently be found outside the professional field, and to an easily frightened older person, these are usually far more welcome.

FRIENDLY NEIGHBORHOOD SERVICES

Often what an ill old person values most is someone who can bring in with the groceries or the floor-mop a breath of the outside world. Everywhere there are women with nursing experience gained in their own families, who usually can be persuaded to help out a neighbor. They may not be eligible for a practical nurse's license. Yet if they have learned how to care for people the hard way they seem to be endowed with sympathy and the willingness to do ugly tasks with friendliness that usually makes up for technical lacks, especially if a person is not acutely but merely chronically ill.

Old-time general practitioners, particularly in small towns where professional nurses are scarce, often know and will recommend such women. Ministers, even Chambers of Commerce, are other sources to tap to be sure someone will be on hand if an emergency comes. Or a local woman's club, the American Red Cross, or perhaps one of the men's service clubs—Lions, Rotary, Kiwanis—frequently can call on someone to drop in occasionally to see that all is going well without letting the older person known he is being watched with a too anxious eye by a distant or near relative.

If this seems too simple a remedy, and you are still doubtful about the wisdom of letting an octogenarian, or someone even a decade younger, stay where he is, remember these thumbnail sketches. They are a random selection from a large number of cases Dr. J. H. Sheldon investigated to find out how typical incapacitated old people get along. (10) They lived in an English industrial town and were in moderate circumstances.

"In some instances," Dr. Sheldon relates, "the heavy burden willingly undertaken by or for the neighbors is remarkable, especially from the point of view of continuity."

As proof, he cites the case of a woman of over eighty-five who lives by herself, but is infirm. A neighbor on one side comes in every morning, dresses her, and puts her in her chair. Another comes at night, undresses her, and puts her to bed. A religious organization sends a representative every day to see to her meals.

Here is another one of his cases:

"An old lady of eighty-seven," says Dr. Sheldon, "treasures her independence and lives by herself, but finds the housework a strain. A subject of the survey, a woman of seventy-three, goes to see her every day—after doing her own housework—and helps to put things right."

A third woman—this, a "young" one of sixty-three—has stood in the queues that have become a part of the life of the average British housewife, for six years. She does the shopping for some older neighbors in addition to her own.

Industrial towns in England are very much like towns in this country. And not all the good neighbors, by any means, live in Great Britain.

NOTES TO CHAPTER VIII

(1) Kardiner, Abram, M.D. "Psychological Factors in Old Age," in *Mental Hygiene in Old Age*. New York: Family Service Ass'n of America, 1937. P. 20.

(2) Smith, Gertrude A. "Case Work Needs of the Aged," in *Proceedings*. New York: The National Conference of Social Work, 1938. P. 587.

(3) Johnson, Ralph J. and Pond, M. Allen. "Health Standards of Housing for the Aging Population." *Journal of Gerontology*, Vol. 7, No. 2, April, 1952.

(4) Graham, Lee E. "Old Folks at Home—Their Own." *New York Times Magazine*, Nov. 9, 1952. P. 53.

(5) Goldfarb, Dora. "Homemaker Service for the Aged." Address delivered at National Conference of Social Work, June, 1949.

(6) "Our Older Citizens." Hartford, Conn.: Family Service Society, Feb. 1939. (Mimeographed.)

(7) Hill, Ruth. "Understanding the Problems of Older People," in *Case Work with the Aged*. New York: Family Service Ass'n of America, 1938-9. Second Printing, 1944.

(8) "A Different and Economical Service to the Aged." Report on Community Homemaker Service for the Aged, 1945-1950. New York: Jewish Family Service, Jan., 1951. (Multigraphed.)

(9) Randall, Ollie A. "Living Arrangements to Meet the Needs of Older People," in *Planning the Older Years*. Ann Arbor: University of Michigan Press, 1950.

(10) Sheldon, J. H., M.D. *The Social Medicine of Old Age*. London: The Nuffield Foundation, Oxford University Press, 1948. Pp. 178-9.

CHAPTER NINE

PREPARING THE OLD FOR CHANGE

There may come a time when an elderly person must make a drastic change in his living arrangements—or you feel he should. If it does, take your own attitudes sternly in hand. The job ahead will be much less difficult for you, and far less a strain on the other person, if you don't try to tie up his remaining years in a tidy plan, like a Christmas package. Life may slow down at four score and ten, but it is not going to be static. Unless your relative has abandoned all hope and is merely waiting for death, he will probably require different types of living at different stages. As Dr. Robert T. Monroe remarked about patients in his geriatric clinic, "There is as much difference between a man of sixty and one of ninety as there is between a boy of twelve and one of two."

Your responsibility is to help an elderly individual make a new bed so that he will like it *now*—not in some distant future that may never come. The idea which one vigorous septuagenarian had is the right one.

Mr. Britton was a Wall Street employee of modest means. When he retired he continued to live as he had done for many years. "Home" was a small room and a neat shelf of groceries over a two-burner gas stove. A former fellow-worker dropped by to see him one day and asked, "Aren't you going to try to get into some old men's home?"

Mr. Britton's answer was: "No, but I might when I'm ninety!"

Every person, no matter how old or how infirm, wants to make his own decisions about how and where he will live. The most important step toward helping him accept with equanimity whatever lies ahead, is to make him feel he is capable of judging what he ought to do.

DANGER OF OVER-PROTECTION

In our anxiety to spare them worry and make them comfortable most of us put much emphasis on protecting older people. In the process we run the danger of undermining their initiative. Even more frequently, we underestimate their capacities. Such over-protectiveness is not always for the sake of the older person. We all tend to make decisions that will spare *us* worry.

If his bank account is lean or his body feeble, you may have to do what newspaper reporters call "legwork" for a parent or a grandparent. But unless he is actually mentally incompetent—and only a physician, not the family, can determine that—his fate ought to be in his own hands, or as much so as anybody's can be who lives in a world where other people have rights. If your relative has a fractured hip or a bad case of asthma, he may have to go to a nursing home or a hospital. But even then, he ought not to be coerced into it, or treated like a child, incapable of attending to his own affairs.

Psychologists say recognition that a man is really old often comes painfully and abruptly as the result of some change thrust on him. Yet, if it is necessary, what should you do?

PLAN WITH, NOT FOR, THE OLD

The only safe rule is one every social agency practises. Their workers plan with, not for, old people. They know, what a good many of us forget, that well-meant advice from the young may seem like patronage or condescension to the old. A man who has earned his own living for four or five decades, a woman who has reared a family, a couple who have weathered the hardships of life, handling their own problems as they arose, can't be expected to take kindly to plans devised for their well-being by someone years younger.

One worker, who has had long experience in helping older

people make shifts in environment, calls relatives "complicating factors; they are sure they know what should be done, and equally sure of the incompetence of the aged to manage their own affairs."

Even in an emergency, you can help most if you restrain your natural desire to show some man or woman a way out of a dilemma before he is willing to admit there is a dilemma.

Ollie Randall of the Community Service Society of New York, states the problem in these words:

"Most older people have acquired certain habits of thought and of living which do not yield to change without painful wrenches and sometimes bitterness and unhappiness. They want independence at a time when others, if they think about the matter at all, believe they should be emotionally and personally as well as financially dependent. Yet with this desire for independence there is paradoxically the conflicting desire for security, for freedom from fear of what the future almost inevitably holds—sickness and the need for care because of it. . . ."(1)

In practical terms this means that if grandma wants to stay in the tumble-down ancestral mansion whose worn-out furnace eats up coal, and whose rooms are too vast for even a slavey to clean, let her do it. At least let her stay till she has a chance to find out that it is uneconomical and unhealthy to cling to a worn-out past. She'll find out sooner if no one puts pressure, however well-meant, on her. Forcing her out "for her own good" means you are taking a chance on having a disgruntled old woman on your hands the rest of her life.

Similarly, if grandfather wants to stay down on the farm and struggle through the harvesting again, let him try it. Perhaps he'd rather die in harness than live through what he may consider dull years somewhere else. Or he might be just stubborn enough to believe he knows when to move—in his own good time.

OLD ARE SLOW TO ADAPT

The old need this chance to mull over new proposals. As Dr. A. Kardiner, the psychologist, points out, "Old age is a phase of life with the fewest adaptation possibilities. The plasticity of the ego is gone, as well as the ability to modify the environment."(2) If you can remember that the pace of the old is slow it will keep you from being exasperated at the reluctance—the young are apt to term it obstinacy—of the aging even to try the unknown.

The wrench from old-time moorings is bound to be hard, no matter how you try to cushion it. The poignant story of the widower who feared his growing blindness would make him a burden, is an example. When his physician urged him to accept his married daughter's somewhat tepid invitation to share her home, Mr. B. declared he was "too ill and old to make the change, and too worried to go on living."

Neither the daughter nor her husband really understood Mr. B.'s fear of dependency. Consequently they resented what they called his "ingratitude"—a situation far from unique. It was the visitor from the state Commission for the Blind who gave him courage. Week after week she came to teach him simple leather-tooling. The day he sold his first billfolds was the day he actually accepted the fact that a shift in environment was necessary, and might be bearable.

Even a relationship which is warm and tender between two generations can suffer at the crucial moment when an older person has to give up familiar surroundings. It is then you need to be like the psychiatrist whom Alfred A. Knopf, the publisher, described as "at once wise and compassionate, tough-fibred, hard-headed, and understanding."

CANDOR IS NECESSARY

How can you best help an older individual face reality?

In the first place, prepare yourself for the likely prospect that most older people are wary, if not suspicious of the enthusiasm of the young for the unknown. They have lived long enough to regard change with a jaundiced eye. A fresh approach to an old problem may seem no solution to them at all. Or they may be fearful of the changes new persons or places may bring, or fear change itself.

This terror of the devils they don't know often makes many older men and women willing to endure the devil they do know to the point of discomfort, or actual harm. It may complicate your best-laid plans for placing your uncles or aunts in a well-run boarding home, or even make your parents hold back from moving where there will be an elevator instead of steps to climb.

Yet, if you berate them because they prefer a damp city basement to a sunny cottage in the country, you will only add to their confusion. If you treat them as if they are too eccentric or too old-fashioned to know what to do, you will only strengthen their conviction that they are being insulted or abused. If you bring pressure to bear through doctors, nurses, or family counsellors when they are facing a devastating break in long-established routine, they will feel you are persecuting them.

Any individual who is usually a "dear old soul" can turn cantankerous if he thinks his authority or his prestige is threatened. If this happens, and barriers arise between you, there will be sore places in your relationship that may never heal.

To prevent it, and to save yourself—and him—wear and tear, be candid. Older people can stand more shocks than younger ones think they can. What they can't bear is to feel baffled and helpless because well-meaning relatives too often act as if crises in family life ought not to be discussed with them.

If you think a change advisable or urgent, don't be afraid to say so. Tell them how other people in similar situations have met their predicaments. Even the most irascible person wants to feel he is not the only person in his world with trouble.

If he lives with you and it is no longer wise or feasible for him to stay, screw up your courage and say so, but give him reasons, not excuses. If he knows you are trying to be honest with yourself and with him, he will listen. Explain why the situation will bring unhappiness if it continues, not only for you or someone else, but for him.

If he is sick and a convalescent home, a nursing home, or a hospital seems a better place for him, tell him frankly why you and the doctor think so. It will keep him from feeling his family is conspiring to get rid of him. If he is rational at all, he will want to know exactly what arrangements are being made for him. He deserves to know the pros and cons of this place or that, and have a chance to express *his* own opinion and know that attention is being paid to *his* preferences, no matter how much you feel worries ought to be kept from him.

If he becomes "cranky" or dejected while the change is pending, ignore it, and coach your family to follow your example. These are normal manifestations of fear.

THE NEED FOR REASSURANCE

To combat anxiety, give old people reassurance. They need to be told—sometimes over and over—that those who know them best believe they have enough youthful resiliency left to make any adaptation, given enough time.

Instead of bemoaning the fact that he is obstinate, put your efforts on making an older person feel he is not going to be sent out to sink or swim alone. If a mistake is made, he ought to feel it is not irrevocable.

For no older person should ever feel that a decision which is uprooting him from an accustomed mode of living, good or bad, has the terrible finality of the laws of the Medes and the Persians. Conditions as well as people change. If you hit on what seems the perfect solution now, and your relative is content with it, it will probably not be what he (or you) will want one, ten, five, or fifteen years from today. You need to make your own relative feel as Clara Morrison does, that no matter what happens there is someone who will cushion the blows.

Clara Morrison, a lady who never tells her age, is constitutionally restless. For years she has lugged about with her, from one set of light housekeeping rooms to another, an old coal stove. She cannot believe that a gas range or some other woman's oil stove can produce a kettle of soup with the same flavor as her own. Her nearest relatives, two nieces, view their aged aunt's idiosyncrasy with amusement. Every few months she rings one or the other up and confides that her current landlady is "impossible." Then the hunt is on. They patiently look for suitable quarters and a tolerant landlord who will permit the introduction of the old reliable stove.

If Miss Morrison's nieces were not wise enough to perceive

that to their aunt change is veritably the breath of life, she would probably by now be a dour, not a merry old lady. A few hours is a small price to pay, they think, for that.

COUNTRY LIFE VS. CITY

The best recipe for a successful placement is one which matches older people's past environment. Most of them will eventually learn to tolerate, even to like a new setting, particularly if they have had a hand in choosing it, if they know they will not be torn from a background that gave meaning to their lives.

This is not always a possible solution, of course. But it is possible to remember that if your aging relatives were born and reared in the tumult of a city, it is far better for them to remain there. Living in a rural area or even in a small village, requires a certain knack. If a man or woman has attained the age of seventy or more without it, the taste for rural living is not likely to be acquired, however wistfully they may have looked at "come-on" advertisements picturing contented couples fishing or gardening their old lives away.

Those of us who have an enthusiasm for country air are likely to be carried away by it. We forget that the older generation who have lived with the roar of railroads or automobile traffic in their ears for decades will feel lost and miserable away from them.

The opposite is true, naturally. Fiction like Ruth Suckow's Iowa stories has dramatized the tragedy of many older men and women who have farmed most of their lives, and then are compelled to give it up. If this means they will spend their last years in a city environment, no matter how cushioned, there is more than an even chance they will be miserable.

The case of Mrs. Timothy is a typical instance of such misplaced devotion.

Mrs. Timothy's son and daughters were sure they were "doing right" by their mother when they installed her in a comfortable rose-embowered cottage in one corner of her son's country estate. Mrs. Timothy, a gentle woman, not given to speaking her mind, and cowed by long years of living with the late Mr. Timothy, docilely packed. When she was finished she went where she was bidden. Behind her, however, was a period of forty years of urban living, much of it spent in hard post-immigrant years in a tenement.

The first Sunday after her arrival, her son arrived from the city and called on her. He found his mother outside her cottage, comfortably settled in her favorite armchair. However, she was not facing the adjacent lake and countryside, but the six-foot garden wall. When her son expressed astonishment, Mrs. Timothy said, plaintively, "It seems so much more like home!"

If you recall that what you wanted at fifteen or twenty is rarely what you appreciate or want now, you will understand more easily why a good situation from your point of view may be intolerable to someone twice your age.

EASING TRANSITION

The gulf between generations is too wide to leap with good intentions. Nevertheless, there are ways to ease an older person's going if he must move. One of them is not to urge him to change his daily habits late in life.

In one of New York's most crowded areas, for example, there is a home for the aged. Its directors are genuinely concerned about their charges' comfort. On the roof they built a garden which would do credit to a resort hotel. Yet even on the hottest summer days it is nearly always deserted. The old men and women continue to congregate about the front stoop of the Home. Or on rainy days they gaze out of their windows at passing traffic—just as they enjoyed doing day after day in the past, when there was no one at hand to force a luxury on them they neither appreciate nor want.

Even though an older person's home might have been physically unsafe, medically impossible, or economically unsound, it was filled with possessions which were heavily vested with emotional meaning. They may or may not have had monetary value. Psychologists say old people often hold to worthless objects and reject valuable new ones, for they tend to identify themselves with a certain object or place. And if they admit the usefulness of a certain thing is over it is an unconscious admission that their own usefulness is past.(3)

The second way you can make a transition less difficult, therefore, is to accept their own valuation of what is important, what can be left behind. Tolerant superintendents of homes for old people recognize it makes a resident happier to look at a bedside table groaning with familiar knickknacks or sit in a chair brought from a familiar setting. For the same reason be tolerant if your mother-in-law wants to boil the mutton in an iron kettle instead of using the pressure cooker or your father-in-law wants to clutter up your modern décor with an old-fashioned rocker. It may comfort them for whatever they have had to give up. And what can be more important than that?

Sarah Barton's concern with a broken-down chaise longue is an example of this dominant urge you will find in many people once they pass the half century mark and realize that life brings irrevocable change, if not progress.

Sarah was one of those devoted unmarried daughters of whom the world is full. She supported her widowed mother faithfully for many years. One of the comforts she gave her was the chaise longue; the maternal invalid spent long hours on it during her last years. When the mother died Miss Barton clung to this piece of furniture, dragging it after her to one furnished room after another. When she was seventy-three, crippled with arthritis, and unable to work at the fine embroidery and beaded bags which had been her livelihood, Sarah finally took the advice of her pastor. She applied to her church's home for needy gentlewomen, and was accepted. Some months later she was notified there was a vacancy. At this point, however, Sarah balked. She refused to take up residence until she was assured by an understanding matron that she could install the chaise longue, delapidated and forlorn remnant of a beloved past.

ADAPTATION TO NEW SETTING

How your own relatives will adapt themselves to proposed new ways of living depends on several factors. One of them, we repeat, is the important first step of whether they are presented with a *fait accompli*—something decided by the family—or can choose between what they may consider at first, if not finally, two evils.

Sometimes all the potentialities between permanent discontent and content will lie in the framing of a simple question. There is a vast difference between asking: "Do you think you'd like to live with the X. family where the children are clamoring for a grandmother in the home? Or would you rather look around for some place to board where there will be several people your own age?" and making the flat statement, "We've found something we think you'll like and can afford." The love and concern may be equal in both cases but the applied psychology is certainly not.

Whether your relative will be happy or miserable, however, is often not a matter of how good or how bad a particular situation is. It is, rather, a question of how he has met other life crises. Throughout life we are constantly forced to adjust to limitations and this is the same in old age, when general slowing up makes the adjustments harder. You can only measure the degree of difficulty any older person will have against his own earlier self, not by what others have done under the same circumstances. Health, of course, is an important factor, but so are psychological and mental factors in deciding what he is going to be able to do, and what he cannot do.

A so-called "trial period," if it can be arranged, is always a good bridge to a new life. It has the merit of making an individual feel he is not sealed off irrevocably from his old life. Agencies who have trouble in getting clients to move out of buildings that are unsanitary or have too many stairs for old legs to climb have found that the device of short vacations or even day-trips helps. The new environment sometimes has the effect of making even the set-in-their-ways realize that fresh beginnings can offer stimulation. The watchword is: "Do it slowly."

If a person is an invalid, physicians and nurses can give the best reassurance. So-called "friendly visitors," whom churches and lodges sometimes can supply, also may make more impression than family urging. It is not flattering, but often true, that older people are frequently more receptive to a word from a trusted stranger than to arguments, however good, from their own family. Possibly this is because the old think those nearest to them by blood ties are too much steeped in what they think is right and proper for their kinfolk.

A welfare agency head has a list of "types" which she says she keeps in mind when families present themselves to ask for aid in taking their old outside the family circle. They are not flattering portraits, but you may recognize yourself—or someone else—among them.

The well-meaning relative: He is earnestly pursuing at great effort on his own part some airtight plan he has thought out. He is usually firmly convinced that (*a*) the old must be relieved of all responsibility for their own fate; (*b*) family problems should not be discussed with them or in front of them; (*c*) the elderly must not know the secret of circumstances which necessitate a change in his living habits; (*d*) they must be spared the knowledge that arrangements which may alter their whole future are being made secretly for them.

The self-sufficient relative: His attitude of mind can be summed up in one sentence. He thinks he is in the best position to know what the older person ought to do; what the latter thinks about it or wants to do is of no importance.

The sorely-tried relative: He is weary of the struggle to maintain the rights of the younger generation against the equally imperative demands of an older man or woman. He is incapable because of his anxiety of realizing that it is the older person's misery which frequently makes him concentrate his thoughts and his actions on himself to the point where everyone else around him is wretched.

Whether or not you put yourself into one of these categories, you can do your best for an older individual when you realize without equivocation that the later years offer little time for experiment. He may be willing to make the best of "second best." Yet, to be asked to re-shuffle one's living patterns late in life in the hope of finding a satisfying combination at the least must draw on vigor and endurance that is depleted.

You may be able to secure a happy, serene old age for someone dear to you in a place where he will have both comforts and affection. This is certainly the ideal to strive for. But perhaps all you can do is to aid him adjust to a poor environment. In either case, there is one thing of which you can be certain. If any older person has to change his mode of living, the plan most likely to succeed is the one he thought of, or thinks he thought of, himself.

NOTES TO CHAPTER IX

(1) Randall, Ollie A. "Living Arrangements to Meet the Needs of Older People," in *Planning the Older Years*. Ann Arbor: University of Michigan Press, 1950. Pp. 31-59.

(2) Kardiner, A., M.D. "Psychological Factors in Old Age," in *Mental Hygiene in Old Age*. New York: Family Service Ass'n of America, 1937. P. 20.

(3) *Ibid.*

CHAPTER TEN

HOMES FOR THE AGED: PROS AND CONS

If a man or woman has to resettle himself late in life, should he go into an old people's home?

The answer may be "yes" and it may be "no." In either case, the idea should be frankly discussed. One thing is true: you may be sure any elderly person is thinking about it, whether he tells his family so or not. The reason is that when he was young there was no other solution for a person who could neither live with relatives nor stay in his own home. And thinking about it, unless the person is unusually perceptive and aware of changes that have occurred in his lifetime, means dreading it. For people of your grandparents' generation, and even your parents', grew up on those lachrymose verses, "Over the Hill to the Poor-House." Most of them still think in terms of this stereotype of their youth.

The attitude of one woman, alone and frail at eighty, reflects the deep-seated anxiety among older people uncertain of their future.

"When I had to think of an old ladies' home," she said, "I had to steel myself to visit one!"

This lurking fear of an institution is so firmly rooted that you have an obligation to make any elderly person realize homes for the aged have radically changed since Will Carleton wrote his dismal verses. You should point out that a Home is not the sole, or even the chief, choice open today; that this life is a fitting choice for only a few. But for those few it offers a better life than they could have anywhere else.

National studies bear out the conclusion of the Federation of

Protestant Welfare Agencies in New York, that seventy-five to eighty per cent of the men and women who apply to homes for the aged don't belong in one. Whether or not your relative is in this category is something you and he ought to find out.

Homes for the aged are something most of us think of as a last resort. Actually they may be a quite successful prop for the old. There are distinct advantages in having your relative aware of the pros and cons of so-called "congregate life" even if he ultimately chooses some other way of living. But before you can discuss them intelligently, you will probably have to rid yourself (and him) of some prejudices.

WHO ENTERS OLD PEOPLE'S HOMES?

"Something there is that doesn't love a wall."

The poet, Robert Frost, was not thinking of institutional life when he wrote that line, but it does express the instinctive recoil most of us have against the idea of being shut in. It is especially difficult for anyone under sixty to comprehend that there might come a time when he would prefer to sit back and watch life pass by. The question, however, is not whether you would choose an old people's home for yourself, or even for someone you love. Rather, the query you should pose is this: *Does a home for the aged offer what my relative ought to have now, and if it does, is he eligible for one?*

It will be easier to arrive at an honest answer if you understand what prompts people to ask for a place and a life which will make few demands on their self-confidence.

Mrs. Ruth Laverty, Field Director of the Peabody Home for elderly women, in New York, tells this story about the eighty-seven-year-old woman who came to see her. (1)

Mrs. Laverty says she bustled in as spry and alert as a woman half her age. "I'm so glad I got here on time," she said. "I just flew up from Florida; the weather was bad and I was afraid the plane would be delayed."

She was assured that another appointment would have been

arranged in that case. "That's not the point," the little lady said. "I've got to catch a plane for Massachusetts this afternoon!"

Mrs. Laverty asked her how she thought life in any home for aged women would suit her since she still obviously was so vitally active.

"Mercy me!" her visitor exclaimed. "I'm not applying for myself. I'm much too busy for anything like that. I'm looking for a home for my niece; I'm getting worried about her. She'll be sixty-six on her next birthday!"

What the niece's point of view might have been is another story, but the incident illustrates that neither chronological age nor pressure from relatives is a sound reason to expect an old age home to provide shelter and care.

Why do homes admit some applicants and not others?

Admission policies vary somewhat, but roughly speaking, successful applicants fall into these groups:

The physically well: They may be partially or wholly economically sufficient. This is the smallest category of all. Nowadays if institutions have such residents it is usually because they have come in years ago before we were ready to acknowledge that people of both sexes—especially the "younger aged" from sixty-five to seventy-five—if they are not incapacitated, should stay in the community.

The financially insecure: Some older people prefer to live in a home for the aged where they have paid an admission fee, however small, to living on relatives' bounty. Others, buffeted by life, would rather use an Old Age Assistance grant to pay board in a home, if state laws allow it, than eke out a meager existence outside it for themselves.

The feeble, or nearly so: More and more homes are admitting chiefly older and sicker people. This is to meet the sad fact that many who find the fear of illness more frightening even than dwindling resources, have nowhere to turn. A study by the Health and Welfare Council in Philadelphia, for instance, showed that eighty to eighty-five per cent of those who applied to eighty-two homes in three counties did not really need institutional care at that time. The majority frankly said they would prefer to remain independent. But what they did want was assurance of a place where they could have nursing and medical care if they should ever need it. In other instances relatives may cherish old people and still find them too much of a burden when they become enfeebled, or when they need supervision a home can provide.

The emotionally dependent: There will always have to be special places for some people, not necessarily ill and not necessarily extremely old. Elderly men and women whose friends and close relatives are dead, or who are removed from them in spirit or geography, think kindly of life with their contemporaries under a common roof. Sometimes they come willingly when they are merely tolerated strangers in a community, or if there is tension in a two- or three-generation household. There are also those—generally women—who have depended on a spouse all their lives; if death comes, they are too bereft to remain alone. The widow who cannot manage her own finances is a familiar figure in most institutions.

ATTITUDE OF THE AGED

Are all these people happy? The answer, of course, is "sometimes yes, sometimes no." Characters do not change; the timid remain so and the aggressive are not tamed. Nevertheless, relatives who have found elderly men and women "difficult" are sometimes surprised when they come to visit to hear that Mr. X. or Mrs. Y. is known as "a sweet old thing." When conflict is removed, the reason for ill-humor is no longer there.

The lonely, or those who find the pace of the young has been too swift, find it pleasanter and easier to share memories and experiences with people their own age. In a new environment, relieved of the strain of competition with the young, many become more alert and find life takes on zest that was lacking before. This was true in Mrs. Flora G.'s case which is not atypical. Widowed at seventy she tried living alone; later she lived with a friend. Neither satisfied her. She had no close relatives who cared to share their home with her, nor did she herself want that. Finally, after months of hesitation, she applied to a home which was small and had a moderate admission fee. The monthly board rate the contract called for was also within her means. Since she knew she could leave if she decided this, too, was no life for a lonely, childless woman, her trepidation was less. A year later, however, this is what Mrs. G. wrote a cousin:

"I came here resigned to hoping for nothing more than a clean bed and good food. But how much more I have found!"

The home had an excellent recreational program, which included a well-equipped arts and crafts workshop. Spurred on by the director, Mrs. G. took up again the ceramics which had interested her as a girl. Before she died a few years later she had the satisfaction of having her work exhibited in a metropolitan art gallery. It was praised by critics, not because it was produced by an old woman, but because Mrs. G. really had a fine sense of color and design.

Like Mrs. G., your relative may feel he doesn't know how or where to live out the declining years ahead. Even if a home for the aged is not his sole choice, its advantages may outweigh, as they did in Mrs. G.'s case, its disadvantages. If he seems to have no other option, he still has a right to know the good and bad points of congregate living, before he has to face them. As Dr. Elon H. Moore points out, "One should select his home as he would choose his wife or his house, with deliberation, and not as too often is the case, in desperation."(2)

ADVANTAGES VS. DISADVANTAGES

The home which we usually think of is one that is supported by a lodge, a church, a charitable agency, or an endowment, whether or not it requires fees from the applicant. Homes differ from one another, even in the same city or rural area, as much as county almshouses do. But before any attempt is made by your relative or by you to match his personality with an institution, he should weigh carefully the advantages and disadvantages common to any one of them.

Advantages

(*a*) In a home a guest does not have to make difficult decisions beyond his strength. He does not have to worry about his meals, his bed. Even his clothes are often bought for him and his amusements arranged to suit his capacities.

(*b*) Private homes for aged people generally provide a higher standard of living than they can procure for themselves on a limited income. This is a guaranteed way of life.

(*c*) If a resident decides to leave, he can always do so, even under a lifetime contract. Usually he has assurance of being charged only for the time the Home has supported him.

(*d*) Good homes have recreational and occupational therapy programs and opportunities for useful work. They encourage residents to participate in civic, religious, and avocational activities in the community outside the home.

(*e*) Healthful surroundings, periodic physical examinations, prompt remedial measures in case of sickness, are common. Large homes have resident physicians and consultants of all kinds on call.

(*f*) Life in a home is often superior to an unhappy existence forced on all members of a family in a crowded apartment or small house. There is opportunity for congenial companionship and new interests.

Disadvantages

(*a*) Unused minds soon become apathetic. The minor decisions made every day are what keep a steady stream of life pulsing in aged veins. Where this necessity is taken away, people often rust out their lives.

(*b*) A resident, in actual practice, is financially dependent. He retains only the amount of spending money a Board deems adequate.

(*c*) A lifetime contract means every asset must be turned over, present and future. All personal claims, even to inheritances, are given up.

(*d*) The change from community life to any institution is a psychological shock. There must be regulations about mealtimes, room furnishings, radio, visits and visitors, and amusements.

(*e*) Applicants with diseases which require constant care are not accepted. Admission requirements often bar those who need institutional life most.

(*f*) A shared bedroom or dormitory life are general and prove a hardship for most elderly people. There is frequently friction between residents under such conditions.

(*g*) Applicants on waiting lists are often aided to find alternative methods of living, or given visiting housekeepers and/or visiting nurse service, occasionally even financial aid.

(*g*) There is no guarantee that those who pass the required physical examination at time of application will be in sufficiently good health to be admitted when their names are reached.

THE SECOND STRING

If your relative puts his name on an application blank when he is trying to plan for his last years, he will have a valuable *second string* to his bow.

Note that emphasis. As Ollie A. Randall says, out of her years of experience in the Community Service Society of New York, "It is incredible how many people, and their children, in this day and age, in an emergency turn to look for a 'home' for themselves or their parents, with no glimmer of an idea that waiting lists are often years long and that admission requirements are strict."(3)

But if your relative's name is on an application blank, and he has been accepted, there is nothing to prevent his making other arrangements while he waits for a vacancy. If they prove satisfactory, he can always withdraw his application and no one will think the worse of him.

Progressive homes give an applicant a clear understanding why he cannot be accepted immediately, or if they must reject him, also frankly tell him the reasons. At the same time they try to help him find an alternate solution, such as a boarding home, a nursing home, or a cooperative club residence for old people. Frequently several homes, particularly in large cities, cooperate in sharing the services of an "intake worker." She calls on the applicant not only to give him a chance to ask questions, but to get acquainted with his background and family relationships, and gives him help in determining whether he really wants, or needs, a sheltered existence. (See Chapter XIV, *Where to Turn for Help*.)

DEFERRED APPLICATIONS

There is another, not so minor advantage in urging any elderly person at least to investigate homes in his own neighborhood. If he decides they don't meet his requirements (whether or not he meets theirs) he will be more tolerant of other alternatives. Or if he tries another way of living in the community and finds it wanting, he can still apply for admission to some home he already knows about, with facts, not fears or prejudices, as a measuring-rod.

If he applies and is accepted but put on a long waiting list, which is usual, and still wants to enter two or three or five years later when his name is reached, he can have first claim on the vacancy. Even then he may often ask to be put on the "deferred" list.

This is a proviso made for those who feel they still want to make their own way but also want the assurance that they will be cared for when they can no longer manage by themselves. The story of Miss Smith shows its advantages.

Miss Smith was seventy-one when she filed her first application to Ward Manor, a suburban home on the outskirts of New York. She was working as a "companion." A few years later, when a vacancy occurred, she was notified. She was reluctant to retire, however, as long as she could be self-supporting. When she finally did ask for admission, she was eighty-six. Because she had already had long years of adjusting herself to other people's ways, and was a friendly person with a sense of humor, no one doubted Miss Smith would make this final adjustment with ease.

WHAT THE STATISTICS MEAN

If his situation, however, calls for immediate action, it will probably come as a shock to learn that no one can select an old people's home as a place of first choice in an emergency and let its gates clang behind him on the morrow.

This is one instance where statistics, to paraphrase an old saw, are worth a thousand pictures.

The deep-seated belief in most people's minds that a great many old people spend their last years in homes for the aged is a glaring fallacy. When Dr. Moore made his study, based on U. S. Bureau of Labor Statistics, he found that only one person in eight hundred past his sixtieth birthday—about 1 per cent of all our aged population—*can* have a place in an old people's home. There are approximately fourteen hundred privately supported(4) homes for the aged in this country. Whether they have low standards or high ones, they are all filled to capacity, all the time. When a new one opens, it is flooded with applications.

Does this mean that most old people long to adopt this way of living out the last third of their lives?

The answer every federal and private survey gives is a resounding "No!" It does mean that "over the hill to the poorhouse" never was, and is not today, an answer for more than a fraction of our older population. It also means that construction of homes by fraternal lodges, social agencies, trade unions, churches—their usual sponsors—reached its peak in the latter part of the nineteenth century and has lagged far behind the jump in our aging population in the twentieth.

Moreover, it means that if a person needs or wants to enter a home, he should find out if he can meet its requirements long before the necessity to go there becomes imperative. Homes, good and bad, vary in their admission requirements not only from state to state, but in the same town. An applicant can be on a waiting list anywhere from one to five years, or even more.

ADMISSION POLICIES

Based on years of accumulated experiences, admission policies are framed, by and large, as much for the happiness of the applicant as the comfort of those already in residence. These are the factors that are taken into account:

Age: A minimum of sixty-five years is still general, but anyone who applies at that semi-youthful age now will be urged, and quite often helped, to find some other way to live.

Citizenship: In some states American citizenship is a requisite; others accept long-term residence, sometimes as little as five years.

Residence: Local residence, varying from a substantial part of the applicant's lifetime to several years, is a common requirement.

Race and Sex: Some homes limit themselves to members of one sex; others accept both. Either type may have racial restrictions.

Health: Most homes require a physical examination, usually by a physician designated by the Board, before acceptance, and another at time of entrance. Some limit themselves to the ambulatory. Often all chronically ill persons are automatically excluded along with alcoholics and the mentally ill. However, if a guest falls ill after he enters, he is taken care of in the infirmary or through some temporary arrangement elsewhere in a hospital, usually one a home is affiliated with, which supplements the interim, less specialized infirmary care.

Membership: This depends on whether a home is largely supported by a fraternal lodge, a church or group of churches, a trade union, or some other type of organization. If it is, the applicant will have to be a member in good standing, or a close relative, such as wife or husband of a member. Occasionally privately supported homes of this type, when they have vacancies, allow others to enter at a higher fee.

Homogeneity: Most homes, particularly small ones, try to take men and women who will be congenial. Usually they are screened to find out if the person who wants to live in a home has a similar social and economic background to those already in it. (They seldom go quite so far, however, as an Illinois home which restricts its admissions to impoverished men of former wealth and position.)

This is not snobbishness. It is a practical recognition that problems arise when people live together whose life patterns were set long before they met each other. Homogeneity helps to eliminate sources of possible friction.

Let this typical resident bear witness:

Arthur Mueller in his seventies moved to the Bethany Methodist Home in Brooklyn, New York. He had lived previously with his daughter and son-in-law for several years. "But when the family grew," he says, "we were too much 'crammed in.' " Those who share the home with Mr. Mueller, like him are of German background, many first-generation immigrants, all members in good standing of some church. There is room enough to house forty people comfortably.

"Every month," Mr. Mueller says, "I go home to my folks for a week. But when you get older you long to be back again in your own comfortable room here, where you have everything in its right place, each book on its proper shelf, and all the conveniences for your personal requirements handy."

He ends his little homily with these words: "In our Bethany Home we are more like a large family; everyone knows each other, and all our people are happy and satisfied. In fact, nobody would be admitted who would not fit into our way of life."

FINANCING ADMISSION

Unlike Mr. Mueller, a great many people are dissatisfied because they never clearly understood the provisions under which their contracts for care were made. Fees for entrance, charges for board and room, and all other financial arrangements between the aged person and the institution, should be in writing. See that there is a copy for each, to avoid possibility of any misunderstanding. Some of the things to ask about *before* the agreement is signed, are these:

1. Will a refund be made if a guest leaves or dies before the end of the period paid for, if there is no life contract?
2. When cash and other personal property owned by the residents is turned over to the home for safeguarding, is a receipt given, and all withdrawals accounted for by signed receipts?
3. Is there an inventory of other personal property held by the home for residents, and a copy given the guest?

The agreement itself should show: (*a*) value of the property transferred; (*b*) amount of care to be furnished; (*c*) manner in which care is to be furnished. If a deposit is accepted be sure assurance is given—in writing—that admission is guaranteed within a specified time limit. It is possible that the home will refuse this guarantee because its waiting list is too long and it has no indication when vacancies will occur. If this is so, then find out whether the agreement is definite on the point of a full refund in case you make other arrangements or your relative changes his mind. (The shoe has to be on the other foot, too; if grandma or grandpa makes a deposit, or his family does it, and then backs out after he has arranged to take possession of a room set aside for him, he usually won't get his money back.)

To be sure your relative won't harbor resentment or feel his confidence has been abused, see that he understands these fine points:

Admission fees: They vary widely. The usual norm is between $500 and $5,000. Most elderly people, with a vague idea of what their money covers, feel they have fully paid their life way. They resent being asked to give up any other property or investments if they sign a life contract. The facts are these: Studies show that the average applicant's admission fee pays his upkeep for a year, two, or possibly three years, but that he is likely to live and be supported in sickness or in health for another ten, fifteen, or twenty years—or even longer. Older people in institutions, well cared for and living without strain, are living longer than was expected when those admission fees were set. They also benefit by all the preventive measures and the drugs and operation procedures that make their sisters and brothers of the same age outside the institution healthier and able to withstand death longer. At the Presbyterian Home in Pennyslvania, for instance, a life care contract costs $500 only. But their accountants' figures show that the average guestship costs the managers of the home more than $4,500.(5) (As Mr. Mueller says of the Bethany Home, "We have a full house at all times; once in a while there is a vacancy because our people are mostly between eighty and ninety-four years old.")

Requirements: You should explain gently to elderly people, who may be sunk in memories of the days when eggs were ten cents a dozen, the troublesome business of transferring assets. Homes which guarantee to take care of a person as long as he lives, require a transferral of all money, securities, and property, real and personal. This includes pensions, income from annuities, social security, workmen's compensation, etc., as well as any property or money which might come through future bequests or gifts.

This is not nearly as harsh as it sounds. The homes are merely trying to make up the difference between what they pay out and what they receive from a resident. If he happens to be unlucky enough to die and leave a residue of funds, then someone who lives longer than he will profit by it in board-and-room benefits. (This is exactly the same principle the insurance companies operate on; those of us who get benefits for a policy on which few premiums have been paid are "carried" by the many others who pay and pay, and receive little or nothing.)

Most homes will arrange for interest to be paid, at a low rate, on money surrendered over and above the admission fee. They also arrange for even the penniless to have the equivalent of some spending money for little purchases (and fellow-guests will not know its source).

On the other hand, there ought to be a clear understanding, preferably in writing, about any extra charges. These may be for mending, laundry, hair cuts, shaves, shampoos, cleaning dentures, or other personal services. It is especially important to discuss charges for physician's and extra nurse's services and medicines, if they ever are necessary.

Most homes will permit a full refund if a resident withdraws after a trial period (usually thirty days), or is told he must leave (when he is a misfit). However, he will probably have a deduction made for board and room he has already enjoyed.

This may all seem elementary to you, but elderly men as well as women who have not handled their own finances for some time, quite often have only a vague idea of the spending power of today's dollar. Like Clarence Day's mother, Vinnie, they may even be oblivious of the fact that dollars withdrawn from the bank always leave that much less. One woman who collected $5,000 in insurance after her husband's death lived on it for nearly two years. When she applied to the Peabody Home in New York City for admission she brought out her bankbook. The person who interviewed her noticed there was a long record of withdrawals in small amounts. All she had left were several hundred dollars. When this was called to her attention she exclaimed in horrified accents, "Oh, no, that can't be so! I've never drawn more than $10 at a time!"(6)

Boarding care: Life contracts are going out of fashion. This is not only because they carry a sense of finality about them which is depressing to many. It is also because homes for the aged have suffered from high costs and low endowments. Many homes, large and small, now encourage persons to pay a monthly board rate which can be adjusted in relation to the economic picture as the lump sum payment for life care could not be. Older people who have limited amounts of their own, or are not positive they can count indefinitely on contributions toward their maintenance from friends and relatives, can still enter the home, but are expected to apply for Old Age Assistance when funds are exhausted. The money is sent directly to the resident and he or she pays board just as before.

The boarding-by-the-month plan gives many elderly people a sense of freedom that the life contract seems to take away. One woman said frankly at her first interview, "Knowing I can pay my way as I go takes the sting out of coming here. I was afraid I would have to sign my life away!" (Parenthetically, when she did eventually become a happy resident, the amount she paid represented exactly one-third the cost of her upkeep, though neither she nor any other guest knew it. Like colleges, homes have to be subsidized; private ones, like this one, depend on annual campaigns, allotments from the Community Chest, or special contributions from organizations and individuals.)

Range of accommodations: Fees sometimes vary within the institution itself. An old building may contain a few private rooms, or some which have to be shared between two or among four or six persons, or dormitories, or all three. The price will be scaled accordingly. A new edifice, erected along modern lines, gives every individual or couple a room although it may be small. To most people—though not all—this is a great boon. Some place to keep one's keepsakes in privacy, and a piece of furniture associated with memories, a spot by a window to retreat to with the door closed, would make necessary adjustments to group living easier for most of us, and for most of the older generation.

On the other hand, beware of mistaking your personal preferences for someone else's. Not all older people care for privacy even at the end of their lives. Some like sharing a room along with their reminiscences, especially if they have been alone or lonely.

If everyone were like Mrs. Adele Carson, the problem would be simple. The day she was sixty-five she marched into a long-established "home for indigent females" and announced, "I've kept house, child and woman, first for my father, and then for my husband. I've been worried and fretted for over fifty years. I want to live now where I won't ever have to think for myself again!"

As she had no children living, and no funds, eventually she had her wish. Today she sits with her cronies in the dormitory, or rocks the time away on the porch. Apparently she has not bothered to "think" since she entered the home, and at eighty-one, is still enjoying it.

TYPES OF HOMES VARY

What will be available where your relative lives? In the long run he may have to content himself with what he can get. But if he is to exercise any degree of choice, he ought to know what kind of homes exist, and how widely they vary, so that he can have something against which to measure those for which he is eligible.

When the U. S. Bureau of Labor Statistics made its last study of homes for the aged,(7) New York, Pennsylvania, and Massachusetts had one third of the total number in the United States, though this does not necessarily mean they were the best. Geographic distribution, like the accommodations themselves, is very uneven. The types to look for fall into the following classifications. Tell him about them before he visits any place.

The Congregate Plan: This is the most usual. It means that a group lives together, usually in one large building. There may be private rooms, semi-private rooms, or dormitories, or all three, under one roof. Happily, the days have vanished when married couples were placed in separate dormitories, able to see each other only at a certain time on Wednesday or Friday, as Dr. Carol Aronovici says the custom was when he began work early in this century. The best homes try to provide residents with the type of living, medical supervision, recreation, etc. that corresponds most nearly with their capacity for normal living *when they enter*. As passing years work their changes, temporary or lasting, and residents require a greater amount of attention or nursing care, they are shifted about.

The way this plan works is shown at its best in an institution like the Hebrew Home for Aged and Infirm in New York City. Its main building is typical of those you will find in many cities—an old-fashioned, inadequate, unprepossessing brick and stone edifice. But in spite of this, the men and women who live in it are kept mentally alert, as well as physically alive, as long as possible.

About three hundred and fifty people are housed there on the "congregate" plan. Those with sufficient physical vigor have rooms, two to each room (because space is so scarce) on the upper floors. The less sturdy live in ground-floor dormitories. There is a dining room on the same floor, and a tree-shaded small garden within easy reach, pleasant, even though it is overlooked by tall apartment houses.

These dormitory residents are not allowed to feel they have retired from the main stream of activity. (If you can find the kind of program, or something similar, to that given them, you can be certain your old are not going to rust away.) There is a well-stocked library, where residents are assistants; a synagogue in which they serve as well as pray; clubroom and handicraft shops, all accessible, and all well-used. For those who find this too taxing, there is an infirmary wing. But here, too, even the bedfast are made to feel part of the community. The occupational therapist brings lessons and handicraft materials to their bedside, and a mobile book wagon furnishes them with whatever they want from the library. When concerts are given for the residents who can attend them, strolling musicians play, before or after the performance, for the infirm. The residents themselves from the many home clubs make regular visits to keep their neighbors in contact with all that is going on.

There are few places as well-organized, as well-supported by the community, and as well-staffed as this, but its standards are those to keep in mind.

The Cottage Plan: This calls for small cottages built around a central edifice. The cottages are the property of the home and under its control. Such homes for the aged as the one at Elyria, Ohio, built by the Methodists and in operation for more than a decade, or by the same group at Claremont, California, are past the experimental stage but are not numerous. They offer these advantages:

1) Independence: A married couple or two friends, or several, share a house and have all the independence of normal home life, with added protection when they need or want it. For instance, they can either eat their meals at the main dining-room or in their own home.

2) Security: Cottages are always built in close proximity to the main building. Near at hand, then, they have nursing care, an infirmary or hospital wing, congenial friends, and counselling.

When cottage residents are no longer able to care for themselves or when one spouse dies, a move can be made to the main building. This does not have the drastic emotional effect of other types of removal because the same friendships in the same environment and the same staff arrangements for care continue. Usually these cottages and their main building are set in spacious, well-landscaped grounds. Sometimes cottages are scattered through a community, but are under a central administration.

Apartment Plans: A few, very few homes have incorporated into their programs an opportunity for some aged to live semi-independently. One plan is to have small efficiency apartments located in a building where residents have some supervision, usually taking their meals together in a common dining-room. Another permits still able-bodied men and women on waiting lists to live in an apartment house where they have well-furnished rooms. They either partake in a special recreational program provided for them or participate with people already residents of the home itself in their activity projects. In either case they have access to medical care, and assurance that when they no longer can care for themselves they will be taken into the institution.

One home, for instance, offers to a limited number efficiency apartments consisting of two rooms, kitchenette and bath, or one large bed-living room and bath.

These are modifications of plans already prevalent in Northern Europe, but in this country they are not subsidized by the government or state, and can only be offered the individual able to pay substantially toward their not inconsiderable cost.

Private Pavilions: Even among the tiny minority of people over sixty-five who can well afford homes of their own and servants to care for them, there is a number who need companionship, constant medical supervision or nursing care, and a planned routine without strain.

For this group, insignificant in numbers, but just as much in need of what a home offers as their less well-to-do brethren, a small number of large homes have well-furnished accommodations at rates comparable to good hotels or nursing homes. The guests share in the same recreational, medical, and counselling activities given their poorer neighbors in other wings.

PUBLIC HOMES FOR THE AGED

At the other end of the scale is the tax-supported home for the aged, a descendant of the old-time "poorhouse."

Normally, you would not choose this for your aged, yet the best county farms or city almhouses are sometimes superior to poorly run homes under benevolent auspices in the same area. Since many old people are without savings and need custodial care, it is common sense not to shy away from visiting a public home, if only for purposes of comparison. You might even find your own elderly friend's reaction the same as Auguste Cordelier's. Mr. Cordelier, born in Switzerland, decided to retire from farmwork in his early sixties. He methodically looked over facilities open to him in New Jersey, and choose to turn over his life savings of $4,648 to a county home; authorities will draw on it at the rate of $3 a day. He is reported to have said, "There's nothing like this at home!"

The chief difference between the vicious institutions of the past and the more humane ones of today is in the degree of physical comfort and better medical and nursing care given the senile, the chronically ill, and the disabled. The fact that they, too, are packed to capacity, and sometimes beyond it, is an eloquent commentary on our national inability to grapple with a vital problem, and not evidence, for or against, a particular city or county home.

Yesterday's care of the aged on a "county farm" consisted of three meals, usually scanty, and a roof over the residents' heads as they lay on cots or beds with poor springs, close together in a bare dormitory. This picture has almost, though not quite, faded away. The dormitories are still there, and the meals are not always appetizing though usually they are nourishing enough. The difference now is largely in the kind of people who are admitted, and our attitude toward their needs.

The great number of public home residents, like those in private homes today, are feeble, or suffer from some physical defect which makes it difficult for them to live alone or in a family. This means they are barred from rendering the assistance in growing crops which was the mainstay of the old-time county farm. The question today is to find sufficient work, of the functional or even the occupational therapy type, to keep these old people happy to the point at least of not becoming "problem old children," as one superintendent calls them.

Medical and bedside care varies widely. The only general rule you will find, and even this has exceptions, is that if you look for a place in a larger home you can also expect more extensive nursing and recreational services. One large home in Indiana, for instance, has a staff of four physicians, two registered nurses, a licensed practical nurse, and men and women listed on the payroll as nurse's aides or attendants, all of whom have had practical nursing experience. Smaller homes with a less impressive list, however, may be able to attend equally well to fewer old men and women. The rule is to have physicians on call (sometimes not enough, to be sure) and units or wards where some nursing service is given. This may be by practical nurses, or those waiting for their licenses to be granted, or by those who have "trained" in their own homes. Usually there are male orderlies in addition.

In short, what you will find, and how high the standards will be, will depend on how far the community, the county, or the state —or all three—have advanced in their social thinking. In this there is no difference between the private and the public home. You will find there has been a steady improvement in physical surroundings, general standards, and an attempt to introduce occupational therapy and recreational programs which will rehabilitate the individual.

On the obverse side there is the lamentable fact that most of these institutions are terrifically overcrowded with those whom society has rejected, with staffs too small to do an adequate job. Nevertheless, public homes for the aged perform a definite service which cannot be ignored for the simple reason that often there is no other place for an old person to go.

"It could happen to anyone!"

This is the dramatic heading of an article in Indiana's *Public Welfare* magazine.(8) It tells the story of a county commissioner who vigorously opposed any improvements in a home, even to changing the regular fare of beans and bacon. In true movie-thriller fashion circumstances compelled him late in life to seek refuge in the very place he had contended was "good enough."

It is hardly likely that anything so dramatic will happen in your friends' and relatives' lives. If it does, remember there is no disgrace to living in a tax-supported institution. If the ones to which they must apply are badly run, it is only public disinterest which keeps them so.

WHAT TO LOOK FOR EVERYWHERE

What makes one home, public or private, good, and another bad?

The answer can't be found merely by visiting an institution, or more than one. However, if an elderly person knows in advance what makes life in a home for the aged not only bearable, but pleasurable, his talks with a superintendent or with guests will be helpful.

Old people's homes everywhere have conscientious boards trying to determine what role this old-time institution ought to play today. In many instances the programs are in a state of flux. As early as 1932 the Welfare Council of New York set up standards for communities to follow and has revised them from time to time to keep pace with the changing public attitude. The essentials, nonetheless, will remain the same. Help your relative to judge a particular home by these basic elements, not by the "trimmings":

Physical surroundings: Most of us are impressed when we see an imposing building set in beautifully landscaped surroundings.

Nevertheless, a warm-hearted management which treats old people as individuals worthy of courtesy and consideration is more important than glamour.

The important thing to look for is a place not so rundown that employees are overworked and good housekeeping principles impossible to follow. Where life is easier for the staff the atmosphere is happier for those they serve. The location is even more important than that. It should not be isolated, so if he goes there, your relative will not feel cut off from everything and everyone he knows. If he is well enough, he will want to get out and see friends. He ought also to be near enough to members of the family so that some of them can visit often. This will mean more than the most elegant of exteriors or interiors.

Licensing and regulations: State and municipal laws may be good but inspection weak. Find out what the licensure laws are and whether they are being lived up to in such matters as the number of fire-escapes, fire drills, sanitation. If medical care is offered, there will be regulations governing the number of the staff and their qualifications. Don't be hesitant about asking to see emergency exits or the plumbing. If possible, look into the kitchen, or even where the garbage is deposited.

Degree of freedom: In the best regulated homes able-bodied residents are free to come and go as they please. A rule may require them to leave word at the office if they are to be away at dinner or overnight but this is no more than the courtesy they should extend to their own families. Visits to friends and families—usually from a week to a month—are encouraged. So are activities in the neighborhood, including retention of church and club memberships.

Where groups of people live together, a selfish person can be a disrupting factor. But common-sense rules about promptness at mealtime, time to turn off the radio or turn out the lights are not restrictions but necessities.

Nutrition standards: As the publication of the Welfare Council points out, "Well-planned meals (with an element of choice), served in a pleasant, relaxed atmosphere, pay rich dividends in better health and greater happiness for the aged."(9) (See Chapter IV, *Getting on in Years—Safely.*)

If a home houses more than fifty residents it should have a professionally trained dietician, or at least the consultation services of one, to insure well-balanced meals, not occasionally or on special holidays, but all the time.

Activity program: "By their deeds ye shall know them" was never truer than in a home for aged men or women. If residents are sitting about, just "resting," or are herded in a group doing nothing, no matter how luxurious the parlor or how handsome the lawn, take your relative somewhere else. A chance to develop new hobbies or cultivate dormant ones, to help with small duties in accordance with strength, to retain contacts with the outside world—these are the balance wheels which keep people from desiccating in a small, enclosed community.

You can judge whether a home has high recreational standards by these three forms of activity:

1) *The activity which people watch:* This exists everywhere. It means that there are movies, concerts, even plays in the institution, either participated in by the residents or given by outside performers.

2) *The activity which people themselves engage in:* Some, not all, homes have facilities for arts and crafts, carpentry, gardening, etc., but all afford a chance for reading, sewing, knitting, cards, etc.

3) *The activity which enables people to work and play together:* This is the one most often lacking, and the most important. If older people are stimulated to produce their own plays and act in them, make their own costumes and sets, arrange their own parties and act as hosts, or undertake a joint project for the benefit of some cause outside the home, they will never stagnate. A home for aged and disabled men and women in San Francisco illustrates that even though your aging relative may end his days in an institution, he can still lead a productive life. Here is an incomplete list of the busy program carried on by residents in this West Coast home:

Ex-carpenters build tables, stage-sets, and make arbors for the dramatic groups which ex-actors have organized.

Former upholsterers decorate chairs and keep couches and other furniture in repair for rooms in which former lawyers and accountants lead forums.

Old ladies who used to make tidies now employ their skill in sewing and embroidering tray clothes, bureau scarves, and bed jackets for their sicker comrades.

Others make dolls for a crippled children's hospital, roll bandages for the Red Cross, and write letters to wounded soldiers.

Writers, editors, and just ordinary people prepare, edit, mimeograph, assemble, and mail a magazine. Its covers are the work of an eighty-five-year-old artist who paints from a wheel-chair.

Work as therapy: If you find guests working in a vegetable or flower garden, acting as receptionists, or switchboard operators, or drying silverware, etc., it is not necessarily a sign that the institution is understaffed. If these are voluntary tasks, they have a value. They keep a sense of productivity alive. Sometimes it helps a person with a temperament like Simon Frankel's to feel he is fully paying his way.

Mr. Frankel entered a Masonic home, largely because he could not bear to be separated from his wife. He had nursed her for many months after he sold his small jewelry business. Finally, he realized she needed more care than he could give her. By that time his funds were nearly exhausted. Luckily, he had little difficulty in obtaining admission to the home after his many years' membership in the Masonic Order. Once there, however, Mr. Frankel grew unhappier day by day. A wise superintendent was aware of it, and finally asked him if he would keep the institution's many clocks in order, and take on the additional job of repairing watches for staff and fellow-guests. Today Mr. Frankel is one of the most contented and busiest people in his little world.

Opportunity for earning money: This is an expansion of the "work as therapy" idea. It is valuable, provided you can be certain that residents are not being exploited or depended on for the operation of an institution. More and more, however, it is recognized that people who want some paying work on a basis compatible with their strength, ought not to be barred from it simply because they are institutionalized. Nowhere is the possession of some small funds more important in achieving little satisfactions than in an old people's home. Traditionally, homes have conducted annual bazaars or gift shops to exhibit work made by residents. That gives them the feeling they are contributing to their support. There are other ways elderly people of different backgrounds and interests can utilize their time and have a chance to earn—and have fun. If you and your relative wonder if initiative is stifled, study this list of novel earning ways the National Lutheran Council uncovered in homes for the aged in Minnesota: An ambitious member of one home organized a crocheting class. An exhibit of the work brought enough orders to make the project profitable. A disabled man made weathervanes; orders came from many parts of the country. This hobby grew into an industry and employed some of his elderly friends. A group of men at one home go fishing regularly in a near-by river and come back with large fish and larger stories. Residents in another location pick berries and use the proceeds for rental of moving pictures. No old age bugaboos here!

Medical care: In many ways the attending physician, in residence or on call, is an institution's most important officer. It is important to find out whether regular periodic physical examinations are given, and what means exist to alleviate suffering, both emotional and physical.

It is not necessary for each home to follow the same medical plan. The type of medical services will vary with the number of old people who have to be protected. Look for these:

An infirmary is a *sine qua non* no matter how small the home. It may consist of a couple of rooms, or a whole floor. This depends on whether admissions are limited to the able-bodied generally or include the infirm, and whether the policy is to remove the sick to a hospital or keep them in the institution. Every infirmary ought to be under the supervision of a registered nurse.

Only the largest institutions will have hospital wings with diagnostic and treatment facilities. The majority remove seriously ill guests from the infirmary to a hospital with which the institution has an affiliation. They return when they are convalescent. Or they may have to be discharged to another institution; for example, in case of mental illness. (If you are apprehensive on this score, inquire what disabilities incurred after a guest enters, require his removal.)

Institutions which charge monthly fees are apt to have smaller facilities for the sick than those which give life-care contracts.

Also, commercial institutions tend to have a smaller per cent of beds set aside for their "sick bay" than non-profit-making institutions.

Dr. Robert Monroe estimates(10) that a home for one hundred residents should have a nursing unit equiped with fifteen to twenty beds. Where you find this ratio, you can be reasonably certain the institution is admitting people with advance knowledge that most of them will eventually need special care and that it is prepared to give it to them.

The staff: Ideally, the home which houses only those able to get about freely needs approximately one person on the staff to every five guests. If the latter are sick or infirm the ratio should be one patient to about every two staff members. But this is only a small part of the story of relationships between residents, and between residents and staff.

The intangibles are the hinges upon which swing most of the happiness or unhappiness in congregate living. It has been said that with the same facilities two distinctly different types of homes can be created, depending on the personnel and their operational procedures. Even on a single visit you can tell something about the atmosphere of a place.

Sometimes there are legal regulations covering age, health, training, and experience, which you can easily determine from any local welfare organization. These cover the bare bones of qualifications for a post as staff member. But it does not need a trained eye or a law to make it evident that if guests seem dejected or look vacantly at nothing, an institution is not well managed. It may be giving them excellent food and adequate shelter and clothing but it is not offering them an opportunity to retain their independence, initiative, or even self-respect.

A good staff member will be patient, kindly, and will respect the privacy and dignity of a guest. He will knock if the resident is in a private room. He will not discuss his problems or the resident's condition in the presence of strangers. He will show interest in placing an applicant with congenial roommates if he has to have any. Anyone can make up his own scoresheet to add to these fundamental qualifications. A good way to find out if residents are receiving the benign care they need is to ask these questions, or use them as a guide when you make your own observations:

Is there a social worker to whom they can turn for counsel?

Does the manager or superintendent appear to recognize psychological as well as physical needs of old people?

Are birthdays and such small attentions as food likes and dislikes always remembered?

Are guests chatting or working at something together, or do they just seem to sit, lost in their own thoughts?

THE CRITICAL POINT

Presume that these and other questions can be answered satisfactorily. Presume, too, that a person who is experiencing frustrations and insecurity wants to accept this traditional way out of a troubled situation. How can you be sure it is only because he knows no other alternative? The only answer to that, of course, is to be sure that he does know.

For if an active and independent man or woman is admitted to a home before he is psychologically ready for it, regardless of his need he is likely to break mentally or physically, or both. One case worker in an aged woman's home says, "How often I have heard a woman say that entering an institution was the last thing she really wanted but she thought she ought to do it because her relatives and friends advised her it was the best thing to do!"

To enter a home with such strongly negative feelings means that no matter how excellent a place really is, she is going to find the slow pace of institutional life depressing and discouraging. (The same is true for men, naturally.) Either the person becomes so discontented and critical of everyone and everything that he develops into a personality problem with which the home's staff and the other residents cannot cope, or he will slow up his own pace and hasten his own mental and physical deterioration. Obviously, he doesn't belong there.

But to compel an adult child to take on the care of an aged parent when he is unable to carry the extra burden, or is unwilling, only intensifies an already serious problem. "What would the neighbors say?" or "What would the minister think?" are not important. If keeping an elderly man or woman in the family circle means putting an increased strain on already weakened ties, relationships will grow worse and nothing but unhappiness for all concerned will result.

What is the solution?

You can find the proper answer in the comments made at the Second Gerontological Congress, held in St. Louis, Missouri, in 1951. There it was pointed out that a well-designed institutional home which meets the medical, social, and recreational requirements of the aged has much to commend it. It was also pointed out, however, that even when a man or woman appears to require this maximum protection from the blows of life, he has a right to know what other choices society has to offer him.

Your own lingering doubts and the hesitations of the person most deeply affected can only be dispelled by one means. Before he makes a final decision your relative should have the comfort of knowing that his family want to help him explore every other possibility that will give him a substitute for his own home.

NOTES TO CHAPTER X

(1) Laverty, Ruth. "New Ways for Old." Address delivered at 46th Annual Conference, New Jersey Welfare Council, Oct. 31, 1947. (Mimeographed.)

(2) Moore, Elon H. "Homes, Hostels, and Other Institutions for the Aged." *Journal of Gerontology,* Jan., 1948. P. 207.

(3) *These Harvest Years.* Edited by Janet Baird. New York: Doubleday and Co., Inc., 1951. P. 208.

(4) Moore, Elon H. *Op. cit.*

(5) *The Presbyterian Home News.* Admissions Committee Edition, Vol. XIII, No. 2, Nov. 1948, Newville, Pa. P. 2.

(6) Laverty, Ruth. *Op. cit.* P. 9.

(7) Evans, Louise. "Providing Institutional Care for Recipients of Public Assistance. *Public Welfare,* Nov. 1945. P. 248.

(8) "It Could Happen to Anyone." *Public Welfare in Indiana,* July, 1952.

(9) *Suggested Standards for Homes for the Aged.* New York: Welfare Council of New York City, 1948. Sixth Edition.

(10) Monroe, Robert, M.D. "The Role of Homes for the Aged in the Future." Address presented at conference of Federation of Protestant Welfare Agencies, Inc., New York City, April 6, 1948. (Mimeographed.)

CHAPTER ELEVEN

SUBSTITUTE HOMES FOR THE WELL

There is much more recognition now that older people who want to spend their last years as an active part of the community should have that right than there was when your parents faced their parents' problems.

That is one of the reassuring facts you can offer any able-bodied older man or woman. Since one out of every dozen of us is over sixty-five, where people live when they age is no longer a mere family affair. It has become society's business.

In the decade from 1940 to 1950, when the number of people past their sixty-fifth birthday rose by thirty-seven per cent—nearly three times the rest of the population(1)—businessmen as well as philanthropists saw the need of some bold housing experiments. New York led the way with state-aided housing projects in which apartments are set aside for the elderly. In the state of Washington old people have aid to maintain cooperative residences. Florida real estate men are beginning to develop housing designed expressly for retired people. A Midwest architectural firm is one of several which is designing houses for clients in their seventies, including such features as ramps instead of stairs.

These, and a dozen other projects, are encouraging straws in the wind. Everywhere, communities large and small have taken the first, basic step toward helping the old. They are taking an interest in them.

YOUR OBLIGATION

But you would only be deceiving yourself, and injuring the people you want to help, if you did not recognize clearly our present tremendous lacks. Housing suitable for the old, particularly any erected especially for them or which gives them a chance at semi-independent lives, is pitifully insufficient, not in one place or in one region, but everywhere. What was said in a report presented in 1950, at the first Conference on Aging this country ever saw, is still true and likely to remain so for some time:

"In the area of housing . . . the total supply available to meet the fundamental needs of aging couples and individuals is grossly inadequate and there is almost none that has been designed directly to meet the needs of the aged. We don't know enough about how the aged are living, how they want to live, and how they should live. . . ."(2)

By the time we have reached the last third of our own lives, the pilot plans which have already proved successful, and others now in the blueprint stage, may be widespread. The mounting tide of old people will force some action. But until the picture radically alters, anyone who cares deeply about how an older individual lives has two major obligations:

The first is to be certain he knows what he can expect and how to judge whatever is available where he is, or has to be. Once he understands the standards he has a right to ask for, then help him decide on what points he can safely compromise.

The second obligation is to make an effort to find out the nature of new experiments that give old people quasi-independence. If some promising plan seems suited to the community in which your relatives reside, lend your active support to an effort to introduce it there.

If you are at that common, bewildering stage where you are afraid every step may be the wrong one, or if there is need for immediate action, what should you do?

A GUIDE FOR THE PERPLEXED

It's a good idea to start from the sound premise that the "young old"—roughly, those between sixty-five and seventy-five—do not voluntarily seek out homes for the aged and do not want to live in them. Chronological age, however, is no real criterion of what a person can or cannot endure. A hale man of eighty or a woman of ninety in sound health may still want to live in a community setting. They can do so if they are willing to re-locate themselves by this rule: There is no ideal solution or place. The right one is simply the one which best meets a particular older individual's requirements *at a time when he has to choose between it and something else.*

Miss X's mother may be perfectly happy in a wheel-chair, living alone in an apartment hotel. Your own mother may be in a fair state of health and hate the idea of hotel life—or lack the necessary bank account. Mr. Y. may be a cheerful patient who gives an example of fortitude to everyone around him in the boarding home. Your own grandparent may be a hellion with nothing much the matter with him but his disposition. Yet he may be capable of wearing out a succession of paid companions as he flits from resort to resort.

Whether they are to live in an old-time boardinghouse, a newfangled "retirement colony," a cooperative residence club, or an apartment house under social service supervision—and each is possible—the basic factors to judge by remain the same.

Before a final decision is made, take into consideration these questions. When you know the answers, help the person gauge the good and the bad so that he will know in advance just what essentials are offered and which are missing:

1. In a proposed new setting, is he going to be near his children, other relatives, and special friends?
2. Will he meet congenial people?
3. Is his church near by?

4. What about shopping and transportation facilities?

5. Are parks, theatres, libraries, clubs, accessible?

6. If he wants to pursue a hobby, or go back to school to learn something new, is an educational institution close by?

7. Is a good physician quickly available? How about hospital, nursing, and infirmary care if he should be disabled or seriously ill?

8. If it is in a new community, how is the climate—too moist, dry, windy, calm or too many electrical storms? Too hot or too cold? (Many are sensitive to changes of weather.)

9. Is there ragweed in the area which will affect his hay fever, or some other nuisances that may make other allergies worse?

10. If he has furniture, how is he going to transfer or dispose of it? (It may be worthless from a cash standpoint, but he won't think so.)

11. Does the cost of living run higher than he is accustomed to, or so low it outweighs other disadvantages?

Some of these and other queries may seem unimportant, even childish. But if they are answered to his satisfaction before he makes a move, you will have a much happier or at least a much less complaining person later on. There is no need for exhaustive research to show that contact with people and events, the sense of belonging, of friendliness with the young, promote well-being and psychological health, and should be objectives.

As a beacon light, take this warning, issued by the Community Service Society of New York as a guide to those who have to move the Society's own aged clients to a new setting:

"Consider carefully the importance of a familiar environment to someone who is being buffeted about by a constantly changing world. . . ." And this added, significant note from the same source is the root of the matter. "Physical needs are so obvious they are usually met to some degree at least, but emotional needs may be by-passed because they are not easily recognized by those associated with the older person or himself."(3)

It is easy enough to translate physical needs into a check-list. No one needs to be told that if you make sure there are no physical hazards wherever an elderly man or woman lives, you are forestalling the likelihood of accidents. Steep stairs without firm banisters, narrow halls without bright lights, unscreened fireplaces or windows —and so on, through a long list—are undesirables, not only for the old, but for anybody.

Beyond this, it is not impossible to satisfy a hunger for personal attention which lapses in none of us till the day we die. It may mean meeting the complaints of a person who is "fussy" about the height of a bed or the softness or hardness of a mattress, or arranging for his between-meal snacks or a magnifying glass so he can use a telephone directory with ease. The real danger most of us face is that we relax and feel we have done our duty when we have provided the best possible physical environment.

NO SOLUTION SATISFYING TO ALL

Geriatricians never minimize the pain old people suffer from parting from all they have considered "so firm a foundation." But they also believe that once a break is made many elderly men and women experience real relief. There is no blanket solution which you can apply, however. The amount of resentment and inflexibility an individual shows toward a contemplated change depends on his past attitudes, just as in every other act of life. As Dr. Stieglitz says, "If we have a man who for thirty years or forty years has been turning the second bolt on the fourth unit two turns to the right every time it goes by on the production line, after that length of time is it surprising he is in a mental rut?"

One grain of comfort exists which many of us overlook. If we give a person, no matter how ancient, a chance to work out a troubled situation himself, he often uncovers hidden strengths, as Mrs. Fitch did.

At eighty, Mrs. Fitch's peaceful life was shattered. First, her husband died. Then she had to face the unpleasant and unexpected fact that he had left her little but their home and some heavy debts. Next, she had the shock of finding her relatives—distant in all respects—expected her to take refuge in a home for the aged. But Mrs. Fitch did no such thing. This woman, who all her long married life had never handled finances, sold her house and paid off her debts. Then she was told she was eligible for Old Age Assistance. When she was sure what monthly sum she could expect she approached the purchaser of her old home. She knew he expected to rent a couple of rooms and she asked if she might occupy the ex-maid's quarters, and eat dinners with his family. A few months later she could write, with pride, to a cousin who issued a belated invitation for a long visit, "Thank you, no; I am very well provided for!"

Mrs. Fitch's way might never occur to or appeal to your own mother or aunt, but it does carry a meaning you can apply to any family dilemma. Finding a way of living within the means of the individual's or the family's purse is important, of course. But it ought not to be the major, or only concern. The touchstone which will be a good test to apply against every alternative which exists in any area, is this:

1. *Which environment offers the fewest problems at the time a particular individual has to break with his past?*

2. *Which offers the nearest equivalent to his accustomed environment?*

3. *What matters most, the locality, companionship, or special services he should have?*

4. *What best suits his current—not past or future—capacities?*

It is possible, of course, that your relative may provide a safe and happy future for himself if he can take advantage of one of the new ways of housing the old. But everyone of them—like Tompkins Square House in New York City, and the cottages in New Jersey's cooperative colony—have applicants far in excess of accommodations.

If some new development arises to his liking, there is every reason why an elderly person should take an interest in finding out about it, and if he likes it, put his name on the waiting list. In the meanwhile, however, he has a problem to meet, and the greatest part of it probably will be reconciling himself to what is actually available as long as his health is good and he requires no special care.

What are his choices?

APARTMENT HOTEL LIFE

At one extreme there is the apartment hotel, a familiar sight in all cities. Quite often there are some largely filled with elderly people, usually women, and the advantages are considerable. Life will be leisurely for the people who have the means to afford this physical comfort; there will be independence, and even some protection in a night and day staff, always on call.

For the not so well-to-do, there is an equivalent, the small, often somewhat shabby, "residence hotel," or "club," with or without an impressive sidewalk canopy bearing a fancy name. Usually these places are off-shoots of an era of high rents. Generally they offer a good address at a modest rate. This is something not to be despised, though the room may be small and the flick of the dust-mop weak. "Keeping up appearances" can mean a good deal to a man or woman who has lived long enough to see financial as well as physical resources dwindle.

Many men, and an even larger number of women, prefer this type of living to any other. As one tart-tongued octogenarian said, "I'd rather live in a hall-bedroom, have only a chambermaid to talk to, and get my food out of cans than live with the clatter of old fools' tongues in my ears in some 'genteel' home!"

If your relative, like this Mrs. G., wants no interference from family or friends and has some regular, permanent income, however small, help him hunt for the place (and the address) which suits him. When he finds it, let him live in peace. He will have privacy, no responsibility, and yet will not be completely alone. A friendly maid can let you or someone else know if he should ever need more than that.

"FOSTER" HOMES AND FAMILIES

"I want to live with a family!" is a much more frequent cry than a plea to be let alone. It may spring out of a hunger to continue a relationship that has been satisfying in the past, or because the person cannot accept either with grace or resignation the idea of institutional life.

Happily, this is one instance when he can take advantage of a new trend no matter where he lives.

"Foster" homes for the aged are offsprings of ideas for children's placement, first launched thirty or forty years ago. It is generally accepted now that the normal place for a child is his own home, however poverty-stricken. If this fails him, second-best is a home with a substitute family. We are just now catching up to this point of view about the aged. Today, those who work professionally with and for the old know that next to living in their own homes or happily with a close relative or sometimes closer friend, a foster family is a good substitute.

What a foster home is: The term may vary from town to town —boarding home and "private residence plan" are typical alternates. The theory behind them all is the same.

A good foster home for the aged, as for the young, is one which gives a boarder most, if not all, the advantages of family life. The sum he pays may vary with his surroundings, but the living standards should resemble those he has had. He must feel part of the family group and take part in most of its group activities. If he can remain in his old neighborhood, or near it, attend the same church, get books from the same library, meet his friends at the same clubs, so much the better. A good foster home will offer permanency, without the rigidity of a lifetime contract.

Where found: It may take time, and it does take judgment, and a knowledge of the difference between non-essentials and fundamental requirements beyond bed and board, but the right foster home can be found even in a village.

If your relative lives in a city where a social agency has a home-finding service for the aged, the matter is comparatively simple. (See Chapter XIV, *Where to Turn for Help.*) Where it exists at all, the service will be available to anyone, regardless of income. Homes are carefully investigated and when the client is "matched" to his prospective environment, the landlady and the older person are brought together. If they think they will like each other the agreement is made, usually for a trial period. Trained workers supervise both this adjustment and later relationships to be certain that everything continues to go well.

The Jewish Community Service of Long Island, for instance, has not found it difficult to locate foster homes in various parts of New York. One reason is that it pays a room and board rate of $145 a month, sufficiently high in 1952 to guarantee its high standards. The client is expected to pay full maintenance out of his funds or those he receives from relatives or friends, if he can. If he cannot, he pays $90 a month at least, either from his own income, or from a sum contributed to his support by the Department of Welfare. The agency makes up the difference.

Occasionally you may find a commercial home-finding agency listed in the classified telephone directory. Before you attempt to use it, check with the Council of Social Agencies to determine whether it is considered trustworthy.

Or, lacking other sponsorship, try to find a family listed with a children's agency. Occasionally applicants are rejected for juveniles but may be well adapted to take adults into their home. Parish priests, ministers, rabbis, denominational papers and even "ladies' aid" societies are good sources. On one occasion, when the Catholic Charities of Brooklyn launched a campaign, "adoptive" families were found most easily through announcements from the pulpit by parish priests. (4)

If you must rely on personal investigation, check replies to advertisements carefully. A pastor, the neighbors, even the grocer and the druggist in the neighborhood, all will have a fair idea of the antecedents and the habits of a family. You will need safeguards to be sure an older person will not be exploited as an extra "hand" in the kitchen or with the children. This is different from feeling sufficiently at home so than an offer to help mind the baby or make the bed is accepted as a favor.

Basic standards: A woman like Anna Morrison, a former schoolteacher with a cardiac condition, had no family to help her when she was no longer able to do even light housekeeping. But eventually her physician found a place for her in the home of a nurse, also retired. She took a couple of people to board who needed someone able to keep a watchful eye on their symptoms but no actual nursing. She was even willing for Miss Morrison to bring her bad-tempered little poodle with her. In this peaceful environment, not even a strain on her teacher's pension, Miss Morrison looks and feels younger than her seventy-four years.

Your relative may not have a physician close at hand to find a proper home, and he may not be able to secure one through a welfare agency. But it ought to be obvious that a shining, immaculate interior and exterior is not all that has to be looked for. What may be perfectly suitable for a good-natured not too fastidious older man or woman may repel a meticulous one. "It is as though you had the last piece of a jigsaw puzzle in your hand," says Margaret Wagner, Director of Cleveland's Benjamin Rose Institute, "and must find the almost complete puzzle into which it fits."(5)

It will be easier if you know the essentials professional workers look for:

1. A foster family should have younger members who actually *like* older people, not merely tolerate them.

2. The home should be a place where an older woman can putter about occasionally in the kitchen if she likes or help with the dusting, or a man can use a saw or do a bit of gardening, without feeling in the way.

3. The elderly boarders should sit down at the family table on all occasions and join in holiday festivities. Occasionally, at least, they should be invited to go with members of the family to church, the movies, or share some other recreation outside the home.

4. Each boarder should have freedom to have his own guests and a place to entertain them, at a stipulated time so that he won't interfere with other family arrangements.

5. He should have his own room, no matter how small or how modest.

6. He ought to feel that if he needs help once in a while with bathing or dressing or in some slight illness, someone will be at hand to give it to him ungrudgingly.

7. Extra care, such as a special diet for a diabetic, ought to be

paid for. But experience shows that if the relationship begins well and remains good the little services any human being craves when he needs them are often given with no thought of remuneration.

8. Agreements, verbal or written, should be on the basis of a permanent relationship. But it also should be understood in advance that if the aging person becomes so infirm he needs special care, or conditions in the family change, a move can be made without recrimination. Actually, there may be regrets on both sides.

Life with a foster family may be a good bridge to another type of living, especially for those on the long waiting lists of homes for the aged. Sometimes the attachment between landlady and guest becomes a lasting one as it has in the case of Holland-born Mrs. Zept.

There were tears on both sides when she left, and the reason for her going, the only reason, as she said, was because a home which had finally accepted her had many Dutch-speaking residents and she had had practically no one to talk to except her landlady. Mrs. Zept has lived in the home for nearly two years. Her landlady has not missed a week calling on "Aunt Sarah." Each time she brings some small gift as proof friendship has not waned.

A very important point, whether you cull advertisements or rely on an agency's investigation, is to be sure the way of life, and as far as possible the physical setting, will not be far removed from the newcomer's background. Sometimes old people suffer and are unwilling to complain, even to their nearest and dearest, because they dread another shift.

Ideally, look for some such fortunate conjunction of personality and standards which have made the last years more than just bearable for Miss Everett and Mrs. Shaw. For fifty-seven years they had lived together, working at dressmaking. When Miss Everett developed a cardiac condition and Mrs. Shaw became almost totally blind, they were both in their late seventies. For a year they struggled on until they and their funds were practically exhausted. With extreme reluctance, then, they applied to a home for indigent women. But the social worker and the physician there decided the bond between the two old friends was too firmly rooted to be broken. A home was found for them with Mrs. Berwick, British-born like themselves. She is a childless, middle-aged widow, glad to have the money from their Old Age Assistance grants, gladder still for companionship.

"It's like having my old grandmother and the great-aunt that brought me up!" Mrs. Berwick told a recent visitor.

BOARDINGHOUSE LIFE

There are some people, on the other hand, who prefer to keep at a distance. Even their families come under this ban. And the intimacy of a strange family would be something not to be borne. If your relative falls in this category, he might find life in a boardinghouse, either with a mixed group of young and old, or with his contemporaries, a comfortable solution.

This old-fashioned *milieu* has the merit of many years of trial. It also has the advantage of being widespread. Even a farmer's traditionally large household is often not averse to an extra person at the table, whatever his age.

If you are like the majority of young people, you will probably scoff at this way of life. But don't try to measure your preferences today by what they may be a quarter-century from now. Mrs. Anderson's fashionable daughter, for instance, cannot understand why her mother lives in what she terms the "desolate atmosphere of a brownstone front" when she could have a well-furnished room in her daughter's elegant Park Avenue establishment. But Mrs. Anderson's landlady carefully nourishes her rubber-plants and her golden oak furniture along with the independence of her elderly roomers. When they meet at meals in her dining-room under a massive chandelier, they feel perfectly at home in an atmosphere redolent of their own youth.

Advantages: There are more people than Mrs. Anderson who would choose this way of life if they knew how to make it secure for themselves.

If your relative has some means, yet finds life in a hotel sterile even if he can afford a paid companion, or if he cavils at the idea of living with an adult child of different tastes, a boardinghouse will give him privacy without isolation. He will have companions, yet no obligation to make intimates of them or the proprietor. He will have, of course, his own room, and what is just as important late in life, meals under the same roof. Though a boardinghouse is not a nursing home, there will be someone to report an illness; in some instances arrangements can be made for short-term care in case of sickness or an accident.

Definitions: One way to help a person decide whether this is the way of life he wants, is to let him try it for a short period. But old people who dread a move may stay on under circumstances which are not suited to them. A better way is to understand clearly just what a boardinghouse is and what a boarder ought to be to get its benefits.

When a licensure law was under consideration in Pennsylvania the Health and Welfare Council, representing three counties which included Philadelphia, drew up this definition:

"A boarder shall mean any active individual who needs no service or care other than room and board and who is able to go up and down stairs unassisted and able to bathe and dress without assistance or supervision. . . ."

The important clause relates to the state of health of the prospective boarder. If your relative is too feeble to help himself dress and bathe, if he needs a special diet, or assistance in walking, he does not belong in a commercial boardinghouse.

Standards: Nevertheless, the average boardinghouse keeper, though she is in business to make a profit, is not necessarily a harpy. There will certainly be one you can find to equal the good record made by fifty-six out of sixty-two investigated by the New York Department of Welfare a few years ago.(6)

The budget allowed by the Department for its aged clients was modest in the extreme, so that the surroundings were exceedingly modest. Also, the income from boarders was often the chief support. Yet the report states the attitude of these landladies was one of "interest, sympathy, and appreciation of individual problems." Special services—not paid for—included everything from meals planned at irregular hours to suit a temperamental old man, snacks at midnight for a finicky old woman, personal shopping, or acting as a guide for the dim in sight.

As this indicates, the moral integrity of the people he lives with is more important than the physical surroundings. A good deal will be determined by the attitude of the other boarders. Do they seem depressed or depressing? If they are younger than he is, do they seem likely to resent an old person? Do they talk well of their quarters and the food? Most people will talk freely on this point and rarely are over-optimistic. Since any older person is far more dependent on the good-will of those around him than a young one is, pay at least as much attention to the other boarders as to a room with a possible view.

If he is fortunate in personality and temperament, he may find, as Mr. Metzikoff has, that life at eighty and more can be fuller and richer in this environment. When his wife died Mr. Metzikoff served notice on his two married sons, both of whom lived at a distance from his favorite haunts, that he had no intention of making his home with them and their many children. Neither did he intend to invest his life's savings in an old people's home. Through cronies with whom he played chess in Central Park he found the Gerson family. They are jolly, friendly, middle-aged people, with young sons and daughters in their late teens, and several elderly boarders, all widows. Within a month Mr. Metzikoff had become cock of the roost. He makes a fourth at cards with the young people when they lack one, and is always ready for backgammon, the movies, talks or walks with the older ones.

So far as physical surroundings are concerned, common sense will tell you that these other points ought to be thoroughly investigated—in advance:

1) *Interiors:* with particular attention to possible violations of multiple dwelling laws, fire laws, and the sanitary code of the community.

2) *Cleanliness:* This means the kitchen as well as bedroom and linens, and the state of the bathroom.

3) *Furnishings:* A comfortable bed and armchair and suf-

ficient closet space are minimal necessities; so is good lighting, not only in the bedroom, but in hallways.

4) *Stairs:* If there are any, how steep are they, and how wide are the stair treads, and how firm is the banister? Will your relative have to climb stairs up or down to reach the bathroom or is it on his floor?

5) *Dining-room:* A nourishing diet is a minimum but you may have to visit a few times to sample the menu to find out what it is really like. Tray-meals ought not to be the usual practice, however attractive the idea may seem at first thought. An older person needs companionship as much as food.

6) *Exteriors:* Close proximity to a park or open space is desirable. Nearness to transportation and one's friends, church, shopping, etc., is more important.

7) *Freedom:* A resident ought to be able to have guests and some place to entertain them besides his bedroom. An old man or woman is probably going to spend much more time at home than a young one, and he should feel free to have friends and a radio or television set of his own, if he wishes—and doesn't disturb his neighbors.

PROTECTION THROUGH LAW

Whatever type of living your relative elects, see that he receives whatever protection the law allows him.

Licensure laws, unfortunately, are in a national tangle. By July, 1953, each state which includes payments to individuals in private or public institutions as part of its plan to aid the old, must have set up some state authority to establish minimum standards, if it shares in federal funds. And where these minimums are set up, it is probable that eventually all the old will benefit by more stringent laws to protect them at least from fire hazards, food toxins, and brutality.

In the meanwhile, however, your relative may live where homes for the aged and commercial boarding homes both come under regulation; or in his state perhaps vigilance is concentrated on regulating nursing homes only. Or licensure laws may affect him only if he is living on an Old Age Assistance grant in an institution giving nursing and medical care. These, and dozens of other variations, exist. To be certain that there are no violations where he intends to live, it is necessary to investigate not only state laws, but the jurisdiction of the county or the municipality, too.

If this seems too much effort, remember the grim all-too-true horror tales which appear periodically in the press. A typical one tells of a fire in a nursing home in Maryland in which three elderly women were suffocated. The story was the more pitiable because a license had been withheld "because of certain health and fire decisions."(7)

To understand how this can happen you must realize that though there may be good laws on the statute books, there must also be a regular inspection to see that they are enforced. Also, some perfectly honest officials allow sub-standard boarding homes and nursing homes to continue because if they were shut down the only other alternative would be the county almshouse—or someone's doorstep.

You will usually find a cordial welcome when you make inquiries at the city hall or the county court house about local regulations, or when you write the state Department of Health or Welfare to find out about their legal responsibility. The reason is that more civic-minded citizens are needed to convince legislatures of the necessity for larger appropriations to compel observance of whatever laws there are, and to improve on those which exist. As Dr. Vlado A. Getting, Commissioner of Public Health in Massachusetts, once said, regulations are important so that old people "can be taken care of in pleasant, kindly surroundings and with at least a minimum degree of care and protection against the danger of fire or other hazards."(8)

These "other hazards" could include everything from open dumps of garbage to a "Typhoid Mary." You can't look for uniformity in the law to cover them; even terminology differs from place to place. For instance, in Pennsylvania, when licensure laws were under consideration in the legislature, a boardinghouse was defined as ". . . Any institution, however named, which is operated for profit and advertised, announced or maintained for the express or implied purpose of providing service or domiciliary care for three or more elderly people who are not ill or in need of nursing care."(9) But in Massachusetts a boardinghouse legally is a place where the elderly are given some slight nursing care "incident to advanced age."

All you or anyone else can do is to be sure the law, whatever it may be, is observed, report violations to the proper authorities—and work for better laws.

For the rest, your major concern for an old person, still able to make his own choices, should be to make sure he really understands what will make life happier for him. It is more important to secure toleration of his food fads, his eccentricity in dress or manners, or of the way he stores his possessions wherever he goes, than it is to see him sheltered under a luxurious roof.

NOTES TO CHAPTER XI

(1) *Statistical Bulletin.* New York: Metropolitan Life Insurance Co., July, 1951.

(2) *Preliminary Report, First National Conference on Aging.* Washington, D. C.: Federal Security Agency, Aug., 1950. (Mimeographed.)

(3) "Aging, Guide for Public Health Nurses No. 8." *Family Health Series.* New York: Community Service Society, May, 1948.

(4) Casalena, Katherine F. "A Foster Home Program for the Aged." *The Catholic Charities Review,* Mar., 1951. P. 60.

(5) Wagner, Margaret W. "Personalized Care for Aged Clients." *Journal of Social Case Work,* Oct., 1946.

(6) Galpern, Marie, and Runcoli, Fanny. "Boarding Homes for the Aged in New York." *Public Welfare,* Vol. 4, Feb., 1946.

(7) *New York Times,* Sept. 19, 1951.

(8) *Regulations for Licensing of Boarding Homes for the Aged.* Boston: Division of Hospitals, Massachusetts Department of Public Health, Jan. 10, 1949.

(9) House Bill No. 1431, introduced June 6, 1951, by Representative Wilbur H. Hamilton of Philadelphia.

CHAPTER TWELVE

COMMUNITY CARE FOR THE SICK

Do sick old people need different medical and nursing attention than younger ones? If so, where can they get it in the place they live? What is available for the chronically ill? And at what cost?

Finding the answers to these questions ought not to be postponed till a crisis is actually at hand. Even if your parents or grandparents are still sound in wind and limb a disability can occur abruptly.

Facing what may lie ahead with realism does not mean you are an alarmist. Possibly you may never have to meet a situation of just the sort Mrs. Cunningham did. But if something like it does come, you ought to be better prepared for its shock than she was.

Mrs. Cunningham's mother was apparently in good health when she came to keep house for her daughter and her grandchild the year both women were widowed. However, less than twelve months later she had a stroke which left her partially paralyzed. The younger woman held on to her junior executive job in a department store, relied on neighbors to look in occasionally during the day and give her mother and her small daughter a noon meal, and at night did the housekeeping and nursing. Within a year Mrs. Cunningham had developed a cardiac condition. Her physician warned her the older woman would probably have another, more severe stroke. He urged her to consider putting her mother in some institution. Mrs. Cunningham's answer was to shut her eyes to possible consequences—and keep on struggling.

When the second stroke did come, she collapsed. The mother

was rushed to the county hospital, not because it was the best place for her, but the only possible one at the time. Mercifully, she died soon after admittance, in a ward so crowded that some beds, hers among them, had to be put in a corridor.

Her physician might have been wrong about his advice, but one thing is clear. Like most of us, Mrs. Cunningham lived too long on the theory that "it can't happen here." Her story is grim, but no more so than hundreds of others in the files of any hospital.

Your own relatives may never have anything more drastic than the ordinary run of ailments. Even for them, arm yourself with foreknowledge of just what a local community can do for its sick old people. If there are lacks in the one where your older relatives live, you will be better able to cope with them.

THE PRESENT OUTLOOK

Most of us already know that sufficient medical care of the right kind is one of our most costly and scarce commodities. But what many of us don't realize is that our sick aged population has, in addition, some pressing problems of its own. They arose chiefly because our life expectancy has more than doubled since the average ancient Greek died at twenty-nine.

This seeming paradox has a simple explanation. The chances of the newly-born baby dying from the infectious diseases had been reduced by 1945 to only one in ten. This was in marked contrast to 1901, when the potential eventuality had been more than one in three.(1) But it is just because we are saving so many more thousands of young lives that we have ever-increasing numbers of old ones. These old people may be disabled wholly or partly from cancer, hardening of the arteries or any other of the chronic diseases which are the main foes of middle and later age, but they can go on living a long, long time. Lamentably, the facilities to care for sufferers, like the cures, are lagging far behind the numbers of men and women who need them. This is true, not only in the country, or in a particular city, but everywhere.

Against this gloomy picture, however, there are some fine things to chalk up on the credit side.

GAINS TODAY VS. YESTERDAY

Today's elderly patient is far ahead of even his immediate progenitors. Old people are coming out of hospitals today on their way to recovery from illnesses which would have caused their death only a decade ago. As late as 1924 young Calvin Coolidge, Jr., died from blood poisoning because the known treatment then was no more effective than that physicians gave Alexander the Great some three hundred years before Christ. Today, we have the antibiotics that prevent infection in old people as well as young ones. There are drugs that have cut post-operative complications to a minimum, so your elders can undergo surgery no physician even of the Victorian era would have dared perform on people past their seventieth birthday.

If your great-grandfather at that age went to the hospital, it would only have been for some then virulent disease, like pneumonia, and he would have expected to die. Even if he had been one of the few lucky older folk to survive, he would have been hospital- and bed-bound for a much longer time than his son or his grandson at seventy—or more—today. The average length of stay in a hospital has been decreasing steadily. New techniques, drugs, and new approaches to infections or the acute phases of chronic disease enable old people, as well as young ones, to recover much more quickly. In 1929 the average hospital stay was fifteen days; by 1940 it had come down to 12.9 days, and declined even more spectacularly in the succeeding decade by twenty-two per cent. Grandpa, like other patients, is hospitalized now usually for no more than ten days. (2)

The statement is sometimes made that a hospital is "like a hotel" and hence shouldn't cost a patient more than room and bath. But the hospital today provides room and board as only a small part of its twenty-four-hour-a-day service. A hospital even in the smallest town today has operating rooms with expensive equipment, skilled nurses, experienced technicians, extensive laboratories, diet kitchens, pharmacies, blood banks, X-ray departments, better surgical instruments, facilities for much more accurate diagnoses—plus a staff which now averages almost two to a patient.(3)

HOSPITALIZATION VS. HOME

But old and frail people don't always need a hospital, and except in rare cases, shrink from it. If you can find some other means in the community which will keep your relative out of one that in itself may speed his recovery.

This fact, that a hospital bed is a hard couch for most older men and women to lie on, is difficult for a younger person to understand. We belong to a generation which takes hospitalization for granted for everything from tonsillectomies to delivery of babies. Our parents and grandparents would have never thought of going to a hospital for either. They grew up in an era which regarded hospitals as a place of last resort, like blood transfusions, to be used only in dire extremity, and quite often, as a prelude to death.

Consequently you will find that, if your relative is like most older people, he will have to be cajoled into accepting hospital care. If he goes against his will, you may find he will show his hostility by refusing to adhere to regulations or ignoring prescribed treatment. At Fordham Hospital in New York, for instance, Mr. Gagliono perished of a rare form of food poisoning, botulism. He died because he refused to take a serum, in spite of all the coaxing of doctors and nurses. He insisted he didn't believe in serums. At Montefiore Hospital in the same city, a man in his eighties obstinately refused to allow a thermometer to be put in his mouth. As the nurse hovered over him that first day, he suddenly opened his lips. When she popped the thermometer between them, he clamped down hard—and bit it in two!

Not all older people are so belligerent, or misguided. Yet practically every physician will tell you an elderly patient will get well faster and have far fewer physical and psychological complications if he remains in his own home than he will if he is removed to a hospital. This is true whether or not he can afford a private room with a private nurse twenty-four hours a day, or has to put up with a crowded ward.

NURSES: COMMUNITY BULWARK

A professional nurse, or a practical nurse, either on full- or part-time basis, may help you keep a man or woman at home. You should be fully aware of the differences in their training, and when each can best be used.

Professional nurses: Registered professional nurses are almost as precious as jewels, and practically as costly on a round-the-clock basis over a long period of time. At acute phases of a severe illness, their skill and experience is invaluable. There are over a half million of them in the United States and its territories, though just half that number are on active service. This number is about 50,000 less than most authorities think we need. Nevertheless, you can secure one if absolutely necessary and your physician recommends it. They are obtainable through regular employment agencies (called nurses' registries), listed in telephone directories. (See pp. 466-72 for list of approved registries.) Hospitals also have lists of both men and women who are registered for private duty, or know where to get them.

Practical nurses: It is more economical and often easier to secure a practical nurse. If she is a licensed one, you will pay about three-fourths the daily rate a professional registered nurse receives, and she will be worth it.

Practical nurses are well equipped to take care of the elderly who are infirm, mentally confused, or suffering from a chronic disease in its quiescent stages. You must, however, be on your guard to see that she is really qualified.

Thirty-six states now have licensure laws, and the number is increasing annually. If your old live in a state which still has no licensure law or where it is not compulsory, you may still secure a practical nurse who has a license from other states.

There are still thousands of women who call themselves practical nurses, whose knowledge is acquired primarily through experience, not training. They may perform a combination of housekeeping and nursing duties very well, but don't mistake them for practical nurses. (To secure someone with adequate training, find out if she is a graduate of a school approved by the National Association for Practical Nurse Education. Schools approved by the Association exist in states with and without licensure laws. In many cases their requirements are higher than those of state legislatures.)

Visiting nurses: This is one aid which is widely spread in cities and in most towns, and in some rural areas. The visiting nurse (whose title varies) is a public health nurse who has special training. Her chief advantage for the family is the fact that she can be secured on an hourly basis (which enables her to spread her good deeds among a large number of patients). That means the expense of having a professional nurse at the time you need her most—for enemas, injections, specials types of bathing or exercise or medication—is a small drain on the budget. It also means that if an elderly person can have this comfort, there is often little reason to insist that he leave his home to get it elsewhere. (Any hospital or physician will know where to get this nurse.)

A visiting nurse can make the best of whatever home equipment and facilities there are, and neither requires nor demands hospital furnishings. She stays only as long as she is needed to do specific work ordered by the physician, and is paid only for the time she is waiting on his patient. Most organizations which supply these smartly uniformed nurses are supported by citizens' contributions. The fees they charge are often based on the patient's income.

One important adjunct of this public health nurse is her training in giving the family instruction in home nursing. She can also be relied on to help an elderly invalid adjust to his condition. In Boston, for instance, a veritable virago of some seventy-seven winters terrified motorists and pedestrians alike. She insisted on weaving her way across the street from her furnished room to a restaurant, supported by nothing more than ill-matched crutches. Finally, the inevitable accident occurred. It was the visiting nurse called in by the landlord who persuaded the irascible old lady to reconcile herself to a less dangerous, more supervised existence in a nursing home.

Local visiting nurse organizations are autonomous. They function under a variety of names. If your telephone directory doesn't list a recognizable title, the local chapter of the American Red Cross, or any hospital, will know if the service is available. Or, if you live at a distance from your relative, write the state Health Department at the capital city.

In country areas, you may have to do more scouting about. The county Health Department is a logical place for inquiries. Some cities, like St. Louis, have the whole county covered through their nurses' organization. Other plans, like Minnesota's, provide district or visiting nurse offices in small towns which farmers near by can also call on.

If you can secure one of these valuable part-time nurses, think of her in these terms: One of her reasons for existence is to enable a man or woman to return home earlier from the hospital than he might otherwise do. Her second purpose is to help a man or woman who does not want to, and often cannot, go to a hospital at all. You may have good reason to remember this some day when you are trying to secure hospitalization for some older individual.

Most of us take hospitals for granted as part of the background of any well-regulated community. Like the police force or fire engines, we assume they stand ready from dawn to dawn every day in the year for people—any person, any age—who need them.

This is one of those generalizations which may have exceptions where elderly people are concerned.

If Uncle William is stricken with coronary thrombosis he can be virtually sure at least of a bed, if not a room, in any general hospital. However, if he survives this crisis and becomes a permanent invalid with a heart condition which needs watching and some care, the family may be perfectly willing to have him get it, and pay for it, in the hospital, but the authorities are quite likely to feel that other arrangements should be made.

If this, or a similar problem arises you will be better able to handle it if you know how hospitals differ, what each should and can do, and how to judge whether they are good or indifferent.

TYPES OF HOSPITALS

In essence, any hospital is a corps of trained persons and a repository for complex technical equipment and supplies. Together, the machinery and the personnel are there to relieve distress and suffering. But not always the same kind or for the same type of patient.

General hospitals: The one we think of first, and the most common, is the general hospital. This is the designation given in medical circles for the institution which exists to take care of "short-term" illness, accidents, surgery, and the kind of emergency that struck down Uncle William. Most of the over five thousand general hospitals in our country belong to the voluntary type. That means their income is derived not only from patients' fees (no matter how high these are they cannot cover all the expenses of the ordinary hospital), but gifts, endowments, and special local campaign funds.

Proprietary hospitals: These are operated for profit. Usually they are small, and not numerous. They are conducted under the supervision of a single physician or a group of physicians, or other citizens. Many excellent sanitariums for chronic diseases come under this classification.

Governmental hospitals: This is a general term for any medical institution supported by tax funds, whether it is operated under federal, state, city, or county jurisdiction, or a combination of them. All have a large number of free beds, and a great many are used by old people. Over ninety per cent of the so-called "long term" diseases, mental and physical, are taken care of in this type of hospital. Usually they are very large, often well equipped, but overcrowded. The corollary is understaffing.

WHAT MAKES A GOOD HOSPITAL

Regardless of auspices, what you need to know is how to determine whether medical and nursing care is the kind that will benefit the elderly person who goes there.

First of all, size has nothing to do with high standards. We are primarily a nation of small hospitals. The one in a small town can be, and often is, just as good in its personnel, equipment, and nursing, as its counterpart in a large city.

A hospital of fifty beds or one of two thousand ought not to be judged by its physical plant alone. Beautiful grounds which allow ambulatory patients plenty of sunlight, fresh air, and exercise are, to be sure, as good for old patients as young ones. So are numerous elevators of large capacity so wheel-chairs can be moved freely from floor to floor. Sun porches, well-furnished rooms, general visiting hours—these are all pleasant and desirable.

But the prime requisite is a medical and nursing staff, laboratories and diagnostic facilities that meet high standards. You can determine this in a simple way. Ask: "Is this institution approved by the Joint Commission on Accreditation of Hospitals?" Ask the hospital itself, or write the Commission (660 North Rush Street, Chicago 11, Illinois), or inquire of the local hospital or medical society. If the answer is "yes" you can be certain that there is good patient care.

If there is any choice, of course you will want anyone you know to go only to a hospital which has met the Commission's requirements. For your reassurance, however, it is only fair to say that some hospitals do commendable work but haven't yet been able to meet stipulated requirements because of limitations in size or resources, or both. (This is one more of the numerous instances in which public concern and support can raise standards. Before this problem comes home to roost, investigate, and raise your voice if it is needed.)

WHY HOSPITALS MAY REFUSE OLD

Whether it is an accredited hospital or not, some day you may be brought up short against the reluctance, perhaps the refusal, of a hospital to accept an older person as a patient. Be forewarned about the several understandable reasons.

When young people have a disease it is practically always sudden in onset and short in duration. In old age, just the opposite is true. The average duration of illness in men and women over sixty-five, according to Dr. Louis I. Dublin, formerly Vice-President and statistician of the Metropolitan Life Insurance Company, is seventy-five days every year.(4) This is approximately seven times the number the rest of us have to endure.

When your parents or your parents-in-law are in need of hospitalization how will these rather wry statistics affect them?

The answer is short. They will be in competition chiefly with other aging and aged people. As Dr. Dublin says, they "are utilizing a large fraction of our hospital facilities and a major portion of the time of physicians and nurses."

Dr. Marcus D. Kogel, Commissioner of Hospitals in New York City, puts it in even blunter terms:

"An important reason for the disinclination of the general hospital to treat the oldster is that there is often the strong possibility that the bed will be tied up indefinitely. Delays are frequent in discharging elderly people after they have received the maximum benefit from hospitalization. Often there is unwillingness on the part of the patient to exchange the sheltered environment of the hospital for the discomforts of a home long since pre-empted of affection or warmth. Then there is the resistance on the part of the family to the return of the aged one to the family hearth. . . ."(5)

Even where Dr. Kogel's pessimism about family relationships is not justified, there are other causes for a general hospital's hesitation to take the old. Not only are they overcrowded, but their beds are urgently needed for the acutely ill who require the particular type of service these hospitals, and no other, are set up to give. They are not suited for what Dr. Kogel calls the aged patient's "apathy, garrulousness, irreversible damage and incontinence."

WHERE CAN THE SICK OLD GO?

There is no general rule by which you can determine whether Aunt Susie, with high blood pressure, or her aged spouse with hardening of the arteries, will be accepted in a general hospital in their town. If you feel there is a likelihood any time in the near future that they will require care of the type only a hospital can give, take the time to find out where local lines are drawn. In the main, you can take this example as a guide:

Mrs. Discomb's father had always been self-reliant and seemingly in good health. Several years after his seventieth birthday he was still going to his brokerage office every day. Long a widower, he was comfortably situated in a "family" hotel. As his seventy-fifth birthday neared his large family planned to gather and celebrate it in lavish style. The day before the birthday dinner, however, Mrs. Discomb, the only child who lived in the same city as her father, had a telephone call from the manager of the hotel. Her father had had a cerebral hemorrhage.

The local general hospital took care of him while his life was in danger and assessed the extent of damage. The hemorrhage resulted in partial paralysis. At this stage the authorities informed Mrs. Discomb her father would have to be transferred, either to his hotel, if he could have proper care there, or to some other institution.

The Commission on Chronic Illness attempted in 1951 to query hospitals the country over to find out their admission policies.(6) For various reasons, the report was not published, but a summary of what the replies revealed will give you more than a hint what to expect, and what type of inquiries to make.

1. Many general hospitals reported that they feel they have a community responsibility to accept any patient in need, whether for acute or for chronic illness. On the other hand, others have policies which preclude acceptance of persons afflicted with chronic illness, even for a short time. (The only way to determine what the rule is in a particular hospital, is to investigate.)

2. About half the replies from general hospitals, public and private, stated they will *not* provide care for the mentally ill, or for the tubercular (or poliomyelitis, the children's foe), even for a short stay. When it is known these patients will requre care for a long time, or if other patients are suffering from cancer in its last stages, paraplegia, or cerebral vascular disease, and will need care for more than a month, an even larger number of hospitals reported they would not admit them at all. (Here, again, you must make your inquiry locally, but be sure you make it before a crisis arrives.)

3. Nevertheless, the shortage of beds is great. As a result, nearly every general hospital of significant size does have some patients receiving long-term care because very often there is no other resource in the community that can take them. Surveys show that in a number of communities from ten to twenty-five per cent

of the total bed capacity of general hospitals is now occupied by patients who ought not to be there, not only for their own good but for the best use of the hospital's facilities for intensive care. In Chicago, for instance, at one time nearly three per cent of the total number of beds in general hospitals were occupied by cancer patients alone, all of them in the last drawn-out static stages which may run for several years.

4. In an effort to deal with this stupendous problem some hospitals have established special wings or wards for the chronically ill. (If a hospital has no such wing or ward and you want to know where one can be found, inquire at the state Department of Health at the state capital. At least eleven state Health Departments have divisions which deal exclusively with the care of the chronically ill within the state's borders.)

If you wonder why, in view of the constantly growing numbers of the aged, no one has thought of hospitals exclusively for them and their less dramatic illnesses, the answer is that some medical people and long-sighted private citizens have. There are a few voluntary hospitals for chronic disease of a very high order. The bulk of their sick population is older people. There are others which describe themselves as "geriatric hospitals." Their standards and the kind of care they can provide vary tremendously. Usually they are tax supported and exist chiefly for the sick who have little or no money. They are large state, county, or municipal institutions usually, also usually overcrowded and understaffed. (The state Department of Health or hospitals will have a list of both kinds.)

Geriatric clinics are rarer; they are also a still-debated subject in medical circles. Where they exist, they are primarily for the low-income group, suffering from long-time illness in non-acute stages.

PLIGHT OF CHRONIC DISEASE PATIENT

As you can see, the chronic disease patient has been the neglected stepchild of medical and public health efforts. He cannot be ignored today if only because two-thirds of our deaths are caused by the chronic diseases, compared with only one fifteenth seventy years ago.(7)

By the time our generation has grown old, there will probably be better answers than anyone can give today to a situation like Solomon Barthold's. At seventy-four he is a sufferer from diabetes. His wife, some six years younger, is bedridden with heart trouble. He was a fairly prosperous grocer who retired at sixty-five but his savings have been used up. For two years Mr. Barthold has tried to take care of both his wife and the house, and take an occasional job clerking part-time. This effort, and worry about money and his wife's health have aggravated Mr. Barthold's own condition. Meanwhile, lack of proper nursing has made Mrs. Barthold worse. Now she must be hospitalized, the physicians tell him, permanently. However, there is still a long waiting list at the only institution in town which can take her. So the Bartholds continue to live in their home as they will have to for several months longer. The social agency which the doctor approached has sent a visiting housekeeper to help Mr. Barthold and will aid him in making plans for his lonely future.

The worst aspect of this story is that it is not unique. Dr. A. P. Merrill, Director of St. Barnabas Hospital for Chronic Diseases in New York, sums up the present national story in this capsule statement:

"An integrated and standardized program for chronic patients is non-existent. Some are in nursing homes and homes for the aged not properly equipped for their care; others who should be in hospitals are at home. Still others are in hospitals when they should be at home."

You don't want anyone you know to fall into either of these classes. What can you do to avoid it?

The first constructive thing is to recognize, as physicians do, that elderly people with chronic troubles fall into three classes. This will help you determine where they belong, and what they need.

WHAT SICK OLD PEOPLE NEED

1. *Your relative may be one of those who need a large amount of intensive medical and nursing care.*

This usually means the kind only a hospital can give.

2. *He may require chiefly skilled nursing care, under regular supervision of physicians.*

He may be able to get this at home if he has funds for professional nursing, and means to equip the home with apparatus and devices needed. A convalescent home if it is a short illness, a nursing home if a long one, are easier solutions for most people.

3. *He may need only "custodial" care under medical and nursing supervision.*

A home for the aged can give him that. A great many publicly supported hospitals have aging and aged people in this class, largely because there is no one to take care of them elsewhere, or the community lacks other facilities. However, if a person is well enough to live at home and attend a clinic, this often will obviate his going to an institution.

If your relative falls into one class, he may improve and progress to another, or a sudden attack may throw him back again. Sick older people, like well ones, are not necessarily going to continue indefinitely in the same way, which is one of the most hopeful things you can say to yourself.

Also, as Dr. Morton L. Levin, former Director of the Commission on Chronic Illness, says: "In many communities the services are there but are not used, either because those responsible for the care of the chronically ill patient do not realize that he needs them, that the services are available, or do not know how to get them."(8)

Don't rely merely on a doctor's telling you what is available; keep your ears open for anything new that happens in some other community—a home medical care plan, for instance, such as was inaugurated in New York City by Montefiore Hospital—which needs support if your own town is to have it. (You may someday need it yourself.) Remember that there are other things besides drugs and doctors which a sick older person needs urgently. Dr. Levin numbers them as:

1. Housekeeping and maintenance services "to provide cleanliness, warmth, and comfort."

2. "Preservation of ties with family and close friends.

3. "Recreational activities and other wholesome use of leisure-time consistent with the patient's capacities and interests.

4. "Special services as needed, including particularly (*a*) social workers to help with emotional, economic, and social problems; (*b*) the visits of clergymen and opportunities for religious worship; (*c*) training to help the patient overcome residual disability and to become as self-sufficient as possible."

To find all these services in one community is difficult, but not always impossible. It means you ought to make a search for them *before* they are needed, both as insurance for the older person and to give yourself peace of mind. Then, in an emergency, you won't be in a panic.

From the point of view of an older person whose purse is limited a hospital is usually a most expensive proposition. Quite often, except in the terminal stages of chronic illness, it is a temporary one. Convalescent homes are the usual way to bridge the gap between hospital and home, and they may have an additional purpose. They often give a "breather" to the family while some permanent plan is being worked out.

RIGHT USE OF CONVALESCENT HOMES

Like every other facility for the sick, convalescent homes are in tremendous demand, and vary widely in both rates and standards. This means that if you want your conscience to be free of twinges, you must do personal investigating. Start with names secured from a hospital. The social service department will furnish them, and discuss them from the point of view of your relative. Physicians also usually know a few to recommend. Where a state licensure law is non-existent or lax, or where inspection is infrequent even under a good law, a visit may uncover conditions you would not want to expose your relative to.

Convalescent homes fall into different classes, and what you have to do is to help an elderly person decide which best suits his temperament, condition, and pocketbook. Some nursing homes advertise their ability to take care of those recuperating from short-term illnesses and operations, as well as to care for others who may never leave the home. Some states forbid the mixture of patients, and make sharp distinctions as to their care. On the whole, it would probably be a better idea to place an elderly person in an atmosphere where everything is geared to fit the man or woman who cheerfully looks forward to complete recovery in a short time. Most convalescent homes try to give patients a chance to have country air. Apprehensive old people might prefer to be close to those who can visit them often, with or without the delights of the countryside.

These are the usual types:

1. *Homes maintained by lodges, churches, or other organizations.* They may be limited to members exclusively, or be open to the general public. While they are sometimes heavily endowed, and quite often are luxurious, they ordinarily operate on a fee basis, waived in certain needy cases.

2. *Homes affiliated with a particular hospital or group of institutions.* These, too, must try to operate without deficits, though often, like hospitals, have to supplement fees with contributions. They will have varying rates, depending on accommodations, and take patients free of charge when a vacancy exists if the hospital recommends it or a social agency asks it for a client.

3. *Strictly commercial ventures.* These range from institutions offering a palatial country-club atmosphere, at commensurate rates, to shabby domiciles, peopled with forlorn, neglected people. Personal recommendations are good, but personal investigation is better; advertisements which appear in practically all newspapers of any size, particularly in urban areas, will give you a list to start your tour.

A convalescent home of any type, if chosen wisely, always can serve and serve well the person suited for it. The case of the Wadsworths illustrates the use of one at its best, and carries a hint to a thoughtful person.

The Wadsworths, like many other older people, suffered from false pride. It prevented them from letting their two sons, who lived far away from their village, know their real circumstances. Mr. Wadsworth's stroke was severe enough so that he should have remained at home. Instead, he took a part-time job as night watchman on a large estate. This was all he could find to do in between nursing his wife. Mary, like himself in the seventies, had never rallied properly after a kidney operation. When her sons heard their mother was still ill, both urged her to re-enter the hospital. Her doctor thought differently.

"What your mother needs," he wrote each with some acerbity, "is a chance to rest and get away from housekeeping. Apparently she has never been able to do that in all her married life."

The money for a month's stay in the convalescent home he recommended came by return mail. While Mrs. Wadsworth took the rest she long ago had earned, her husband was learning to face the fact that he would have to accept some financial help from his children for the first time in his long life. When his wife returned, however, she was better able to help him plan for a future which would not be completely independent, but need not be bleak.

NURSING HOMES: VITAL NEED

There has to be something more than the scanty number of beds in hospitals, or the temporary care of a convalescent home, for the multitudes that need nursing. That "something" is the nursing home. Good, bad, and indifferent, it has mushroomed all over the country, and is here to stay. It is a badly needed part of our social economy, useful, and a haven for the chronically ill.

It is a comfort to know that wherever old people live there is always a possibility of finding a place to put them when it is physically difficult, or economically or socially unwise to keep them as part of the family group. Yet if there is one place which anyone who loves and cares for an older person should know intimately before he enters it, it is the one in which he has to have—or is supposed to have—constant nursing attention.

No one knows how many nursing homes have sprung up in the country. A study which you can accept as typical of all states showed that in New York seventy-nine per cent of the patients in nursing homes were over sixty-five, and three-fourths of those were bedridden and required considerable care.

This can have two interpretations. One is that the remarkable increase in the number of older people in the past two decades, and scarcity of other facilities for the sick ones have forced nursing homes to open.

That premise is certainly true.

The second is that a nursing home can give to a sick aged individual services better than he can get elsewhere.

That may or may not be true. If you put the adjective "good" in front of nursing home, you can be more optimistic. Yet, as Ollie Randall, of New York City's Community Service Society, points out, "to close the poor ones during the present shortage may present the patient with the alternative of making his bed on the sidewalk or in a state mental hospital."

LOCATING THE RIGHT NURSING HOME

The job of locating the right nursing home, like genius, requires an infinite capacity for taking pains. Personal investigation is not fool-proof, but it is the best method to reassure yourself and to give confidence to the person going into this semi-institutional life. You may not be able to tell if patients are getting the right kind of care for the type of illness they have or whether they would be better off in a hospital. But you can certainly judge the physical surroundings, and at the same time get a good idea of the temper and the temperament of the proprietor and her staff. Linger long enough to see them in action.

State Departments of Health or Welfare, whichever is the licensing agency in a state where this safeguard exists, have lists of institutions they will send you. Occasionally, as in New Jersey, these lists give some information about a nursing home's admission policies and rates. This will give you a starting point. But if you have to rely solely on advertisements, you will necessarily need to be more wary.

A list of desirable assets may range from button signals in bathrooms to sun porches, but above all, there is an absolute necessity to fit the place to your—not someone else's—relative's needs.

One young woman who came to visit her great-uncle was

grieved to find him in a nursing home which did not meet her ideas at all. There were unshaded light bulbs in the halls, and oilcloth on the bed-tables. The dormitory room her uncle shared with seven other men had no curtains on its windows. But the old gentleman himself was perfectly contented. For twenty-three years he had been confined to a wheel-chair. He had never married, and after the fall which injured his spine had been compelled to live on relatives' bounty in one boardinghouse after another. As soon as he became eligible for Old Age Assistance, he had found his present home. Its appointments were no better and no worse than those he had known before. More than that, he felt independent there for the first time in years. His new friends included a couple of men who like himself were chess enthusiasts. His grand-niece's sympathy was wasted, and her comments only aroused the ire of the proprietor.

Some states, like New Jersey, issue lists to inquirers which give addresses, rates, and admission policies. These show the sort of entries from that state's special division dealing with regulations for nursing homes:

NAME* AND ADDRESS	BED CAPACITY	PATIENTS ACCEPTED	MINIMUM WEEKLY RATES Private	Semi-Private	Ward
Fayre Nursing Home, Jersey City	13	Aged and chronically ill. Convalescent.	$45 a week flat rate		
The Norris Nursing Home Montclair	12	Aged and convalescent. (No bed patients or alcoholics)	$60		
Rest Sanitarium Bloomfield	12	Aged, chronically ill, and convalescent	$65	$50	
Vale Sanitarium Newark	17	Aged and chronically ill, convalescent (women only)	$50		$45

* All names used in this sample are fictitious.

And so on.

ADMISSION POLICIES AND RATES

This will give you an idea not only that rates vary, but that admission policies widely differ, too. Some homes restrict applicants by age; others by sex. In the South, particularly, many nursing home operators accept only the patients of one race. Most nursing homes are non-sectarian. The great majority in all states accept bedridden persons, but as you notice in the New Jersey examples, you cannot take that for granted, either. Higher rates are often charged by homes which advertise that they take only a "selected clientele." This may mean a religious or racial bias. It frequently means they reject applicants sent by the county or state welfare board whose fees are paid through Old Age Assistance channels.

Various states interpret "nursing home" and "home for the aged" in their own fashion; sometimes legal responsibility for both is vested in the Department of Health. At any rate, you can always communicate with that department and be referred for information regarding homes in a given area to the specific body responsible for their licensure, or where none exists, for their fire laws and sanitation. The local medical society, a municipal Health Department, or Public Welfare Department, or a Council of Social Agencies, can also direct you.

If you can secure such a list as New Jersey's your quest will be simplified, but you still have the job of finding out exactly what kind of care is given, and by whom. Be sure you have a clear understanding about services included in the quoted rate, and what additional charges are made for such things as special diets. Tell the proprietor in advance *all* the facts. That means everything you know about the physical and mental condition of your ailing relative, his background, disposition, abilities, and attitudes toward life. If she is the person you are looking for, she will then be in a position to tell you whether her nursing home can give him what he actually needs.

For higher rates may or may not mean a better quality of care. When Dr. George E. Meyers of the Moosehaven Research Laboratory made a survey in Florida during 1950 he found charges ranged from a low of $40 a month to a high of $12 a day.(9) In that year, moreover, Florida did not have a licensing law.

LICENSING GIVES PROTECTION

Licensing laws, well framed and well enforced, offer protection to those who cannot help themselves. It is important for you to know the exact legal provisions governing nursing homes in a particular state so you can check conditions and admission policies. (In New Jersey, for example, licensed nursing homes are forbidden to take in mentally ill or contagious disease patients, but this is not a universal regulation.)

Nursing home operators of the best type are eager for good licensing laws because they wipe out sub-standard places which undercut good ones in rates and give the whole group a bad name. Frequently the unregulated ones (and sometimes the others where inspection is too infrequent) suck in old people too helpless, or too forsaken by friends and relatives, to cry out against what amounts to actual maltreatment. (In Florida, for instance, an investigator sent from the Moosehaven Research Laboratory reported one private home whose proprietor admitted that she "pulled the hair of old people when they didn't do as they should since slapping and pinching them was against the law.")

In contrast to this monster, who, unfortunately, is not unique, there are many proprietors who have kinder hearts than business acumen. The woman who sent her son to learn how to teach crafts to aged people with disabilities is by no means an exception.

Because of budgetary limitations at the rehabilitation center in Cleveland, Mrs. W. could not get an occupational therapist to make the eighteen-mile journey to her nursing home. So she paid for her son's training herself. Now he teaches such patients as the old man whose hands are badly crippled with arthritis. When he finally was able to make his first plastic bracelets, and sold one or two to visitors, he wept. It was the first money he had earned, he said, in more than twenty years.

The amendment to the Social Security Act which required states to set up standard-making authorities by July, 1953, will bring about general improvements, tightening of inspection and licensing in those states where standards are low. Even then, unless there are enough members on the inspection staff of the state to make regular, unscheduled, and frequent visits to see if the law is being obeyed, it will remain for the most part a dead statute.

New Jersey is one of the states which for a considerable period has kept a close watch to see that hospitals, nursing and boarding homes accept only those people who belong there. These are precautions outlined by the New Jersey Department of Institutions and Agencies which put teeth into its law. You can use them also as a guide when you do your own investigating.

1. Children and adults cannot be admitted to the same nursing home.

2. Persons with an infectious disease cannot be cared for in a home which accepts patients with non-communicable diseases.

3. A nursing home licensed under the Nursing Home Act may not accept the mentally ill except those cases involving harmless senility.

4. Each patient's illness must be diagnosed by a regularly licensed physician before admission, or within twenty-four hours after his admission to a nursing home. (Sometimes there is a house physician who makes the diagnosis; if the patient has his own physician it is made by him.)

EVALUATING A NURSING HOME

We all would like to think of a nursing home as defined by Margaret Ranck of the Illinois Department of Public Health. The ideal she sets up is a nursing home which has the following characteristics: "Hopeful, expectant, cheerful, dignified, friendly, just, fair, helpful but toward self-help, where people are accepted as they are to be persons of real worth, where no one sect or sex is catered to, where the chair-fast individual has the hope of ambulation and the bedfast is encouraged to work toward the day he gets from his bed to his chair without help. In this home there is diversion and zest for life; there is skilled nursing and medical care. There is an opportunity to share and to do for others. There is spiritual counselling."

This is asking a good deal, and the chances are you won't

find a nursing home that has an operator who sprouts such wings. This is all the more reason why any person, no matter how debilitated, ought to have a great deal to say about where he is going to be put. If he is completely bedfast you can still describe conditions for him. You may even find that like "Aunt Emma," as she is affectionately known in her Indiana town, he may prefer a nursing home to family care, however devoted.

Aunt Emma lived alone in a small apartment. A son living on the West Coast had offered his mother a home but she declined. She always told him she would feel lost far away from her lifelong friends, her church, and familiar scenes. This continued until Aunt Emma fell; her accident was serious enough so that on her recovery anxious friends insisted on her moving to one of Indiana's three hundred licensed nursing homes. The one she entered is less than a mile from her old surroundings. She has frequent callers, is in good hands, and is quite content. Although her son would prefer to have her near him he understands how important living in her home community is to his mother, and gladly pays the cost of her care not met by her own small income.

Dr. Walter L. Portteus, President of the Indiana Public Health Association, has outlined these essential standards: (10)

The building: By necessity it may be any type—fireproof, semi-fireproof, or a fire trap. To avoid catastrophes there should be (*a*) a number of definitely marked exits in good working order to permit patients to leave the building quickly; (*b*) rules and regulations and practice in emptying the building so patients know exactly what to do in an orderly fashion; (*c*) rubbish, trash, inflammable material and solvents kept only in fireproof containers; (*d*) rigid inspection by local and state fire authorities.

(Ask about each of these matters, and keep your eyes open on a visit. Confirm what you see and hear by familiarity with local regulations relating to safety and sanitation.)

The rooms and furnishings: Dr. Portteus thinks an eight by ten room the smallest in which a patient ought to be housed.

(This is an ideal; your relative may have to be satisfied with semi-private or ward accommodations as less expensive.)

There must be comfortable beds and facilities for getting patients up and out of them, such as wheel-chairs and back-rests.

"It is necessary . . . to create a homelike atmosphere," Dr. Portteus says, "at least create a feeling within the individual that all is not lost, and that he has an opportunity to get well, and that everything you're doing for him is in this particular direction."

Food: It must be wholesome, fulfill nutritional requirements, and be attractively served. (This last is of prime importance to people trying to get well, or at least no worse.)

Recreation: Dr. Portteus' comment is, "There's nothing worse than being cooped up in a house, regardless of the ventilation, regardless of the sunshine that comes in. Patients ought to have access to some 'airing ground'; it doesn't have to be large but it ought to be made attractive."

(A roof garden in a city, a screened-in porch in the country, a solarium, a comfortably furnished "common room"—these, or one of them at least, ought to be provided. Sick people, if they can walk or sit in a wheel-chair, ought to have some place to see friends and meet people besides a dormitory or a bedroom.)

Entertainment: Many homes confuse this with recreation. Of course there should be radios, or television sets, or both, books, and current magazines—not discarded ones from doctors' offices or elsewhere.

(Find out if organizations in the community send representatives to read to the blind, or do something for the hard of hearing, or just what there is to make patients' lives more than a drab existence and a dull round of medications.)

Occupational therapy: In Dr. Portteus' words: "I think there's nothing more serious for a sick elderly individual than to feel he has no place in life, that no one cares for him, that he's not productive any longer."

Occupational therapists, like physical therapists, are expensive adjuncts and rare even in high-priced homes. Yet you ought to be certain, before you leave your relative "for good" that someone in the nursing home will at least be responsible for seeing that he does simple exercises, even if he has to lie flat in bed. Also find out if she knows how to arouse the interest of a person who will never recover from a debilitating long-time disease, and needs mental, as well as physical, stimulation.

THE NURSING HOME STAFF

Of all the essentials, it is high-grade personnel that is most important. Some states require a professional nurse to be in charge and available for emergencies at all times. Others say there must be at least one practical licensed nurse to every ten patients, and specify the training the attendants must have who help her. Still others insist that nursing home patients be sent to a hospital when crises arise in their illness, but permit them to return if they recover.

Laws can never do the whole job. As the President of the American Association of Nursing Homes says, "In many states, we have found that even though that state may have a good law, the authorities have failed to enforce it. That has resulted in many unfavorable homes throughout the country. The American Association wants good laws, and strict enforcement of those laws in all states."(11)

This desire for self-regulation is a healthy sign. The days are disappearing when any nurse—or pseudo-nurse—could set up shop merely because an Old Age Assistance grant could give her a client. But the real crux of good nursing care will always lie in the kind of people who are at the head of nursing homes. They not only need to have professional competence but must possess a genuine liking for old people, and have their liking in return.

The first you can check; the second qualification is a matter of judgment, not on one visit, but repeated ones, at unannounced times.

A good nursing home proprietor will encourage the family to maintain frequent personal contacts; make it possible for the patient and his visitors to do things together with a measure of privacy; urge his family and friends to take him out of the nursing home environment as often as possible for home visits on special holidays. An exceptional one will be like Mrs. Robertson who turned her parents' big house into a home for invalid women. She searched diligently in Detroit stores till she found a small weaving frame Miss Sophie W. could hold in her semi-paralyzed hands. Miss W.'s relatives rarely come to see her, and seldom have written in the several years she has been in the home. Making potholders that visitors admire—and buy—makes Miss W. feel not altogether left out of life.

COST OF ILLNESS

One of the hardest lessons many older people and their families have to learn is that there is no disgrace in being medically indigent. The drain on the purse, as well as on the body and spirit, of a chronic illness can be as debilitating as the disease itself. How to pay for sickness, especially long-term sickness, crops up at every medical and nursing convention, but the layman still has to face the problem. We have, however, gone a long way from the days when a man or woman who was ill and without funds was called a "charity patient." You may have to exercise an enormous amount of sympathy, understanding, and objectivity to make your relative accept that fact. Remember it yourself, if you have to ask for a ward rate or a free bed for someone you love.

It will be neither a reflection on your relative's ability to maintain himself, nor on his family's responsibility for him. Nationally, we have progressed far enough to recognize plainly that it is the *community* which has a deep responsibility. Physicians, hospitals, and every other type of personnel and institution recognize that a vast number of people are financially ruined through no fault of their own by the high cost of sickness, particularly chronic sickness, today.

There is one thing you can be certain about. If you choose the hospital, nursing home, convalescent home, or any other facility carefully enough, a ward patient will receive the same *quality*—not quantity—of services, as if he were in a private room.

At any time and at any place, the basic needs of the old remain the same.

BASIC NEED OF THE SICK OLD

When your relative has reached a stage of weakness, temporary or permanent, so that he needs care from others, he should have much more than drugs, dressings, and sick-room supplies. More even than housing that is safe, sanitary, and comfortable. He is still an individual who requires more than someone to bring him his tray, someone to provide warmth and shelter and nursing, if he is not to be a major problem to himself or to others. Whether he is disabled, partially or wholly, for a brief time or for the remainder of his life, he needs to preserve his individuality. He can do it if he has activities that make consistent use of his capacities, however limited, and his interests, however wide.

NOTES TO CHAPTER XII

(1) Dublin, Louis I. *The Facts of Life from Birth to Death.* New York: The Macmillan Company, 1951.

(2) *Bulletin.* New York: Hospital Council of Greater New York, Vol. 7, No. 11, Nov. 1951. P. 1.

(3) Freeman, Lucy. "It's Your Hospital and Your Life." New York: Public Affairs Pamphlet No. 187, 1952.

(4) Dublin, Louis I. "The Aged in the Twentieth Century." Address at New York State Welfare Conference, Fifty-first Annual Meeting, Nov., 1950.

(5) Kogel, Marcus D., M.D. "Hospitals and Our Elderly," in *Young at Any Age.* Albany: New York State Joint Legislative Committee on Problems of the Aging, 1950.

(6) Letter to the author from Dr. Morton L. Levin, formerly Director, National Commission on Chronic Illness, April, 1951.

(7) Merrill, A. P., M.D. "Standards for Care of Chronically Ill." *New York State Journal of Medicine,* Vol. 49, No. 9, May 1, 1949.

(8) Levin, Morton L., M.D. "Nursing Homes and Problems of the Chronically Ill." Address to nursing-home operators, etc. Omaha, Neb., Sept. 21, 1950.

(9) Myers, George E., M.D. "Survey of Homes for Old People in Florida." Report from Moosehaven Research Laboratory, May, 1951. (Mimeographed.)

(10) Portteus, Walter L., M.D. "What a Good Nursing Home Is." Address at Second Mid-West Conference of Nursing Home Operators, Indianapolis, Ind., Jan. 12-13, 1949.

(11) Letter to the author from Clifford M. Dahl, President, The American Association of Nursing Homes, Wayne, Neb., Dec. 22, 1951.

CHAPTER THIRTEEN

WHAT TO DO WITH THE MENTALLY ILL

You have the word of eminent psychiatrists, including Dr. George S. Stevenson, Consultant of the National Association for Mental Health, that impairment of the mind is *not* inevitable in extreme old age. Nevertheless, it happens often enough so that you ought to know what forms it takes when it does strike, and what can be done to prevent or retard it.

If it already looms up as one of your concerns, the best thing you can do for any aging person, as well as for yourself, is to bring the whole subject out into the open. Once you realize that mentally ill persons are merely sick persons, and that many of them, with proper treatment and care, can be cured, or failing that, lead happy, even useful lives, most of the dread and fear will be swept away.

There is nothing sinister in being senile. The word itself—from the Latin, *senilis,* old, or an old man—simply means that stage which characterizes the end of a long life. The difficulty most of us experience is that we find it hard to realize that senescence, as much as puberty, is a critical period. As life goes on, changes occur in mental and nervous reactions as well as in the body's functions. Deterioration must set in; it may be mental, or physical, or both. It proceeds at varying rates in different individuals, and it is not necessarily ugly.

Some persons are able to take the wearing-out process philosophically and make adjustments to changed circumstances, people, and events which are an inevitable part of growing older. But not everyone can accept those implacable facts with equanimity. Of all the adjustments life demands, the realization that most opportunities are gone, that old age has come and must be faced, is the stiffest test of mental stability we are called on to encounter. For a great many, particularly those never able to make easy adjustments or adaptations, at any time of life, the realization of the burdens old age usually brings comes as a serious emotional shock. It *may* result in a mental breakdown, either temporary or permanent.

There is always some reason why an older person becomes "queer," "different," "peculiar," or departs more sharply from normal behavior. Often the personality wavers or fails after a serious crisis—the loss of a husband or wife, the sudden death of a child, abrupt severance from a job, major financial stress. But not necessarily so. Sometimes the crisis may seem too trivial to be taken into account by anyone but a physician trained to detect the straw piled up on other straws which represents the summit of strains and stresses of a lifetime.

Dr. G. H. Hardin Branch of the University of Utah Medical School illustrates this with the story of Mrs. X.(1) She was referred to Dr. Branch because she was in a state of extreme depression. The apparent, surface, cause was her failure to be re-elected as chairman of flower arrangements of her club. She collapsed when she was deposed after a service of a quarter-century. Younger members felt they had a right to expect a change. But the shock of realizing she was no longer indispensable, and that her day, if not entirely done, would have to be lived in another fashion, was something Mrs. X. was unable to accept. The result was a mental breakdown.

You will not be able to diagnose conditions like this when they occur, but you will be better able to handle them if you acquaint yourself with the truth about mental illness—how it develops, how it can be prevented, how it is treated. This is what the National Association for Mental Health urges on all of us for the simple reason that mental sickness is something that can happen in any family.

FACTS ABOUT MENTAL ILLNESS

Mental illness is not a disgrace. It has taken centuries for mankind to realize there is no stigma associated with "insanity," a legal term for which the medical equivalent is psychosis. Today, no sensible person ought to regard a mental disorder as something to be ashamed of. Approximately one out of every dozen children born each year will sometime during his life suffer a mental illness severe enough to require hospitalization. You can't possibly feel alone or "marked" when you think of this if someone in your own family should be afflicted.

Many who are mentally ill are not hopeless cases. The probability of being hospitalized because of a mental disorder is far greater after the age of sixty than at any other period of life. Yet this is no reason to despair. Early diagnosis and prompt treatment is just as efficacious in mental ills as in physical ailments. Some cerebral disturbances in the old can be arrested by proper care and treatment. Others yield to changes in environment. There are forms of mental disease which can't be cured, but sometimes an elderly patient can be helped to the point where he can lead a fairly normal existence. In many cases he does not require hospitalization at all.

Mental illness is not necessarily inherited. If it occurs in your family, don't regard it as a "taint." While the chances of a psychosis are greater in a family where there have been other mentally disturbed people, heredity is not the sole factor, any more than environment is. If major strains and stresses can be avoided, or removed, the chances of this sort of lightning striking more than once will be lessened. As Dr. Stevenson says, "One always has the opportunity of deflecting hereditary tendencies by careful control of environment."

Mental illness in older people. When the human machinery begins to run down the two most common types of disorders that *may* affect the brain cells are cerebral arteriosclerosis and senile dementia. The more dramatic kinds of mental illnesses which find their way into the courts or are luridly portrayed in books and dramas—the cases of schizophrenia, manic-depressive psychoses, general paresis, or alcoholic psychoses—rarely appear after sixty-five. The most recent census of patients in state mental hospitals shows that slightly more than one out of every four "first admissions" to state mental hospitals are sixty-five years old and over.(2)

Mental illness gives warnings. Your parent or grandparent is not likely to be in full possession of all his faculties one day and be without them the next. It may *seem* that a single turn in fortune has brought on a collapse but the fact is that up to that time he has been able to mobilize his forces to combat difficult situations. Under the impact of some blow, weakened forces—"compensatory factors"—give way. But a trained observer can detect prior symptoms of a breakdown. This is one more argument for regular, thorough medical examinations at frequent intervals after a person reaches sixty-five. (See pp. 79-80.)

Mental illnesses vary in degree and kind. There may be considerable overlapping between normal and abnormal states. A man or woman may show simultaneously the characteristic changes found in normal old age and those due to hardening of the arteries of the brain. Don't expect him to "snap out of it" if he acts abnormally. The one important thing for you to do is to see that he gets the right kind of help as soon as possible. If he severed an artery you wouldn't wait till bleeding stopped to call a physician. A mentally sick older person, like a young one, is entitled to the best psychiatric aid available. That may mean going to a clinic, entering a mental hospital, or going for treatment to a psychiatrist in private practice. Don't wait; the further advanced the sickness, the slimmer the chances of alleviating or curing it.

SYMPTOMS OF MENTAL ILLNESS

Before you worry yourself (and the older person) unnecessarily, however, be certain you have some cause for real alarm. If your father forgets where he lays down his spectacles or his newspaper, or your mother jots down what she wants to buy at the market and then forgets where she puts her notes, this is so-called "normal" memory loss. Though it is by no means an inevitable part of the aging process, it is common. Other signs, even those not so blatant, should not be glossed over because someone says, "Oh, Aunt Mary was always peculiar!" Or, "Uncle Jim was a silly young man and now he's a silly old one!"

Just because these things may be true, the Aunt Marys and the Uncle Jims should not be ignored or ridiculed. Still less, they should not be hidden away when company comes because those they live with are ashamed of them, or afraid to admit there may be something wrong. Only a physician with special psychiatric training should decide whether a departure from everyday actions is unimportant or important. There are certain signs, however, you should regard as serious enough to bring to his attention.

You would have no difficulty, if your father acted as Mr. Bard did, in deciding something was wrong. Night after night one cold January, he managed to slip out of his son's house by ingenious means, and wander about the neighborhood clad in nothing more than a nightshirt. Eventually Mr. Bard recovered his equilibrium after a long stay in a "rest home," but he might not have done it at all if his son hadn't regarded his conduct seriously.

Unusual behavior, however, is not always so marked. Or possibly it may be, like Mrs. Trueblood's, the type which doesn't disturb the person himself or those he lives with.

Mrs. Trueblood for some time now has felt eternity is right around the corner and that she and her family ought to be preparing to enjoy it. Most of the day she sits placidly by a window, endlessly stitching pairs of cotton wings for each of her relatives. So far, since her delusion has harmed neither them nor herself, the doctor has advised her children to humor her mild aberration.

A single symptom or two in the following list may turn out to be as innocuous as Mrs. Trueblood's pastime. Recognize, nevertheless, that a man or woman may need psychiatric care, either for a period of time or permanently, if he:

1) lives in a separate world and fails to face his problems;

2) has severe "blues" to such an extent that he is unable to carry on his everyday activities;

3) suffers agonies of indecision in making up his mind, then obstinately refuses to carry out some plan even if it is to his advantage;

4) has a delusion that you or someone else is persecuting him;

5) has moods which swing like the pendulum of a clock between wild exhilaration and deep depression;

6) insists he is ill, complains continually of aches and pains,

and a variety of bodily deviations when a thorough physical examination reveals nothing to account for them;

7) cannot sleep without medication, or relapses into apathy and listlessness;

8) is excessively irritable and given to outbursts of rage;

9) loses interest in his appearance, his environment, and his family;

10) talks feverishly and constantly, repeating the same things over and over without realizing he has said them before;

11) goes on spending sprees far beyond his means, or hoards every cent—his clothes, his food—without reason;

12) is a prey to unfounded anxieties about everything;

13) sees or hears imaginary things and people.

RELIEFS AND CURES

This list of penalties that old age may—not must—incur seems formidable, but is not a cause for hopelessness. Dr. Robert H. Felix, Director of the National Institutes of Health, set up as part of the federal health programs, says this: "Though a great many cases have an organic basis and will follow a downhill course, even in extremely old age mental illness does not always have an unfavorable prognosis."

If the diagnosis is "psychosis with cerebral arteriosclerosis" the condition is progressive. No doctor can give any individual new arteries. The lessened blood supply to the brain will bring on headaches, dizziness, and great fatigue. Commonly there is lightning change of moods, inability to concentrate, and a general letdown on the intellectual level. There may be what the layman terms a "stroke" resulting in one-sided paralysis. Sometimes there is partial recovery; often none at all.

"Senile psychosis," the other common mental ill of the old, in its simplest form is merely an exaggeration of the changes old age brings. Or it may be the type that results in sudden outbreaks of temper, delusions of lost property, accusations that are false, or fabrication of bizarre stories.

Many older people cannot be fully restored to their former

states but that does not mean they all need to enter or to stay in a mental hospital. If they do have to go there for a period, given the right medical therapy and assured continued relief from emotional tension, a good many can return to the community and live peaceably the rest of their lives.

Tremendous progress has been made in the last few years in finding palliatives for some cerebral disturbances.

A group of scientists studying persons past sixty-five in a mental hospital, for instance, reported the kind of good news that ought to stimulate any of us to hope. All the patients were suffering either from senile psychosis or cerebral arteriosclerosis.

In one group of three hundred and sixty-five men and women almost two-thirds improved after treatment.

Group therapy, ordinarily employed only with younger people, gave encouraging results in seventeen women patients aged seventy to eighty.

Four elderly persons suffering from depression, lack of energy, tension, etc., had marked alleviation of symptoms and improved in their reaction to social situations after the operation known as prefrontal lobotomy, an incision in a lobe of the brain.(3)

There are other, simple methods of relief for certain types of mental disturbance that work near-miracles—or so they may seem to the layman. Bad teeth, a disrupted digestive system, or a poor diet, can cause a serious vitamin deficiency. In turn that can be the seat of a mental aberration. The cure is administering the right kind and amount of vitamins under a doctor's orders.

Other serious neuroses, especially in the old who love to dose themselves, often with doubtful old-time "patent" remedies, are due to drug intoxications. Withholding the drugs has proved efficacious. In other cases a change in environment brings about good results.

Any of these solutions is within the power of the average family, and is considerably wiser than pretending a maladjustment does not exist, or will "go away in time" or "is normal for old people," this last a phrase many of us use far too glibly.

What an environmental adjustment did for one eighty-three-year-old woman can be done for many—provided there is someone ready to take responsibility, like Mrs. Warburton's daughter.

Miss Warburton was a librarian who lived quietly with her mother in a small Southern town. Circumstances compelled her to take a better-paying job in a city a considerable distance away. Her only sister, living in the same home town, offered to take Mrs. Warburton to live with her family. The solution seemed excellent. It was not wise, the two sisters felt, to move a woman in her eighties from an environment she had known all her life.

Nevertheless, in a few months, Mrs. Warburton suffered great deterioration. Separated from her best loved daughter, and laid low by a stroke which semi-paralyzed her, she turned into a stranger. She reviled her daughter, and screamed, "You're trying to poison me!" when her son-in-law offered her food. One hurried weekend, Mrs. Warburton's other daughter swooped down and carried her mother off to the small apartment she had taken in a shabby family hotel. She had to leave her mother alone while she was at work, but at least on her librarian's salary she could afford to pay the floor-maid to look in two or three times a day and give the old lady a noon meal.

Today, attacks of rage are rare. Most of the time Mrs. Warburton sits passively, staring out the window, her mind still confused, her body almost useless. She has taken a dislike both to visitors and the radio. So evening after evening, and weekends, the two women sit by themselves. Since no real conversation is possible between mother and daughter, the room is quiet.

If anyone has suffered it is Miss Warburton herself. Fortunately, the same results can be arrived at in most cases without such self-sacrifice.

Probably the hardest problem you will have to face is where a mentally disturbed person should live. Whether anyone should offer himself up on the altar of family feeling is something each one of us has to decide for himself.

HOME VS. INSTITUTION

Only when the mental twist is so marked that it is a danger to the person himself or interferes seriously with the rights of others is it absolutely *necessary* to secure watchful supervision for him in some mental institution.

If, however, the condition is merely irritating—slightly, or more so—to those who see him every day at home, whether or not he should stay is something to talk over frankly with other members of the family, and the proper kind of doctor.

Right attitudes: The attitude you take at this point is as important for yourselves as for the afflicted person. It can be helpful to him and to you, or it can be hurtful. The remarks one young woman made in a letter to a friend are a good guide. When she finally realized that her father, formerly a brilliant lawyer, would never plead a case again, she said:

"When someone first suggests that maybe your mother's or your father's mind is failing, you don't even listen to him. The doctor says, 'Wait and see,' when you say his memory is going, or he's childishly irritable or unreasonable, or complains of things you know simply can't be so. So you do wait. But after a while you realize your parent isn't getting any better. Different well-meaning friends tell you different things about what happened to their older relatives. So you begin to worry about that. Finally, when you are flatly told, by a doctor you trust, that an old man's faculties are going, you just can't believe it. But at last you have to, and you learn to live with the idea, adapt to it, and become tolerant of it if you want to keep your own sanity. It's the only way, even if it lands a man or woman, as it did my father, in the state hospital. You have to live with it; you can't dodge facing it."

Every psychiatrist would agree with her.

Pros and Cons: It is never easy to see the personality of a person you love dissolve, and helplessness is as sad at the end of life as it is appealing at the beginning. In a crowded apartment, or a small house, young people with justifiable rights to privacy and attention may resent a deranged person whose tragedy can only be alleviated by the utmost tenderness and extra care.

No one but yourself and your family ultimately can decide whether you can bear to live with the signs of senile decay, but on the favorable side there is this to say: Many senile dementia patients are quiet, inoffensive, and require as little—or as much—care as you would give a good child. If they are confused, it will help them to stay in their old haunts and to see familiar faces around them. In many instances, they can continue to lead pleasant, even useful lives till the end of their days. A woman who forgets her daughter's name may still be a good baby-sitter if she was one before. Or a man who thinks the boy next door is his long-dead brother may still be able to do a good job of gardening or play with his own son's child as happily and as safely as he ever did.

Even a change in character which makes one person sit endlessly doing nothing when he used to be active, or develops in another a disturbance in judgment which makes his spirits flare erratically up and down and his arguments endless, is not a sign that institutionalization is necessarily required. His family may have to resort to it, if they are no longer able to live with a maladjusted personality, but in that case a mental hospital is an escape for them as well as a refuge for the ill.

HOW TO TREAT THE MENTALLY SICK

If you do decide, with a competent physician's approval, that you want to keep your elderly relative with you, *accept him as he has become*. In the beginning, he may still try to conceal his memory defects or fading vocabulary, or attempt, however inadequately, to cloak his inability to reason clearly. Make up your mind you will ignore his inability to draw the right conclusions or make the proper decisions. Even if he turns against you—as sometimes happens, no matter how good former relations have been—don't worry too much about his reactions. As a rule, the mentally ill person won't be fully aware or too much upset about his own state.

Depending on your temperament, you may find memory failure and false identification of people—if either comes—easier to bear than a tendency to hoard and hide articles, or fits of resentment and suspicion. But don't make the mistake of believing, as many do, that because a person is regressing, he cannot feel anything. He will know it if you are irritable, and he will still experience hunger or thirst, be warm or cold, and have an instinctive animal dread of disease, poverty, and death.

If he has a physical illness, treat him as you would at any other time in his life. That is, don't under any circumstances use bonds or any other form of restraint unless your physician has told you how and what to do.

In an emergency, if you think your relative is becoming violent, you can do what attendants in some mental institutions are taught. Fold a sheet lengthwise in thirds, lay it across the patient's abdomen, and fasten the ends to the sides of the bed. This won't hurt him and will keep him quiet long enough for you to get a doctor or an ambulance.

SPECIAL PROBLEMS AT HOME

Special problems will sometimes arise which make imperative provision elsewhere for a mentally ill old man or woman. But before you resort to this, ask your doctor for suggestions on how other families meet the same situation. Dr. Frederic Zeman tells the story of a patient in her late seventies who used to steal into the kitchen at night and turn on the gas without lighting a match. To let her continue obviously was a source of danger not only to herself and her family but everybody who lived in the huge New York apartment building. The solution in the F. family was a permanent companion-nurse by day, and wood panels especially made to fasten along the sides of the old lady's bed at night. They were effectual in keeping her from prowling about and were no more restraining than the bars of a child's crib.

Other situations may call for much more drastic action. There are cases of men, for instance, who have a sexual attraction toward small children, or make naïve proposals, as one Mr. X. did, to a wife's best friend. Not every old man, let us hasten to say, who is fond of little boys and girls is sexually abnormal, even when his mind is awry. Signs of unusual sexual behavior, however, have to be watched. If they cannot be kept under control, another environment may be necessary.

Eccentricities of a disturbed temperament do not always go to this extreme but they can be distracting, not only to the family circle but to the neighbors. Instead of being morose or depressed, an elderly man or woman may be over-active, excitable, noisy to the point of disturbance.

A shift may be necessary, but never jump to the conclusion that has to mean a mental hospital. Margaret W. Wagner, Director of the Benjamin Rose Institute of Cleveland, states this firmly in a principle you must believe for your own sake, but emphatically for the sake of the person who is helpless to help himself:

"The problem of placing the senile person is always difficult. But unless he is seriously disoriented, destructive, or uncontrollable, the mental institution is not the right place for him."(4)

ALTERNATIVES FOR SENILE PSYCHOTICS

Where, then, can he go?

The answer depends on how many kinds of care are available in the community. The last three words are the important ones. For the present trend in psychiatry is to keep a patient outside hospital walls and to try to treat him so that he can adjust to everyday life. Committing him to a controlled environment is the last, not the first, resort.

This means that a sharp distinction necessarily must be made between psychoses that are dangerous and those that are harmless. This is the business of psychiatrists. But for your own information you might note the categories the Metropolitan Council of Los Angeles arrived at, though not all states have the same facilities nor the same licensing laws as California.

1. Older persons who have suicidal or homicidal tendencies need the kind of maximum protection either a state mental hospital or a private sanitarium for mental patients will give.

2. If they are confused or disoriented and need a protective environment they may be cared for in a sanitarium for mild cases. (In California that would be one licensed by the state Department of Mental Hygiene.)

3. If they are not likely to wander off or inadvertently harm themselves or others, or are not disturbing, and senility manifests it-

self in nothing more serious than loss of memory or mild disorientation, they may be cared for in homes for the aged, or in a nursing or rest home licensed for that purpose.

4. There are many borderline situations. Older persons with varying manifestations of senility get along well sometimes in boarding homes, and are also found in nursing or "rest" homes of the usual type.

5. Behavior patterns determine which facility is most appropriate for a given situation.

Mental nursing homes: You may find one solution in a type of small institution, somewhat similar to a nursing home but licensed and equipped to accept mild mental cases. The state mental hospital authority, if one exists, or the health or welfare department of a state, will have a list. You can write for it, addressing the department at the state capital. Some states will list only the name and address; others, like New Jersey, include mention of admission policies and other information which will save you time when you start your preliminary investigation. The sample entries cited here are from the lists of private licensed mental institutions issued by the New Jersey Department of Institutions and Agencies. They will give you an idea of what is available in some other states:

NAME* AND ADDRESS	CAPACITY	PATIENTS ACCEPTED	HOUSE PHYSICIAN
Landview Rest Home Roseland	22	Mild mental and nervous adults	No resident physician
Beautiful View Sanitarium Belle Meade	65	Mild mental and senile	Two doctors
Fairlawn, Summit	52	Nervous and mental; alcoholics (through Alcoholics Anonymous)	Four psychiatrists

* All names are fictitious.

Family care: "Family" or "foster" care is comparatively new in its use for senile dementia cases. But it has been found that if a family is carefully chosen so that bizarre behavior will be tolerated and understood, the senile person can get along well and sometimes his mental decline can be retarded.

At this moment our public mental institutions are encumbered by great numbers of aged patients who don't need the type of care they are receiving and who would be far happier elsewhere. In 1942, when a special survey was made in New York, there were over four thousand of these patients in that state alone.(5) If you can continue your relative's living arrangements on a semi-independent basis you will be doing something to reserve institutional placements for those who need them more. If only from a selfish point of view, this would be worth while. Your relative—or someone else you know—may be needing those very beds urgently some day.

If your relative has been in a mental hospital the Social Service Department, or possibly the state Department of Mental Hygiene, will select the family and supervise placement of the patient. If he has never had to go to a hospital and doctors advise this solution, the proper place to go for help is a local welfare agency. (See Chapter XIV, *Where to Turn for Help.*) This is a sample advertisement one social service organization placed in the New York *Times.*

> "——— welfare agency seeks boarding homes in New York City, Brooklyn, Bronx, Queens, for former mental patients. Agency provides supervision and substantial board payments."

What kind of patients can profit by such an arrangement? And what kind of families will take them and treat them well?

These are questions any anxious person wants to have answered.

"The type of patient usually selected for family care," according to New York's State Society for Mental Health, "is one whose acute mental illness has subsided, who is harmless to himself and others, and who is in sufficiently good condition, mentally and physically, not to require constant medical and psychiatric care. . . ."(6)

From one to four patients may be placed in a home.

Choosing the right family: The responsibility of finding the quiet home life that a mentally ill or a mentally defective person needs is so great that no family should assume it. It is a risky business to trust someone you love to the care of strangers but if a family is carefully chosen by a recognized agency you need have no fears.

The New York State Society for Mental Health follows a pattern which is general through the country. These are some of its criteria:

"The families selected . . . are those who will be kind and sympathetic toward the patient and willing to follow the instructions of the hospital regarding his care. No families are considered who are not self-maintaining. . . . For the most part the families are middle-aged or even older people whose children have grown up and left home. They usually have good-sized, comfortable houses and often they welcome whatever companionship the patients may offer. . . . The entire family must be interested in caring for the patients. It must be an harmonious family and one with a stable routine of living habits."

Note the provision against the board money being the family's only cash income. This, of course, is to guard against exploitation and something you need not worry about when a man or woman is placed where his care will be closely supervised.

If you examine Mr. R.'s case you can see how much this kind of environment can do for a person not able to manage his own affairs or plan for himself but who can still enjoy simple pleasures.(7) (It will also show you the routine which is followed, which is practically the same whether the person is released from a hospital or comes from his own home.)

Mr. R. had been put in the observation ward of a mental hospital. The psychiatrists who examined him found him senile but not disturbing. They thought he would make a good adjustment in a family group. He had one daughter, married and too preoccupied with her own problems to help him. (In fact, it was because no one wanted him that he had been admitted to the hospital.)

The Catholic Charities which was called on to help, had some misgivings about putting him with a "foster" family. Notwithstanding, a social worker talked it over with Mrs. D., known to like old people and possessed of a warm personality. Mrs. D. was sure she could give Mr. R. the supervision he needed and had no hesitation in accepting the responsibility.

Mr. R. is a far different person today from the depressed man he was six months ago. He is interested in his appearance, insists on a clean white shirt for Sundays, looks ten years younger, and is very proud of his accomplishments. There have been difficulties but no more so than in any other family group. Mrs. D. declares "Uncle Bill" will always be with her family. When she had to change her residence she made definite arrangements so that "Uncle Bill" could come, too, and be comfortable.

Sometimes, under the family plan, or some other form of supervised care, a personality will improve so much that a man or woman may again be able to participate in community life. In a certain small village in upper New York there is an elderly, deteriorated, alcoholic woman who lives with a family not her own. Formerly she was a professional musician. Now she derives great satisfaction in playing the organ in the Presbyterian church, and does it well.

WHEN A MENTAL HOSPITAL IS NECESSARY

The other side of the story is the inescapable fact that sometimes a mental institution offers the only solution—at the time. In those last words you have hope. For mental illness, like physical sickness, is not static. The fact that any person has to have what only a hospital can give him does not mean he has to stay there always. Many old people never recover sufficiently to be removed, but there are a sufficient number who do to keep you from feeling there is an invisible barrier which cannot be removed between the world of reality and your loved one.

Dante's melancholy adjuration, "Abandon hope, all ye who enter here!" has no place in a modern mental hospital. You have the solace of knowing that during the last fifty years, and especially during the past quarter century, mental disease has been put on an equal footing with physical disease. Patients who are mentally ill are not "put away" and forgotten; they receive the same intensive study and skillful nursing as they would if they had any other form of sickness in the *best* hospitals, federal, state, county, or private.

That qualification—a modern mental hospital—has to be made. In many parts of the country the mentally ill are still cared for under shocking, primitive conditions. It is still more shocking that often the community or the state in which evils have been uncovered by responsible investigators still tolerates them. This means that when any person has to be institutionalized his family must guard against his incarceration in such a place. It is equally important to get rid of any fears and prejudices you may have. When Dr. Karl W. Bowman was Director of the Psychiatric Division of New York City's hospitals, he said this:

"Many old persons do well in institutions when they cannot get along at home. Many times a senile man is brought into a hospital because he is impossible to get along with. He is in the hospital a week and nothing is seen of his abnormal behavior. Our first suspicion is that the people who brought him are trying to get rid of him but my experience has been that this is seldom the case. The more carefully you investigate these cases the more you find that these old people are impossible in their own homes but get along better in institutions."(8)

With this consoling thought to go on, visit mental hospitals and see for yourself whether those for which your old people are eligible are really hospitals and not merely places of detention.

WHAT VISITS ACCOMPLISH

There will be no difficulty about arranging a visit to either a public or a private sanitarium. More and more superintendents are freely throwing open their doors, not only to public inquiry and exposés, but to ordinary citizens. The majority are eager to make us all realize that if mental hospitals are not what they ought to be it is due to public apathy which is our responsibility—not theirs—to correct.

When you visit first-rate hospitals—again the emphasis has to be on the adjective—the pall of mystery will lift. If you still feel repulsion when you enter, as most of us do who were reared on tales of what goes on in "Bedlam," it will vanish when you realize that in a well-run institution there are trained therapists in many medical fields. They pool their techniques to provide the fullest measure of treatment for each patient. The emphasis will be on the sickest.

You'll discover something else. You will realize that mental disorders, like the poor, can be found everywhere. Seeing other visitors, knowing there are well-educated, healthy, successful men and women who have relatives with mental and neurotic disorders, will give you a sense of kinship and ought to remove the last vestige of shame from acknowledging that mental disease has struck your family, too.

One woman who had to hospitalize her seventy-four-year-old mother, formerly an able, outgoing person, expressed the attitude that everybody ought to try to achieve.

She said to her neighbor in the reception room, "When you see human beings in the hospital that are remarkably like us, even though they behave differently at times, you realize that to have a sick mind is not just something that is always terrible and awful. And when you meet other folks coming to see their relatives you know a tragedy has not just been plotted out for you."

WHAT TO LOOK FOR

Only trained investigators can fully evaluate services and facilities but you can find out what a good mental hospital should look like, and what kind of questions to ask.

Standards for personnel: Start by familiarizing yourself with the requirements the American Psychiatric Association thinks are necessary to provide "active treatment and humane care" for mental patients.

The amount and kind of attention, medical and otherwise, that patients receive is largely dependent on the relationship between their number and the number and kind of doctors, nurses, attendants, and other members of the staff who must look after them.

This sounds like an elementary premise. But it is not when you consider that the American Psychiatric Association declares that not a single public mental hospital—where ninety-seven per cent of patients are housed—whether it is supported by federal, state, county, or city funds, has met its personnel standards. What you can do is to try to find a hospital which comes closest to meeting these standards of the Association:

For those in an acute stage of mental illness, there should be:

one doctor for every thirty patients;
a registered nurse for every five patients;
a psychiatric aide or attendant for every four patients;
a forty-four hour week for employees;
a superintendent who is a medical doctor, who has specialized in psychiatry and who also has administrative ability.

Other types of patients require less intensive treatment, but they do need what the Association terms "continued treatment." This should include such auxiliary services as occupational and physical therapy, recreational therapy such as music, dancing, psychodramas, and so on. They are frequently helpful in bringing the patient to the point where he can respond to psychiatric treatment. For these the Association advocates:

at least one doctor for every hundred and fifty patients;
a registered nurse for every forty;
a psychiatric aide or attendant for every six.

Existing facilities: There are about 680 mental hospitals of all types in the United States, and about 330,000 more beds are needed in state mental hospitals alone. Since eighty-two per cent of all beds are in them, this shortage is of paramount importance. Although there is a constantly increasing number of beds in both public and private sanitariums, the need has vastly outrun them. This means that you must not be shocked if you find overcrowding; unfortunately it is prevalent in three out of every four state mental hospitals, and in many others.(9)

There are private hospitals, run for profit. Many of them are excellent. If this is what you want, your doctor will help you find one that suits his patient. Be prepared to pay stiff prices that only the well-to-do can afford on a long-term basis if you choose one which has the facilities a mental patient should have. Don't be misled by luxurious bedrooms, well-landscaped grounds, and a handsome building. These are comforting to the family but a minor element in the over-all picture of the treatment of a mentally sick person, unless all he needs is a "rest cure."

Evaluating a state hospital: Since the state hospitals contain most of the beds for the mentally ill, they are the ones to think of first. Before you make up your mind that you can never put a person you love in a public institution, investigate. Find out how strict your state licensing and inspection law is. Ask doctors which sanitarium on the state or county level treat emotionally ill persons as sick people in need of medical treatment, not merely restraint. Find out the ratio of staff to patients and know the kind of questions to ask about medical and surgical units by doing some reading. (See pp. 485-86.)

Take heart from the statement of a man like Dr. Max A. Bahr. For fifty-four years he served the Central State Hospital in Indianapolis, half that time as superintendent. He says he has seen a vast change from the "hideous conditions of mediaevalism" which prevailed when he was a young physician.

Like Central State Hospital, the best mental institutions over the country will have not only operating rooms, a pathological laboratory, diagnostic clinics, research laboratories, a pharmacy and dental facilities, but they will have an amusement hall, an occupational therapy department, and planned recreation for therapeutic purposes. The last group, as Dr. Bahr says, "at times is equally important for the relatives" as for the lethargic patients to whom they give new interests. When you make your visit, check off on your list which of these additions to a good mental hospital are lacking, if any, and find out what is substituted for them. Then talk over your findings with a doctor who knows what alternative facilities exist in the area.

ADMISSION PROCEDURES

Gaining admission to a mental hospital of any kind is not a mere matter of walking up to the door and registering a sick person. Nor is it a matter of reserving a room or a bed, even on the recommendation of a physician.

Each state has its own commitment law and these vary widely. Local physicians know or are able to find out what form of admission is possible and legal. More and more states are changing laws, some of them rapidly, to conform with a Draft Act prepared by our federal National Institute of Mental Health. Its basic premise is this: A statute governing the hospitalization of the mentally ill should assure maximum opportunity for prompt medical care, freedom from emotionally harmful or degrading treatment, and protection against wrongful confinement and deprivation of rights.

This is a high ideal, not always met. You will have to abide by whatever admission policy exists but if it is poor remember that the important thing is not so much what the law is, but whether it is carried out by officials who understand the problems of an emotionally disturbed person.

Voluntary admission: This is probably the least likely so far as elderly people are concerned. It is possible, without formality, in all but a few states. The routine procedure is for the person who feels he needs treatment to make a written request of the superintendent of the hospital he selects. If his condition warrants it, he will be admitted.

Medical certification: This is the most humane way when a patient is too ill to realize his own condition. Certification ought to be by two psychiatrists. There are approximately 6,500 members of the American Psychiatric Association, and in addition, a number of psychiatrists who do not belong but are well qualified to perform this function. The examination will not be harrowing and probably not long. The thing for you to avoid is quacks and the self-styled medical psychologists, therapists, etc., who advertise. Consult the county medical society or your own family physician if you are in doubt about whom to go to.

Certification by commission: This is a process in the legal, not the medical realm. It is not a method the medical profession feels gives protection to the patient. Unfortunately, in some states, it is still the only way a mentally ill person can be hospitalized, and you may have no choice.

Trial by jury: Texas is now the only state where this is mandatory. Other states may use the method, equally frowned on by psychiatrists, of a permissive trial by jury. This can be done on petition of the patient, his family, his friends, or at a judge's discretion if he thinks it advisable. Avoid this procedure. No laymen, however well-meaning, are qualified to diagnose illness of any kind, least of all where the question of mental balance is concerned.

Temporary admission: There are only seven states at the present time which will not allow emergency or temporary hospitalization, though some insist on a court order for it. This is another course of action psychiatrists generally disapprove of. The reason is that the legal period may be anything from two to ninety days. Often the person receives no treatment at all in this time, which can have disastrous results.

YOUR RESPONSIBILITY AFTER ADMISSION

Once an aged person is admitted, however, your responsibility really has just begun. The very act itself requires your most loving thought. Your relative ought not to be sent, like a criminal, in charge of an officer of the law. The greatest proportion of those committed are neither dangerous to themselves nor to others. If you can't go with him, or feel that you or other members of the family can't handle him, then a psychiatric nurse, an attendant at the hospital, a doctor, or some friend he trusts, ought to accompany him.

Because his mind is failing, treat him tenderly. Dispel his terrors as best you can, but in any case use no force. The doctor or nurse will know what to do without harming him bodily or injuring him further emotionally.

If you go with him to the hospital, don't leave him abruptly. He may be highly disturbed at finding himself there. Don't try to reason with him, however, or attempt to make him see why you must leave him. If he could reason intelligently, he wouldn't be there. Do as you would if you were hospitalizing a small child for a tonsillectomy or some other minor operation. Try to appear as casual when you go as if you were leaving on a shopping trip, and tell him you'll be back as soon as you can. He'll know from the tone of your voice what you feel, and even if he is unable to respond coherently in words, he'll be comforted. Save any emotional outbursts on your part until you are alone.

Once you have made the decision and carried it out, have no regrets. You will not be leaving your relative with guards.

If you have chosen the right hospital he will be in the hands of competent nurses, doctors, and attendants. They probably will be overworked, and equally probably underpaid, and almost certainly will have too many patients to look after. But that is no different than the situation in many other types of hospitals.

If you have placed your relative in an institution, private or public, which has a good reputation in medical circles, you can be sure that essential treatments will be given. Little attentions and signs of personal interest which mean as much to the mentally sick as the physically ailing may be lacking. This is usually not due to the indifference of the personnel. The staff in a mental hospital is not a group of hard-hearted, unfeeling people; they simply haven't the time to give the signs of personal regard they have every right to believe a patient's family and his friends should supply.

Make as frequent visits as the hospital rules permit; if you don't live close enough to come often, see to it that someone who has a genuine interest in your relative does come. In most cases he will be as sensitive to neglect as he ever was.

TREATMENT IN A MENTAL HOSPITAL

"What will happen to my relative once he gets in the hospital?"

That is the question which agitates most people. The answer depends to some degree on the hospital but chiefly on the condition of the patient.

If he is not violent, he will see moving picture shows, look at television or listen to the radio, spending part of the day out of his ward, preferably out of doors. If he is capable of reading books, he will have access to them. Most important of all, so far as his improvement is concerned, he will be encouraged to keep busy. It may be at crafts, sewing, gardening or some other form of supervised activity program, but the object will be to avoid idleness. It has as bad an effect on the mentally ill as on the sound. You may see your relative working in the kitchen or the sewing room of a state hospital, or digging up weeds or busy at some "manufactured" job in a private one. Don't be disturbed by it. Many a person has taken his first step toward rehabilitation helping to set the table or plucking flowers for the other patients' pleasure.

If, however, your relative complains of overwork or some other ill-treatment, don't disregard his remarks altogether; rather, make some quiet observations without letting him know you are doing it. If the staff seems reasonably efficient and pleasant, if the other patients appear to be comfortable and at ease, if rooms and corridors are clean, and there are no "back" wards where the old are huddled together and ignored, then it is his illness, not the hospital routine, which disturbs him.

THE ROAD TOWARD DISCHARGE

It is important not to give up hope. Always remember the objective of any good mental hospital is to rehabilitate the sick individual and restore him as a productive member of society.

The possibility of someone being kept in a hospital longer than is necessary is one anxiety you can dismiss. The pressure to release beds for new cases is far too great for any patient to be kept a day longer than necessary. Nevertheless, most physicians feel it is unfair to the sick person to set a limitation on the time he will have to stay. Your relative will not be rushed out before he is emotionally ready to leave, no matter how crowded the wards may be. There will be a step-by-step discharge which generally takes place in this order:

1. The first stride toward liberty in the world at large is granting of hospital privileges. These will be given only after the pooling of professional opinions at a staff conference recommends it.

2. If improvement continues, the decision of sending the patient home or to some other place is made only after a staff appraisal of his condition.

3. Preparation for community life, preparation of the family, and preparation for the community to receive the patient, are the next parts of the discharge program.

4. Many states make legal provision for trial visit periods. At first the doctors may permit a visit of only a few hours, next an overnight or a weekend stay. Gradually, if the patient does well, the time will be lengthened to weeks and months.

5. If he has improved to the extent that he is able to manage his own affairs or handle them with the interest and help of relatives, he will be recommended for discharge. He will then be "on parole" for a time. If he is unable at some later date to adjust to a normal way of life, he is re-admitted.

The adjustment period may be trying and a good deal depends on how well members of the family cooperate with each other. If the trial visits are not a perfect success, Professor Worcester's philosophic attitude is the only sensible one to adopt.

His mother came to live with the Worcesters after his father's death. At that time Mrs. Worcester, Sr., was seventy. She was the perfect pattern of a gracious woman, devoted to her only son, fond of her daughter-in-law and grandchildren, able to live her own active life in the college community. A few years later Professor Worcester was dismayed to find his mother was increasingly unpopular. Friends looked askance when she quarreled bitterly at their table, and neighbors lifted eyebrows when she wept if the postman was late or screamed at the children as they played near her window. The eventual end of her hysterical fits of anger was hospitalization.

Today Mrs. Worcester, Sr., is still in the sanitarium. She has improved and has been able to make several trial visits home. Her son thinks she was glad to go back; the children still seemed to unnerve her.

"Fifty years ago," Professor Worcester says soberly, "my mother would have been regarded as a maniac. I know that she's sick. There's a big difference. We've gone a long way since then."

AID THROUGH ADJUSTMENT PERIOD

One of the most valuable assets of a mental hospital is its out-patient clinic. It has two functions. One is to offer disturbed men and women a chance to get treatments under regular psychiatric supervision which may result in their cure, or at least keep them out of the hospital.

The second function is important because it is a useful link between the community and the hospital, and an aid during the adjustment period. The hospital will want to keep in touch with your relative till all doubt is removed about his ability to live outside its sheltering walls. In New York, for instance, a discharged patient is placed on "convalescent care" status for one year in the custody of a relative or some other responsible person. This means that the hospital will keep close watch on his condition, either through its out-patient clinic, or through its social workers, or both.

You will not be left to stumble alone through the trying adjustment days. The social worker assigned to your relative's case will visit him at home and help with family problems as they arise.

Or, if it is not possible to have an aged person return to his own family, she will help find a boarding arrangement for him. Mr. Howard's case indicates how a difficult situation can be worked out.

Mr. Howard had managed quite well after his wife's death until he was in his seventies, doing his own housekeeping and shopping. But when he began to have serious lapses of memory and exhibit excessive garrulity neighbors called his son's attention to it. The son, who lived in another part of the city, eventually took his aged father home to live with him. There was a house full of young people who soon resented grandpa's queer ways. His tedious, repetitive stories of his Spanish War service bored both them and their friends. The climax came in an unhappy situation when grandpa wandered away from the house, and forgot where he lived and who he was. When he was finally found, he began to babble of beatings and thievery by his family. This, at least, was not so.

A few months later Mr. Howard was admitted to the state mental hospital. In the calmer atmosphere there, he improved. Finally, he made a sufficient recovery to be discharged. He never returned to his son's turbulent home. Now he lives with a "foster" family, supervised by the hospital. Periodically, Mr. Howard returns to the out-patient clinic, but that is all. He is a happy, harmless boarder. He has a tolerant landlady who doesn't mind the fact that occasionally he puts the dishes in the bedroom closet and the baby's coat in the pantry. Ask him where he is living, and he opens wide his bright blue eyes, and says in a puzzled voice, "Why, I'm with my son's wife! She's a dear girl!"

WHAT YOU CAN DO

When mental illness strikes an old man or woman it may be pathetic, or it may be tragic. It is natural to ask, then, "What can I do?" It may be the first time you have had to think seriously about the fact that good treatment for your own family depends on how much there is available for everybody.

Fortunately, we have a National Mental Health Act. Through it a number of approaches have been authorized which will promote the mental health of our nation. There is a National Institute of Mental Health; there is personnel and some funds for research, not only in the more serious mental and neurologic disorders, but in everyday emotional stresses and maladjustments. There is provision for training in psychiatry and related fields. And assistance and public education can be offered so that states can develop or expand their own programs.

How adequate this national program is depends in part on how much each of us do before mental illness strikes home. The National Association for Mental Health has a number of suggestions. (See p. 473.) One of them is to join the citizens' mental health group in your state; its objective is to promote mental health locally. Another is to bring the best possible care to all the mentally ill by seeing to it that enlightened legislation is passed. To wait until your own family needs help is too late.

NOTES TO CHAPTER XIII

(1) Branch, G. H. Hardin, M.D. "Mental Aspects of Adjustment and Preparation for Old Age." Address delivered at Northwestern University Centennial Conference, June 8, 1951, Chicago, Ill.

(2) *Patients in Mental Institutions, 1948.* Washington: National Institute of Mental Health, Federal Security Agency, April 25, 1951.

(3) Branch, G. H. Hardin, M.D. *Op. cit.*

(4) Wagner, Margaret W. "Problems of Placing a Senile Person." *Foster Home Care for the Aged.* New York: Family Service Ass'n of America. (Reprinted from *The Family, Journal of Social Case Work.*) P. 10.

(5) Report of a committee appointed by Governor Thomas Dewey in 1942 on Care of the Mentally Ill in the State of New York.

(6) Crutcher, Hester B. *Family Care of the Mentally Ill.* Reprinted from Publication No. 9 of the American Ass'n for the Advancement of Science. New York: State Charities Aid Ass'n (The New York State Society for Mental Health). Pp. 179-84.

(7) Casalena, Katherine F. "A Foster Home Program for the Aged." *The Catholic Charities Review,* Mar., 1951. P. 62.

(8) Bowman, Karl M., M.D. "Types and Special Factors of Mental Illness in Old Age." *Mental Hygiene in Old Age.* New York: Family Welfare Ass'n of America, May 5, 1937. P. 32.

(9) "Facts and Figures about Mental Illness and Other Personality Disturbances." New York: The National Ass'n for Mental Health, Inc., April, 1952.

CHAPTER FOURTEEN

WHERE TO TURN FOR HELP

When you are confronted with a situation with which you cannot cope, talk it over with someone not personally involved. It is not a sign of weakness or a confession of failure. In fact, it is a short-sighted form of egotism *not* to look for help. An expert who has encountered family problems like yours many times before—however unique they seem to you—may be able to find a fresh approach you might not think of yourself, or suggest a solution you might not know exists.

There is a good chance of finding such help. The fact that the numbers of our elders have quadrupled in the past fifty years, and are expected to double again in the next fifty, has had an impact on communities large and small, urban and rural. Some of them have already set up special agencies to attack the problems of the aged. Others have plans that are still in the talking stage, and may remain there. But at least everywhere there is a healthy sense that something has to be done if living longer is to mean anything worth struggling for.

The important thing to know is where and to whom to turn, at the right time. Don't wait until affairs are at an extremity before you act. Urge your older relatives to find out what their rights and privileges are under federal, state, and local laws. It is just as important for an older man or woman to unburden himself to someone he trusts outside the family circle as it is for a younger one. It may even ward off a serious emotional disturbance. That is, if he can talk to someone who will accept him at his own evaluation

—a human being who neither wants to be handled like a delicate bit of china, nor ignored like a worn-out piece of furniture.

The mere fact that you know what is available for older people in an emergency, and quite as important, what is not, will relieve tension, and may prevent too hasty action.

Mrs. Allison's story shows this fact clearly. A woman with a delicate sense of humor, she revealed the tale to an intimate friend of her own age long after the family crisis had passed.

"When I was hospitalized and very ill," Mrs. Allison said, "unknown to me, my children, in all kindness and love, thought it best to sell off my home and most of my possessions. From their point of view they were freeing me from too heavy responsibilities. When I was able, I smiled at them from my convalescent's bed, and silently thought my way out."

Her way was to confide the story of her relatives' over-impetuous action to a capable young social worker the next time she made her rounds in the hospital. With her tactful help the family was made to realize this seventy-one-year-old grandmother could continue to live an independent life even though she would have to use crutches till the end of her days. It was the social worker who set in motion machinery which helped Mrs. Allison recover her remaining furniture and knickknacks from relatives' attics and cellars. Eventually, with the aid of the now chastened family, a small ground-floor apartment was found for Mrs. Allison. There she serenely lives alone again—very much, it must be said, to the relief of her children as well as herself.

TRADITIONAL SOURCES OF HELP

Where older people's lives are involved, be sure that counsel comes from people trained and competent in their own specialties, as the hospital social worker was. It is an intelligent act to find out about community resources, and old-fashioned and benighted to feel you can do without them.

Traditionally, the older generation has always looked to the learned men of the community—the lawyers, the preachers, the bankers—for words of wisdom. And they are probably still the ones old people turn to most easily.

Certainly, no one can be a better guide than a family lawyer when it comes to such matters as persuading a parent or grandparent to make a will and avoid family dissension over property when he is gone. Similarly, a banker's words about investments or real estate will probably be followed considerably more graciously than the same advice given by a young relative. (On the old-time principle that a prophet is not without honor save in his own country—or his family.)

An older generation, reared in the habit of church affiliations and regular church attendance also turns naturally for advice to a minister, a rabbi, or a priest. Since most old people resent a suspicion that they cannot solve all their own problems, this gives a good starting point. For today churches and synagogues are conscious that more emphasis has to be laid on making places for old people, and very often they take the lead in a community to do it. Neither you nor the older individual has to be a member of a church to secure practical aid from its program and its head.

AID FROM CHURCH AND SYNAGOGUE

Even though a minister may be still a very young man, he has undoubtedly been exposed to the widespread discussion of old people's problems. He may even be a graduate of one of the theological seminaries which now add gerontological courses to their curriculum. If you consult an older pastor, years of work and experience with all types of human frailties will have made him familiar with the snares life holds for the old, and some ways out of them.

Many times situations in family life arise where the intervention of a man of the cloth makes life easier for both generations. Mrs. Searcher, for instance, is eighty years old; she is known in the small town in which she lives for the ease with which she gets along with her crusty son-in-law with whom she must live. She gives all the credit to Pastor X.

"He told me," Mrs. Searcher says, "if you must live in your

daughter's and son-in-law's home, smile, and try to see and say only pleasant things. Stay in your own room except when you are especially invited to join the family circle. When you are with them study to have intelligent, non-personal things to say. Breathe complaints only to your Maker in the dead of night!"

Let us hope the older people you are closest to are saved from such rigid self-disciplining. But in less intimate, equally vital matters, ministers, rabbis, and priests can often give impartial advice that will be honest and well-informed on matters like these:

Homes for the aged: Any minister ought to know about those of his particular denomination, national and local. If he has no personal knowledge of how they are run he should know whom to send you to, to find out.

Local institutions and hospitals: Visits to places where the elderly are housed are part of a pastoral round of duties. As a consequence of this first-hand contact, a pastor should be able to give you a picture of conditions as he sees them.

Boarding care: Occasionally a church will help locate families in the congregation able to board a hale or an incapacitated elderly person.

"Over Sixty-Five" clubs: Various types of so-called "Golden Age" clubs are now high on the list of activities of many churches. If the community has none, and you think the aged will profit by it, don't hesitate to talk to any head of a church or synagogue about organizing one. It is quite possible he can help you and others to secure financial support from civic organizations, or men's or women's clubs. The church usually has quarters, and sometimes the personnel, to offer as its own contribution.

Information from other communities: Often the bond between pastors in one area and colleagues in another is such that they will exchange information. You might need to find out, for instance, what conditions are like in a mental hospital in another state, or a pastor may be willing to secure from a fellow-minister a report on an old ladies' home your grandmother may be considering in a town you don't know.

The job which a good man of the Gospel takes as part of his routine duties is exemplified in the story of Miss Minnie.

Miss Minnie was one of those useful maiden aunts that every family used to have. For most of her adult life she kept house for one or another of her relatives. At the age of seventy-four she found herself about to be turned out of the home where for five years she had given loving care to an invalided older sister before she died. This is the tale this sturdy, still-erect, woman tearfully told her minister:

"My nephew wrote me," she said, "that as a token of appreciation for all I did for his mother, he wants to sell her home and use the money to pay my way into a high-class home for old ladies. But I don't want to go into a home! I can still work!" she cried.

The minister promptly wrote the lawyer-nephew to come and talk things over. However, Mr B. was too busy, he said, to leave his office in the city, but assured her pastor he was perfectly willing to provide for his aunt for the rest of her life. He was jolted out of his complacency when the minister informed him Miss Minnie didn't want his support. What she did want was independence. The solution they worked out was for Miss Minnie to stay in the rambling, well-furnished house, take boarders, and (at her insistence) pay rent to her nephew. Almost a decade later, Miss Minnie still does most of her work, and her boarders brag about her justifiably famous cooking. The old ladies' home is very much in the background.

MEDICAL SERVICES

If the church or synagogue is the first line of defense for the elderly, then a physician is certainly the second. Sometimes the positions are reversed. Bodily ills, and the fear of death, whether spoken or unspoken, are always in the background of every aging person's mind.

A physician can be a good friend. If he is as understanding as he should be, he will know that the relief of talking freely is part of the cure of any elderly man's or woman's troubles. As Dr. Robert T. Monroe, distinguished geriatrician of Boston, says:

"Who is in a better position to give friendly, neutral, skillful, understanding advice than the medical advisor? Even if the older person's chief complaint may have little to do with what really concerns him, he needs to talk over these complaints and many other matters with someone. He has outlived the parents to whom he turned in time of trouble; his friends are gone, and now, still the same human being, in the dark about how to pursue his course or how to find a course to pursue, he must bring himself to turn to someone for advice. . . ."(1)

Choosing the right doctor: If your relatives already have a physician whom they have seen periodically over the years, there is seldom good reason to change, except when specialists have to be consulted. The record of their medical lives, the changes that occur physically, mentally, emotionally in them, the effect of their environment, are all facts which affect a diagnosis. The medical record itself may be transferable but the knowledge gained by a physician of the alterations that have occurred over a long period of time cannot be discerned by a new doctor, no matter how thorough his examination.

Nevertheless, there are times when a new physician is a necessity. It is important then to locate someone who can do these two things:

(1) He should be up-to-date enough to believe even the very old can respond to treatment or survive surgery.

(2) He should be someone who understands the elderly and their reactions to life's situations.

Dr. S. is one of these invaluable assets. He never fails to tell Mrs. Walker when she comes with her daughter for an annual check-up, that she looks as young now as she did twelve years ago when she became his patient. He caps his homemade therapy by urging her to wear more youthful hats and colors to match her cornflower-blue eyes and her still pink cheeks.

"I have to give her some antidote," he says dryly, "to counteract her daughter's gloomy outlook. At home she surrounds Mrs. Walker with so many fears about her health it's a wonder the old lady has the spunk to remain alive."

How can you find the type of physician who understands elderly people's emotional reactions as well as this doctor does?

There are several courses you might follow.

If you have any doubt about the qualities that make a physician a good one, send for a copy of a useful little pamphlet, titled, "How to Choose a Doctor." It is published by the American Medical Association (535 North Dearborn Street, Chicago 10), and is available for a few cents a copy.

The best source for a list of local physicians, and for information about their training, hospital affiliations, and credentials, is the county medical society. This body is part of a nation-wide organization to which any physician of repute belongs. Its offices in cities over 100,000 are usually well-organized, well-staffed, and permanently located at an easily accessible address you can locate in a telephone directory. In smaller towns and in rural areas the society is headed by a physician who keeps its records in his own office. It may be even more dynamic than one in a metropolis. Much depends on local leadership. To find the name and address of the current president inquire at any hospital in the county.

If you must find doctors in a community you don't know, or for a relative far away, write the state medical association, whose office is usually in the capital. (See pp. 400-04 for list.)

If he must have a specialist, the best thing is to rely on the recommendation of another physician in whom you have confidence. There is a *Directory of Medical Specialists* (published by the A. N. Marquis Company, Chicago, for the Advisory Board for Medical Specialists), but it is not for laymen. However, if you are the meticulous type, you can examine it in any medical library and some large public ones. It will give the background and credentials of all types of specialists. There is also the *American Medical Directory* (published by the American Medical Association, Chicago) which you will find in the same libraries. It gives the educational background, hospital, university, and other affiliations of all physicians in the United States.

Don't let your relatives confuse the druggist with the physician. The druggist or pharmacist is not licensed to diagnose, prescribe, or treat. He is trained and licensed only to fill prescriptions of the physician; diagnosing illness and prescribing medicine and treatment are not in his province, though a good many older folk don't realize this.

Geriatricians: More and more doctors are devoting themselves to the care of the old. They have to because there are so many old people. Geriatricians, however, are physicians who specialize in treating the degenerative diseases and other illnesses that affect people past middle age. They are not yet available everywhere but their number, too, must grow, as the population ages. The American Geriatrics Society (25 Mechanic Street, Wakefield, Rhode Island) will tell you if any of its approximately fifteen hundred members are practising in the locality where your parents or grandparents live.

GENERAL HEALTH INFORMATION

The American Medical Association has a Bureau of Health Education from which you can secure much useful information. You must, however, observe these reasonable limitations. Neither the staff of the Bureau nor any other responsible organization or individual will:

make a diagnosis by mail. It is not scientific and can never be satisfactory.

prescribe treatment by mail. Physicians do not treat symptoms or diseases. They treat patients.

prescribe diets. There is no standardized diet useful to all patients suffering from the same disease.

tell an inquirer whom the staff of the Bureau has never seen whether he ought or ought not to have a surgical operation. A list of symptoms or a long case history in a letter is no basis for a positive conclusion as to what is wrong with the patient.

predict the outcome of any treatment in any patient. There is no standard dosage for drugs applicable to all patients.

These are excellent rules to remember, particularly if you are dealing with the older person—and there are many such—who writes for every drug talked about on the radio or over television. See that when they turn for help to medical resources, they find the right ones.

One of them is the Public Health Department where can be found information about local hospitals, sanitariums of various types, nursing homes, clinics, and every other matter which affects the health of a whole community. In a municipality the headquarters is usually the city hall; in a rural area, it is the county court house. For information about medical resources in any state, address the Department of Health which will be located in the capital city.

Another gold-mine of information is our national American Red Cross (in Washington, D. C.) and its local chapters. The latter are spread throughout our country. If its staff cannot tell you what you want to know, or does not have the service an elderly person in your family needs at the time, you may be directed to some other organization, if it is possible for it to fill the gap.

Which resource shall you use? Your own knowledge and the needs of your relatives have to determine that. But do not wait till too late to make a decision or a choice. To be aware of what can be done if an emergency arises, and to prepare for it, as the Sanborns did, is to show intelligence as well as devotion to an older person's interests.

Mr. Sanborn, Sr., consented to live with his son and daughter-in-law in Boston, if he might contribute to the household expenses. However, he had already had one serious heart attack. The son was afraid his father ought not to try to continue selling insurance in New England's rugged climate after years of living in Southern California. To settle the matter he wrote his father's physician. "What kind of diet should my father have?" he asked. "What kind of exercise should he take, and how much daily? What recreation means most to him now? Most important of all, does he have enough stamina to continue working, and is it good for him?"

When the answer to the last query came in the affirmative, the son asked the San Diego doctor to forward his father's complete medical history to the family physician in Boston. This, together with the son's knowledge of the regimen his father had to live under, was a major factor in the latter's recovery from a second heart attack. In the period of adjustment both to new family life and a new climate it was invaluable, not only for the older man's health but in his relations with the young people.

RESOURCES IN MENTAL ILLNESS

Of all matters that touch the aged, mental illness is the one to handle with the most care. A family doctor can give you advice in this delicate matter, and it may be all you need. There are also specialized agencies you can consult:

Mental health associations: There are more than three hundred in many states; often they also exist on a county or city level. They have been formed by citizens interested in fostering right preventive measures, and establishing correct diagnosis and treatment of emotionally disturbed people of any age. If such an association is accessible you will find it well-informed about local psychiatric and mental hygiene resources; or you can obtain help in finding those the elderly need elsewhere.

Any hospital, a county Welfare Department, or a state Department of Health should be able to tell you the address of the state Mental Health Association, and that in turn will advise you of the one nearest your older people's residence. In a city, you can find the association listed in the telephone directory, or secure the name of officers and its address from the Public Health Department (or your doctor, of course).

State Mental Health Authority: This is the department charged with development of mental health facilities and their supervision, etc., within the state's borders. (See pp. 452-58 for list throughout the United States and territories.) The state Department of Health or the state Department of Welfare can also furnish a list of public and private hospitals, clinics, etc. Address both in the state capital.

National organizations: Be certain that whatever step you undertake is one which meets the approval of the two organizations most deeply concerned with mental illness, its prevention, and control. One is the privately supported organization, the National Association for Mental Health (1790 Broadway, New York City) and the other is the National Institute of Mental Health (Bethesda, Md.), part of our federal public health program. Both have educational literature and other information for distribution to the public.

SECURING THE RIGHT NURSE

Whether the sickness of an old person is physical or mental, if a nurse is needed she like the doctor, should be one who understands and likes elderly people. Generally, you can safely rely on the recommendation of a hospital or your physician. Or you can consult commercial agencies (called nurses' registries, listed in telephone books) or the group of registries approved by the state or district nurses' association, which are usually non-commercial. (See pp. 466-72 for list.)

If you need information on fees, licensing, laws, or have the anxious task of providing short- or long-term care for an older man or woman far away, you can consult the following:

Professional (registered) nurses' organizations: In each of the forty-eight states, the District of Columbia, Hawaii, and Alaska, there is a state nurses' association. This is broken down into district groups. Each is a unit of the national organization, the American Nurses' Association (2 Park Avenue, New York 16).

An official directory which lists the names and addresses of the state offices and their executives is published in January and August in *The Nursing World.* You can find this journal in medical libraries and in some public ones. Or you can write for a copy of the directory, obtained through the offices of the American Nurses' Association.

It may be simpler for you to apply to the state Health Department for the name and address of state organization officers. The latter can always give you the names of nurses' registries and any other information about nursing services you want to know, including public health nurses who visit homes.

Practical nurses' organizations: The movement toward licensing practical nurses is so recent that standards differ widely. If you are concerned on this score write the National Federation of Licensed Practical Nurses (250 West 57th Street, New York 19). That organization will tell you the situation in the state your older folk are in, and furnish the name of the state officers of practical nurse organizations.

A directory, listing these state offices and officers, is published semi-annually, January and July, in the *Nursing World* (67 West 44th Street, New York 18). You can write for a copy of the directory, or find it in medical and large public libraries. The state office will tell you where to secure practical nurses in the community.

SPECIAL AGENCIES FOR SPECIAL PROBLEMS

In addition to these traditional forms of help our complex civilization has had to set up organizations on a national, state, and local level to solve problems that bedevil the best of us at times. It is a mistake, a heritage from the days of "Lady Bountifuls" who carried baskets to the poor, to think that welfare agencies are designed only to meet the needs of the nearly penniless or the friendless. As their name implies, they exist to add to the well-being of all of us.

Millions of Americans save themselves heartache and, at the least, considerable time and effort, by making use of one or more of the following organizations. Even if you need nothing more than information, tap this resource.

Community Chests: There are between fifteen and sixteen hundred in the United States now and more form each year. If you want to find out whether one exists in a locality write the national organization, Community Chests and Councils of America (345 East 46th Street, New York, N. Y.).

A community chest is a cooperative organization of citizens and social welfare agencies and has two functions:

1. It raises funds each year for the agencies affiliated with it through a community-wide appeal.

2. It promotes the welfare and health of a community through coordinating existing programs, preventing duplication, conducting research, improving standards, developing better public understanding and support for social work, and so on.

Many Community Chests maintain an information service.

There you can tell your problem to a sympathetic interviewer, and be sure of being promptly directed to the *right* place to find a solution.

Since some communities in large cities have as many as seven hundred agencies, and even small ones thirty or forty, you can have an optimistic feeling about finding one that will meet a need.

Community Welfare Council: A Council—known under various names, such as a "Council of Social Agencies," "Health and Welfare Council," "Citizens' Councils," etc.—is an organization composed of public and private agencies, civic organizations, and individuals, determined to work together for the benefit of the entire community.

There are approximately five hundred and fifty of these Councils now, and they are on the increase. Most of them are in towns of more than 25,000 population, and many of them have an information service. (If the Council has one, the Community Chest will not.) A telephone call, a letter, or a personal visit will be a short cut to learning about any or all the facilities the aged can make use of in that particular place.

Now that the aged have come to the fore in our thinking, their health, recreation, housing, and employment are major interests of Community Welfare Councils. Sometimes they offer help directly; most of the time you will be guided to the agency or institution that is the proper one at that particular moment in an older person's life. Or if it doesn't exist where he lives, the Council's staff will find out about any which might be available to him in near-by communities.

Specifically, what can a Welfare Council do for you? These several queries, selected from a random batch of correspondence which came one morning to the information desk of one Council in a Midwestern city, indicates the kind of queries you can make and expect to have answered:

1. "My cousin wants to apply for Old Age Assistance but she is afraid her telephone will be considered a luxury. As she is semi-crippled and lives alone, how can she convince the authorities this is a necessity?"

2. "Grandfather is seventy-three. His wooden leg now prevents him from working at his own trade but he always had a knack for tinkering with furniture. He wants to solicit orders for painting and remodeling chairs, desks, tables, etc. from housewives. Is there a chance for him to support himself, at least partly, in this way? If so, how should he go about it?"

3. "I have a mother who wants to enter a home for the aged but my sister is opposed to it. Who can help us decide if this is the right thing for her now?"

4. "Aunt Ella wants to go to a nursing home but she has only a limited amount of money and so far none of those she's written to want her. Isn't there some place that will take her?"

How Aunt Ella found her nursing home is a good example of the way Councils work. The niece who wrote that query was referred by the information service to the local Family Service Society. The social worker from the agency who interviewed Aunt Ella and talked to the niece agreed that their solution was a good one, since Aunt Ella lived alone and had no one to take care of her. The niece had her own family and could not add an elderly invalid to it. The worker got in touch with the supervisor of nursing homes in the county Welfare Department. This official knows where vacancies are on any day in the homes approved by his department. As a result of the joint action, Aunt Ella was accepted in a home within a short time. She finds it well suited to her temperament, her illness, and her pocketbook, and is on the way to recovery.

Left to themselves, the family would have continued to "shop around," and without knowing just what to do or where to look, might have landed Aunt Ella in a place which would have done her harm, or at least, made her no better. The niece admits that without the Council's intervention it would never have occurred to her or her aunt to go to the Family Service Society for help.

PRIVATE WELFARE AGENCIES

Too many of us are like this family. In our thinking we are still back in the days when private philanthropy was devoted to helping the needy with cash grants. In our time the job of financial relief has been taken over by public agencies which we all support through taxes. Private agencies turn their skills to giving other kinds of help to those who can pay part, or all of the cost, as well as to those who cannot pay at all.

This change is reflected in the names of agencies. The national organization which used to be called the Family *Welfare* Association of America is now the Family *Service* Association of America. Many of its two hundred and fifty member agencies in communities throughout the country have changed their own names to reflect the same trend from old-time "charity" to recognition that a family problem can be urgent even if there is not a strained income.

Service for a fee: If you cannot pay, the kind of aid you will receive is no different than that given Mr. or Mrs. Goldrocks. Nevertheless, as Clark Blackburn, Executive Director of the Family Service Association of America, says, "Paying a fee actually makes it easier for most of us to ask for help. By paying even a small amount of money we assert our freedom of action. We're buying, not begging. Also, we tend to put more value on service we've paid for than we do on even the most expert assistance if it is free."(2)

Fee-paying is a comparatively recent innovation, and not all agencies have it. (See pp. 463-65 for list of those who do.) However, the practice is growing. Where it does not exist, feel free to go to any community agency and ask for help. If it will make you feel better, say you will make a contribution toward its budget. (Just as you probably would if you were taken to a hospital's free ward after an accident.)

Fees are often arranged on a sliding scale, according to the income of the applicant. (This is what physicians try to do when they base bills on a rough calculation of what the patient can pay so the modest income class won't be penalized.) The range is generally between fifty cents to $10 for a single visit to secure professional advice, the latter sum reckoned as actually covering the cost of that service. (This again has a parallel in the medical field. The hospital-room fees that may seem exorbitant actually cover the cost of patient care in only a few cases.)

Whether you look to one of the sectarian agencies—such as

the Catholic Charities, the Jewish Social Service, or the Protestant Family Agency, which exist under some variation of this name in all cities, or whether you approach the Red Cross or the Salvation Army, you should feel no more hesitation than if you were going to a hospital to have an appendix out. In fact, the relationship between a social worker and her client is as intimate as that between a physician and his patient, and as confidential.

If you have doubts that you belong in the waiting-room note that the Family Counselling Centers of the Jewish Social Service Association in New York have had more than a half million clients over a period of five years. Among them are housewives, factory workers, stenographers, ex-service men, plumbers, teachers, artists, musicians, physicians, and scientists. This roll-call could be duplicated in any other agency, perhaps not in numbers, but in the company you would keep.

The procedure: You can go to any welfare agency and ask for an appointment. If you don't know which one to choose, or can't find the right one in the telephone book, ask the Community Chest, Council of Social Agencies or, if these don't exist, a hospital, a minister, or for that matter, the police department.

One visit may be enough in some cases, but it is likely to take more. Casework is the handling of an individual problem; and problems that have taken a long time to develop cannot be unraveled in a hurry. Yours may require from one to several months.

When you or the older person call or write for an appointment, you may be put on a waiting list if the matter is not considered an emergency. The need is far greater than the capacity to fill it, as in practically every other field which touches the old. But when your time comes, you will be received by a social worker assigned to you, in a private room. What you say and what she says to you there will be held inviolate. She will not discuss your affairs with anyone but her supervisor in staff conference (just as a doctor talks over a medical problem with a specialist called in on one of his cases). Specialists will be called in here, too, if they are needed, whether from the field of medicine, homemaking, vocational training, finances—whatever is required.

A social worker is not a difficult person to talk to. Among

the essential qualifications for her job are a warm personality, a genuine liking for people and an interest in their lives. Often she will be a highly skilled, carefully trained specialist. She has helped many people like yourself with similar troubles or questions. She will know how to deal with problems in human relations, but she will offer no pat solutions. There are no sulfa drugs that work magical cures for strains of everyday life, but there are ways of meeting situations and she will know how and when to take the proper steps. If she cannot help you she will know where you can get help.

The "typical" problem does not exist but you may recognize similarities to your own in this one. The manner in which it was handled will show you that any social agency can offer you guidance and counsel if you are a person with need for it, regardless of race, color or creed, or the condition of your pocketbook.

The problem Mr. Nevins, an advertising executive, brought to a Family Counselling Center concerned his anxiety and guilt about his elderly mother. He was about to be transferred to another city and he didn't know what to do, since she had lived with him and his wife since the first of their three children was born. In the beginning things had gone well. But when the babies grew into toddlers the elder Mrs. Nevins quarreled constantly with the wife about discipline, and from that turned to criticizing the way she kept the home. At the time Mr. Nevins came to talk things over his young wife was threatening to divorce her husband. Mr. Nevins, out of his desperation, said this in his first interview:

"If only Margaret and I could start over again, alone, in a completely new place! I think our marriage would have a chance to succeed. But how can I leave mother behind? How can I hurt her that much when I am her only child?"

Skillful questioning by the social worker elicited the fact that Mrs. Nevins, Sr., had a number of cronies in the town, and also a small income, sufficient to support her if her son would supplement it a little. The counsellor at that point suggested that the mother be asked to come in and talk over her side of the story.

"Maybe," said the worker, "your mother is as miserable as you and your wife are. Maybe she'd like to start over, too."

The son didn't think so, but he agreed to mention a visit to the Counselling Center to his mother. To his surprise, she leaped at the idea. Within five minutes of her entry into the pleasantly informal office some days later, she said this:

"I'm so glad I have a chance to talk this over with someone. How can I break the news to my son I'd like at last to live my own life? After all, at sixty-nine I'm a little too old to keep on changing diapers; but my son and his wife depend on me so!"

The upshot was that the counsellor helped Mrs. Nevins, Sr., to "break the news" to her son, and the latter aided his mother to complete arrangements to live with a semi-invalid friend. She is quite happy there, dominating the household, as she did her son's, but much more satisfactorily for everybody concerned. Now, when she visits her son for a few weeks once a year, everything goes smoothly. She comes back praising "my daughter Margaret" and the change a move to another environment has made in her!

SPECIFIC HELP FOR THE AGED

There will be more specialized agencies in large cities for the obvious reason that there are more people to use them but you can find help anywhere.

In a large city: There may be a special Bureau for the Aged, under sectarian or other auspices. Inquire at the Council of Welfare Agencies or Community Chest. Such a bureau co-ordinates information about homes for the aged, recreational facilities, nursing homes, adult education classes, etc. It often employs a social worker representing several homes for the aged. She will interview the elderly in their own homes, to get a first-hand knowledge of whether they really need an old people's home. If the answer is "no," she'll find other ways to keep them out of it.

Large cities are beginning to see the rise of special "home finding" services, established on a commercial basis by trained social workers. The staff, for a sizable fee, will find new living arrangements for handicapped older people, whether this is in the physical or emotional field, and aid them to adjust to the new environment.

They usually advertise, but the Council of Social Agencies will know if the service exists.

In small towns and villages: There will not be so many places to turn to or so many agencies working on the same problems, but on the other hand, neighborly feeling is more strongly developed, even among organizations.

The Community Chests and Councils of America suggest that if a problem concerns older family members one or more of the following agencies should be consulted. Not all of them will exist in any one place and their functions sometimes overlap but you will find some one of them equipped to help:

Social Service Bureau (which may be known locally by another name; ask a hospital or Red Cross chapter); Department of Public Welfare; Young Men's Christian Association or Young Men's Hebrew Association (both of which have departments interested in the entire family and its problems between generations); general hospitals and clinics (and of course, the family doctor); county hospital; public health nurse; Red Cross; fraternal or civic organizations (such as the Rotary or Kiwanis clubs, the library, etc.); Travelers' Aid Society.

If your concern is with chronic illness, add to this list the County Health Department and the Public Health Officer (which the department can direct you to); the Blue Cross or Blue Shield Insurance Plans.

In strictly rural areas: There are few privately supported casework agencies and neither mental hygiene clinics nor public health nurses are matters that can be taken for granted. But there are Home Bureaus, the Grange, the Farm Bureau, the county nurse, all of whom play a considerable role, along with churches and schools, in making life easier for older people. Even volunteer firemen's organizations, the town or county clerk, or in a pinch, a committee man of any of the political parties, will at least take the time and have the knowledge to direct you, or see that help comes to an older person if he cannot get it for himself.

An example of this warmheartedness that is not unique is the story of the rural pastor who was determined to make older farmers' lives less dreary. He was convinced that a new life could open for them once they were free of "nose-to-the-grindstone" pressure. To prove it to men who have worked from dawn to dusk all their adult lives was another matter. However, with the slogan, "Living is learning and you're never too old to learn," he started organizing craft classes. Young folk today are the beneficiaries of old folks' "old time" ways. One of the most successful cases is that of Mr. G. who two years ago tried to drown himself because he thought he was no use to anyone any more. Now he is one of the most contented "after school" teachers in the county. In his youth in Norway, he had gone to sea. He teaches eager inland boys who never saw the ocean the art of nautical knots and the way to make tiny ships' models fitted into bottles.

PLACE OF PUBLIC AGENCIES

Whether you live on a farm or in a city, make the fullest use of the departments of government—federal, state, county or municipal. Because a great many people still labor under misapprehension about them, it is worth re-stating that you live in a country which has a growing sense of responsibility toward *all* its tax-paying citizens, not just the unfortunate ones. To cheat yourself—and perhaps some helpless old person—of help when you can get it from these sources is to play the ostrich.

Department of Public Welfare: It exists everywhere, on a municipal or county basis. In sections of the country where privately supported welfare agencies are few or non-existent, it takes over their functions, though its primary function is to dispense financial aid.

Old Age Assistance investigators, in particular, are not prying, suspicious women or men, out to prevent old people from getting more than their due share of what the law allows. Very often they are well-trained social workers, friendly, eager to be helpful, and frequently they stand as buffer between a harsh world and the sometimes harsher treatment of an older individual's own family. They can and do give counsel. They are well able to furnish information and find ingenious means (within the law) to supplement the sometimes scanty financial help. Since they must work closely with all other agencies, the department is an excellent place to call when you are at a loss where to turn next.

Mrs. Pierce, turned down for Old Age Assistance, but helped to find herself, is an example of the not unusual interest in all old people that exists in a well-run department.

Mrs. Pierce had lived all her life in a small town till she came to spend her last years with her daughter Gladys, a middle-aged clerk in a modest store in New York. The crowds and the traffic terrified Mrs. Pierce. From a busy, helpful woman, she became a morose one, sitting idly all day, neglecting her appearance and her daughter's apartment.

When Gladys was told her mother was ineligible for Old Age Assistance she cried bitterly. She told the welfare worker her hope had been to supplement her wages so she could hire a companion to keep her mother company. But the story didn't end there.

"Was your mother a good churchwoman in her home town?" she was asked.

"Oh, yes!" Gladys answered. "Mama was one of the founders of the Ladies' Aid Society. Here she won't even go to a church service!"

The social worker advised the harried daughter to let her mother know there were vast opportunities to do volunteer work in a city and to show her some of them. She took time not only to make out a list but to make appointments for the two women to visit some of the settlements and hospitals during evenings and weekends.

Today the city no longer holds terror for Mrs. Pierce. Laden with small gifts, many of which she makes herself, she takes the long bus and ferry trip by herself to Welfare Island. Rain or shine, in cold weather and in hot, she makes semi-weekly visits to sick old men and women in the wards of the great municipal hospital. To many of them she is their only friend. Mrs. Pierce is again a cheerful, busy woman, important to herself and other people.

Jobs and job insurance: If it is a job a man or woman wants more than anything else, be sure and encourage him to register with state employment services, of course, but go beyond that.

The federal Department of Labor in Washington, D. C., and

its Bureau of Labor Statistics, have information they will send anyone on general working conditions through the country, and trends in employment, and possibilities (both for old and young). For data closer home, send to the state Department of Labor in the capital city.

The Council of Social Agencies may be able to refer older workers to vocational testing and guidance services; the Chamber of Commerce will know job opportunities in both new and old lines of work.

The state employment office, or one of its branches, is the place to go if an elderly person thinks he may be entitled to unemployment insurance.

Aid to war veterans: An aged veteran of any war is not always aware that he, his spouse, and his children, are eligible for many special benefits. They range from hospitalization and insurance to homes for aged ex-service men.

Information can be obtained from a variety of sources. Local chapters of veterans' organizations such as the American Legion, and Veterans of Foreign Wars, have special officers assigned to answer questions on these matters. Or the U. S. Veterans Administration in Washington will supply the address of its nearest office.

Financial aid: If you have a relative, male or female, who has worked for other people for pay, get him to go to the nearest Social Security field office as soon as he is sixty-five. What he will find out there is whether he has worked in an employment covered by Old Age and Survivors' Insurance. (It is a constantly amazing fact to those who compile statistics that older people, unaware of the changes in the Social Security law, do not ask for benefits they are entitled to until prodded.) The office will be listed under "U. S. Government" in the telephone directory, or the address can be found through any post office official.

If your relative is impoverished and needs Old Age Assistance, any town or county clerk will know the address of the county Welfare Department or a city Department of Welfare if he fails to find them in the telephone book.

Aid to the physically handicapped: The main office of the state Division of Vocational Rehabilitation will be in the capital; so will the state agency serving the blind. Both usually have branch offices, the addresses of which are sent to anyone who asks.

LOCATING OTHER AIDS

In other fields—housing, recreation, adult education, etc.—if local facilities cannot be easily found, write to the national organizations. Very often your own community will have groups working independently but securing information and guidance from national headquarters. (See pp. 472-74 for list of national organizations especially concerned with the aged.)

Local or long-distance information services of the telephone companies are always ready to help. A thorough acquaintance with a local telephone book will uncover a number of aids most of us need at some time or other. To find them in an emergency keep these points in mind:

Denominational and sectarian agencies: They are listed in telephone directories under the name of the supporting religion (Protestant, Catholic, Jewish, etc.).

Nursing homes: They will be listed under their own names, but in a classified public telephone directory, available in all large cities and in some towns, they appear under the general classification.

Adult education courses, school social services: See local Board of Education.

Extension services of state colleges and universities: Look under state listings in your telephone book if they have local campuses. Otherwise, you should write. Any school official at the Board of Education can supply you with addresses.

Hospitals: The information service of the telephone company will supply you with a number, or in an emergency connect you directly with the police (or fire) department for ambulance or other suddenly needed help. Otherwise look under "Hospital" in telephone directory. Use any local hospital as a referral point to find other medical and mental health services, addresses of clinics and medical social services.

There are other general sources of information you ought to know are available, though you may never need them:

Housing: Most types featuring aids for the elderly have to be considered experimental thus far but information about them is available from the Committee on the Hygiene of Housing. This is part of the American Public Health Association (1790 Broadway, New York 19, New York). Other information on up-to-date projects is available from the National Committee on the Aging of the National Social Welfare Assembly (345 East 46th Street, New York).

Diet and nutrition: As long as obesity is discouraged by the medical profession and abhorred by the fashion-minded, the pseudo-scientists will make the most of it. To protect the public against unscientific approaches of the exciting, glamorous, always expensive, and sometimes dangerous methods of quackery, be sure any older obese individual knows these sources of help:

1) *A physician* is the best person to prescribe and approve a program of reducing, though it is a dull and undramatic approach to the problem. Information regarding questionable products and unethical practices is made available to him through the American Medical Association.

2) The staffs of state Health and Agriculture Departments are eager to protect the public against products and people who may jeopardize health. This goes beyond the question of obesity, of course.

3) The Federal Pure Food and Drug Administration (Washington, D. C.) is charged with enforcement of the Food, Drug and Cosmetic Act and other laws to promote the purity and honest labeling of all foods and drugs.

4) The Federal Trade Commission (also in Washington, D. C.) has jurisdiction over advertising to prevent the dissemination of false or misleading claims for foods, drugs, cosmetics or devices sold in interstate commerce.

Whatever source you consult, remember that though the aged have problems they are not very different, except perhaps in degree of intensity, from those of any other group. In community planning it is worth reiterating that we are approximately in the same position we were forty or forty-five years ago in planning for the care of children. What has been done in the children's field can be done with the old. Whatever means you yourself use to overcome his economic problems, his physical or mental problems, emotional difficulties, and adjustment to a changing life situation, the best service you can render is to help an older person help himself.

NOTES TO CHAPTER XIV

(1) Robert T. Monroe, M.D. "The Medical Skills and the Services Needed by Old People." Address made at the conference of the Welfare Federation of Cleveland, Ohio, Mar. 17, 1949.

(2) Ross, Walter and Stratton, Lynn. "Where You Can Get Help." *Redbook Magazine,* Oct., 1952. P. 92.

CHAPTER FIFTEEN

WHAT'S NEW FOR THE OLD

If the nineteenth was the century of the child, the twentieth is unmistakably going to be the century of old people.

It is no small matter for a nation the size of ours to record a gain of twenty-one years in the course of a half century in the average life expectancy of a new-born infant.(1) Each victory in the ceaseless battles waged by medical science adds a little bit more to life expectancy. Till recently this meant only that men and women were reaching the evening of life in larger numbers. Now it is evident that the evening itself is lengthening.

But the plain, hard fact our generation has yet to face fully is that working and living conditions of our new masses of aged people concern not just the Townsendites, but all of us, if we do not want the problem to engulf us.

A prominent speaker, invited to address one of those conferences dealing with problems of the old, which are springing up at every crossroads, was asked what he considered the most important trend today.

"The most pronounced trend, so far as the aging are concerned," he answered dryly, "is the trend to talk incessantly about them."

It is obvious even to the most unobservant that there are a considerable number of radio and television programs dealing with what life is or ought to be like after sixty or seventy or eighty. And articles and books on the proper way human beings, as well as wine, should age, flood every bookshop. Nevertheless, underneath all the torrent of words, there is a tremendous ferment of activity.

It permeates all areas of the country and all walks of life. Some of it is froth, but a good deal is the yeast which will affect the lives of your aged people in the next decade or two, and your own old age a score or more of years from now.

Statisticians, social scientists, economists, medical men—all of them bristle with facts and figures. They talk in terms of a life expectancy of at least seventy-eight years by 1975, and of the old who will form eleven per cent of the total population then.

The sheer weight of these numbers predicted with such confidence is looked on fearfully in some quarters, hopefully in others. To keep pace with them all sorts of experiments and services are cropping up in a feverish effort to make old age more bearable, more satisfying, or even more glamorous—at least by the time we ourselves arrive there.

After a long period of thinking about the aging person as just somebody in need of a pension, we are beginning to discover him as a human being with all the needs that other people have. Gerontology, the study of the aging process, is relatively new, but increasingly important. Another word that we are going to hear a lot more about is "geriatrics," the study of the diseases in old age. Men and women who will reach late maturity in a few years will see their geriatrician just as a child goes to a pediatrician now, or an expectant mother to her obstetrician. Nevertheless, the present accelerated rate of aging of our total population is posing enormous and perplexing problems.

LONGEVITY IN THE FUTURE

The one major fact that will affect any solution we dare to evolve is whether the almost explosive increase in life expectancy since 1920 will continue. How much longer we are going to live is a question of moment to everyone who is not a misanthrope. The best answer we can find is that the scientists have no final answer. At present the average man dies at about seventy. He is a victim of what Shakespeare called "the slings and arrows of outrageous fortune . . . the thousand natural shocks the flesh is heir to."

But those "natural shocks" that are most important in late

maturity now—cancer, the heart and blood diseases—may be as much under control in fifty years as the infectious diseases have been in the last half century. It is this last fact which chiefly accounts for the breathtaking decline of fifty per cent in the death rate since 1900.

We are all going to the hospital more often at the right time; and most of us are learning to pay attention to ailments when they can be cured or halted in their first stages. Both medical care and public health facilities are continuing to spread. All these are big points in favor of a long life.

In 1919, when the average length of life was only fifty-six years, Alfred Scott Warthin published a carefully documented study of old age. In it he predicted, "If the average age of longevity be raised to sixty years, this will probably be as high as the rate can be raised. That it can be raised to sixty-five or seventy-five years is impossible on the face of it."

Less than a quarter century after this scholarly verdict was given, the "impossible" had happened.

Dr. Martin Gumpert, a geriatrician who believes we may stretch the average life expectancy about ten or twelve years more, says this: "Whatever happens to the average life span, the centenarian will be a familiar neighbor on our streets and in our homes, and no longer a freak of nature to be interviewed and questioned as to how on earth he managed to survive so long."

For the next generation, at least, an average life expectancy around the age of eighty is where the scientific imagination seems to stop. But that there will be active, vigorous men and women of eighty, eighty-five, and ninety as a substantial group in every community, there is no doubt.

GOALS TO BE ATTAINED

At the beginning of World War II New York City's Welfare Council issued a study confirming the tenet that old age in itself is not a social problem since it is natural and inevitable.(2) It was recognized that the conditions which surround the aged, including the attitude of younger people, create the problem. The next steps in acquiring sufficient knowledge and understanding for wise and effective action, not only for the individual, but the society he must live in, were outlined as these:

"1. Casting aside all preconceived ideas about the disabilities of the aged and starting afresh in the appraisal of each old person's possibilities and needs.

2. Devising ways and means by which each old person will be encouraged to use all his capacities for his own support and for his contribution to the common life of the community.

3. Provision of a wide range of possibilities in living arrangements so that the varying requirements of aged persons for protection and care can be nicely matched.

4. Extending the range of influence of these attitudes and ideas so that they will be more generally applied by families, employers and friends."

These ultimate goals still remain to be realized, not in New York City alone, but all over the nation. We need more facilities for better medical care and recreation. We need more understanding of the emotional needs of the aged. We need to find new ways of living for old people. We need to learn to care for them with more skill and common sense. We must conquer the unemployment spectre that still haunts millions of old folks. Above all, we need to learn how to differentiate physiological age from chronological age so that we can regard it as a reasonable and rewarding part of everyone's destiny.

Making our communities better living places for both aging and aged people is no simple matter. It is a challenge worthy of our most intelligent and best qualified endeavors. It will require some physical improvements, with local adaptations, community by community, of traditional resources. It will certainly require some drastic changes in attitudes and policies. It will not be easy to uproot deeply imbedded prejudices and even more deep-seated indifference. Some still lack the knowledge that the problem has overtones which affect the lives of every one of us, no matter what our age.

Some partial or personal solutions will have to be improvised around the pressing needs of hapless individuals who cannot wait for perfection. So what is happening today in a number of areas may not necessarily be final or the ultimate solution. Nevertheless, we are making progress. If we examine some of the current trends we can get a fairly clear picture which mirrors tomorrow for older people still alive, and even a shadowy glimpse into our own future.

THRESHOLD OF A NEW ERA

One thing you can be sure of. We are definitely on the threshold of a new era. The most significant evidence of that fact is the quickening of tempo, not of philanthropic services of the Lady Bountiful type, but of sober federal and state action.

The first milestone was marked when the federal government set up a special Committee on Aging and Geriatrics a few years ago as part of the then Federal Security Administration. The second occurred in 1950. The Committee called together the first National Conference on Aging ever held in this country. Eight hundred social workers, ministers, physicians, and other community leaders met during the dog-days in Washington, D. C., to consider the problem of the old from a national point of view. They went home determined to translate into action the inspiration and information they had gained. The immediate result was a rash of state and regional conferences, more in the next twelve months than in all the preceding years. Two years later, when the governmental body called its second conference, this time of delegates from thirty-two states and one territory, fifteen states reported they already had established Commissions or Committees on the Aging.

New York has the credit of being the first to attempt a full-scale program. Senator Thomas C. Desmond, Chairman of its State Joint Legislative Committee on the Aging, says: "Granted a measure of stability, it is clear our states within the next decade are going to make old age a period not to be feared but to be enjoyed."

STATE AND NATIONAL ACTION

That millennium remains to be seen. State commissions and committees, like mayors' committees, and organizations of just plain citizens, still speak and write about the "problem aged" in much the same way we used to talk about "problem children." Only a few have moved into the second phases of trying to do something about the problems.

By now there are legislative commissions or committees either functioning through special laws or by appointment of the governor or municipal authority. There are also citizens' groups, or a mixed body of all three. About half the states with a large population of the over-sixty-five group—such as New York, California, Florida—have made genuine attempts to define the needs of their aged according to their environment, and assuage them. It is safe to predict that as we have more and more old people scattered through the country, the rest of the country will fall in line.

That means, of course, that the over-all national picture is uneven. We have some states which have set up adult hygiene or geriatric bureaus; a few others expect to raise the level of old people's homes and their nursing and boarding facilities by stricter licensing and inspection. Still fewer have tried out visiting housekeeper or visiting nurse plans on a limited basis. Others function, or try to function, in all fields. New Hampshire, for example, with the largest percentage of men and women over sixty-five of any state in the nation in proportion to population, has a Committee on Gerontology which was formed for a year-long study of the problem. Rhode Island has rehabilitation and employment consultants to boost the morale and better the chances of old job-hunters. Illinois is one of the states which is proud of turning antiquated almshouses into modern infirmaries.

All of this, and more, shows a growing recognition that some needs of older people can only be met on a community level or require national or state aid. If your state has lagged behind, politicians will tell you the way to get results is to put "pressure groups" to work. Oscar R. Ewing, formerly Federal Security Administrator, at the time the first National Conference on Aging was held said it in another way:

"The real effort," he pointed out, "if it is to be successful, cannot and must not rest on the shoulders of the federal government. It must be developed by a combination of state and local governments, private organizations, employers, labor unions, and individuals who will work to create a practical, down-to-earth program —a program that will help to make it possible for adult members of the community to approach old age with less fear. . . ."

We don't need to be frightened at the role we, as citizens, ought to play in the future of old people. One group doesn't *have* to be a burden on the other. The thing to remember is that basically old people's needs are no different than other people's. Don't we all want financial security, a decent place to live, someone to care about us? Wouldn't we all like to have a chance to have good health, to be useful, and feel free and independent?

For anyone who wants help, as well as inspiration, in rousing his own community, there are numerous organizations willing to apply the spur. (See pp. 435-37 for list.) The Adult Education Association, for instance, has a committee which functions solely to resolve the knotty problem of what kind of programs best suit older people and how they can be launched and supported. The National Vocational Guidance Association has established a committee which studies the problem of the older worker; another of its committees considers preparation for retirement. Scientific groups, also, like the American Gerontological Society, hold yearly meetings, not only reporting their researches in medicine, biology and social sciences to fellow-scientists but opening their meetings to the public. Since they are well advertised and publicized, this is a contact to pursue when it comes your local way.

You can always get guidance on how to start the ball rolling with kindred spirits in your own community. One major source of information is the federal Committee on Aging and Geriatrics, now part of the U. S. Department of Health, Education, and Welfare. This is a clearing-house for information and a consultative agency for state groups, legislative committees, or for any citizen. If you need encouragement to make a start, you will find it in a report of the national Community Chests and Councils of America. When the membership was surveyed in 1950 to find out which communities had committees to integrate the lives of the elderly into the local scene, eighty-three reported affirmatively. This was in sharp contrast to the mere five who in 1938 thought the aged worthy of special community planning.

OUTLOOK FOR BETTER HEALTH

Whatever else a longer life span brings, we can be optimistic about our chances to have sound bodies for a much longer time.

In the medical field the present has a way of blending very rapidly with the future. Much of the elemental groundwork now being done may emerge as the concrete accomplishments of tomorrow. It is not too daring to say that soon old age will no longer be the age least understood.

Geriatrics is expected to do as much for the aged as pediatrics has done for children. Dr. William B. Kountz, Director of the Division of Gerontology at Washington University, presents the geriatric viewpoint in these words: . . . "Arteriosclerosis and degenerative diseases in general present a biological problem not unlike the problem that the pediatric branch of medicine has overcome. Specific diseases such as diabetes and cancer are simply manifestations of an exhaustive process which to a certain extent can be modified."(3)

These are the sharp pointers which indicate the way we shall probably go, though any one of these new pioneering developments as yet has a painfully limited range:

Geriatric clinics: One of the strong recommendations made at the first National Conference on Aging called for establishment of geriatric clinics in connection with hospitals or health departments. It was felt such clinics could serve old people very much as child welfare stations serve our youngsters by teaching their parents preventive health-practices. In old people it is a case of helping to postpone chronic illness of a grave nature by detecting it and treating it in the incipient stages.

Over a number of years the geriatric clinic of Peter Bent Brigham Hospital in Boston has proved the case. It attracts the elderly, particularly those of small means, *before* they have serious impairments. By guiding them to a more healthful way of life, it has undoubtedly reduced the number of hospital beds that they might otherwise have required.

Home-care medical plan: The idea behind this new medical development is two-fold. As originated at Montefiore Hospital for the Chronically Ill in New York City, and subsequently followed in several other large cities, it means giving the patient, whose disease is not in an acute stage, hospital care *at home*. At the same time it releases hospital beds for those clamoring to use them. (Since the Commission on Hospital Care has estimated that during the next fifteen or twenty years we shall need about 2,500,000 hospital beds—exactly a million more than we have now, and two-thirds of those will be for the chronically sick—this last viewpoint is not minor.)

For the individual who can receive this new kind of hospital care it has proved a boon. In most cases, the fact that he is taken out of the hospital atmosphere, and knows he is well enough to be in his own bed or wheel-chair, boosts his morale immediately. In many instances, even among incurable cases, it has been known to improve the physical condition.

The plans in New York, Chicago, Philadelphia, Washington, D. C., and elsewhere involve sending a physician—usually the one the patient has been accustomed to in the hospital—regularly to the home. Visiting nurses and visiting housekeepers and occupational therapists, as needed, are arranged for and a hospital social worker helps the family make adjustments. The patient knows he will be re-admitted without question if his condition later warrants removal to the hospital. An ambulance is sent to take him back not only then, but for any X-rays, special injections, or other necessary treatments. Since all this costs just one third of the amount needed to care for him in a hospital, community interest is likely to grow.

Rehabilitation centers: The calculations of the Commission on Hospital Care are that the 300,000 beds needed for the chronically sick (many of whom will be old) in the next score of years would cost society $3,333,000,000 to build at present prices, and $750,000,000 annually to maintain and operate. There are developments, however, that may save society the job of digging quite so far into our war-worn pockets.

We have had ample demonstration that with proper treatment few older people need to be permanently bedfast whatever their affliction. The enormous strides made whenever the seven-league boots of rehabilitation are used to their utmost, mean that treatment ends only when the disabled individual actually returns to his daily duties at his highest attainable skill.

Rehabilitation service pays dividends to the community in financial terms as well as in human happiness, so there is hope that more federal and state funds will eventually be appropriated for it. The cost of caring for a sixty-year-old diabetic amputee in one good infirmary, for example, amounts to more than $30,000 at today's rates, if he lives another twenty years. For an investment less than the cost of a single year's care he could be rehabilitated and returned to employment. This is not mere theory. In the Allegheny County Institution, just outside of Pittsburgh, at least half of a group of old patients who had the benefit of an effective rehabilitation program were able to resume their former places in the community. Many others were restored to a self-respecting state of self-care within the institution.

Multiple screening: The successful use of community-wide chest X-ray campaigns for tuberculosis detection, mass diabetes investigations and cancer detection clinics hold out hope for another type of "multiple screening," still in the pilot stage.

The U. S. Public Health Service, in cooperation with state, local, and private health organizations, has experimented with a special technique for "one-visit" testing through clinics. It is believed that supposedly healthy persons can be examined for a group of possible disorders—anemia, diabetes, faulty vision, glaucoma, hearing loss, heart disease, high blood pressure, obesity, tuberculosis, syphilis, etc. If the premise is correct, the cost of regular, periodic examinations can be cut down, and the time for examinations reduced to about thirty minutes. This type of precaution, not now available to the great mass of old people, may prolong life by uncovering and treating incipient illness; what is usually even more important to the person and to his family, it may prevent long-time invalidism and helpless dependency.(4)

TREATMENT OF MENTAL ILLNESS

In the field of mental illness the health picture remains dark for only one reason. The problem for the future, as now, is one of replenishing the present short supply of psychiatric personnel through research and training, supplying of suitable equipment chiefly in state mental hospitals, and organization of more mental health clinics in communities.

Stated in those terms, the solution amounts to little more than overcoming indifference to a problem most of us are reluctant to believe can ever become personal.

If you already have a mentally sick old person in the family, you won't need to be convinced we should have more training programs for ward attendants. It is they who give the major part of care to the hospitalized. At the Menninger Foundation in Topeka, Kansas, a start has been made. Graduates of a year's course went into various states to help set up similar training programs whose chief purpose is to dignify the status of ward attendants and better their techniques.

You may even be willing to write your Congressman to urge him to help get more appropriations. There is urgent need to strengthen the provisions of the National Mental Health Act. Passed in 1946, it offers a powerful weapon for research and training in the psychiatric field—if there are funds for it.

Or you may want to move "heaven and earth" to get your own legislature to appropriate sufficient money to better conditions in your state hospitals so there is a staff large enough to make use of treatment methods already known to be successful in many cases.

But we shall have to go much further before we have taken the right first step—offering to old people the advice and guidance which will ward off any necessity of mental institutions.

The brightest gleam for the future is that the stigma attached to mental illness is gradually fading. Today, more persons are seeking psychiatric help than can find it at means they can afford. It is likely that their number, under the mounting stresses of the twentieth century, will not lessen.

To meet the need of even our present population, Dr. William C. Menninger and other eminent psychiatrists believe that the average community of 100,000 people can and should support a mental health clinic operating on a full-time basis. They feel it should have a staff of a psychiatrist, psychologist, two psychiatric social workers, and the necessary clerical personnel.

On this basis at least 1,500 such clinics are still lacking in the United States. Until we get around to establishing them we cannot say that we can keep older people's frustrations from setting them on a course which may lead downhill.

EMPLOYMENT SECURITY

What do old people worry about most? When the Broome County Social Planning Council in New York made a survey the results indicated that *money shortage,* or the fear of it, was paramount in the over-sixty-five group. Sixty per cent said they did not have enough "to live the life they considered normal" and just twelve per cent were working, part-time. What happens to those who have to pare costs today will surely happen tomorrow. In Broome County nineteen per cent cut down on food, thirty-two per cent on clothes, thirty-one per cent on recreation, nine per cent on medical care, eight per cent on housing. Only eight per cent could report they had made no change in their standard of living after their sixty-fifth birthday.(5)

The greatest hope for a change lies in a paradox. There will be more and more men and women capable of working when they are past sixty-five. There will be fewer and fewer of them in the labor force of the future, if we follow the present path of their decline as part of our working population. Business leaders are uneasily aware that if they are not able to solve this double-headed problem it will become a Frankenstein that will put an unbearable burden on those who must support the idle old.

At business and industrial conferences the burning issue centers around two problems. The first is whether the "official" retirement age should be raised beyond sixty-five to permit those who want to work to continue as long as they are able. The second is whether retirement, when it comes, should be on a flexible, sliding scale to enable those who are unwilling to retire to find other jobs when they are no longer able to hold their old ones.

We can tell just how far the pendulum is likely to swing if we examine some tentative efforts put out as earnest feelers especially by "big business." These are chiefly trial balloons sent up by large companies. Some have the wisdom to realize that an enormously increased number of unemployed older people are a menace to themselves and the national economy. Small, independent businesses may have owners who realize this fact, too, but are either without the means, or have too few employees in the upper-age brackets to try what in many cases are still expensive experiments. Among the tentative efforts are:

Pre-retirement counselling: So far this is confined to a few large companies but it is spreading. Its object is to help workers find avocations, or new vocations; make psychological adjustment to increased leisure before it arrives; secure help with investments or housing or preparation for a changed state of health. Sometimes this is done through individual interviews with personnel employees; sometimes through group interchange among the employees themselves, along the lines of "group therapy" in psychiatric practice.

Retirement ages: This is a bomb-shell which explodes every time the question arises. Much that is being done with an eye to the future is of the trial-and-error variety. At the Dodge-Chrysler automobile plant, for instance, one division was organized so that it included only light jobs suited to the capacities of older workers. But the old people didn't like it. *They* preferred being treated like everybody else, and not set apart. The upshot was that the original plan was abandoned and older workers were re-assigned to lighter tasks within their own departments where they worked alongside of younger people.

The weight of opinion still favors a "normal" retirement period set at sixty-five years for men and sixty years for women in most pension plans. But there have been tiny cracks made in the wall. The Prudential Life Insurance Company, for example, recently raised the possible retirement ages of its women workers to sixty-five years; a practice followed elsewhere permits the severance period of employment for both men and women to advance to sixty-seven or sixty-eight, or be entirely flexible.

A clue to future practices may be found in the personnel policies in two large plants. In one a worker is retained in his job as long as he can produce as much as could be expected from a replacement. In the other, the rule is to permit workers to return if they find after a trial period that they do not like their leisure and are able to work as much as two days a week. (The latter practice is one which some strong labor unions have been able to convince management is wise, especially where established pensions are too small to provide a decent living.)

PROBLEMS TO BE SOLVED

There is general recognition in enlightened quarters that chronological age is not a satisfactory method of determining retirement. Yet the problem of what to do about it is complex. There is, for instance, always and forever the pressure from young people. They cannot be expected to wait in the year 2000 (or the year 1955) for promotion to jobs their elders have held for years.

There is also the perennial question of businesses so small they have no fixed retirement policies. Finally, there is the ticklish question of independent workers, and of professional men and women —teachers, ministers, for instance. They always have worked on too low salaries to save appreciably for retirement. They retire on too small pensions, if they have any at all, to keep from anything but genteel, slow starvation.

We have a few gleams of light which may be permanent lamps:

Self-Help: This is a pious term which has had an interesting interpretation in the educational field. Led by the New School for Social Research in New York City, a few enterprising colleges have invited retiring professors from other institutions to continue teaching and research or give consultative service. This has been a *coup.* Through it small liberal arts colleges, particularly, can afford distinguished scholars whom they might not otherwise be able to offer their student bodies. Men and women, on the other hand, who had to leave their institutions through automatic retirement clauses, can continue in their chosen work.

There is as yet no evidence that other fields have seized on this method of employing high-grade intelligence which does not decline as fast as the ability to climb mountains or to box.

In heavy industry, on the other hand, there is some clear indication of hope for highly skilled older workers. Studies made in this country and in England prove that they can successfully handle jobs at their old trades if the time-stress is lessened. The Industrial Management Council of Rochester reported to New York's Joint Legislative Committee on Aging that a number of concerns were using labor-saving equipment—fork-lifts, electric hoists, etc. —which enabled many older "persons who because of physical limitations would not have been able to perform the work to continue at it." The report emphasized the fact that very little job engineering needed to be done to meet declining physical capacities of older workers. (6)

Counselling: We have established, once for all, the fact that older applicants can get jobs if they can get help through vocational counselling adapted to them alone. The noteworthy experiment initiated by the Canadian National Employment Service in Toronto in 1947 showed that two-thirds of the applicants given special counselling secured employment almost immediately. One-half of the successful applicants were over sixty years old. The leading thinkers in the employment field believe that selective placement is the answer, such as has been highly successful in the case of handicapped workers and disabled veterans.

"Senior Employment Services" which try to find jobs for capable aged people, or re-train them to fit into ones that younger people hold, are presently limited to a few non-profit-making agencies which are sufficiently endowed not to worry about costs. By 1980, when the estimates indicate there might be over twenty million persons past sixty-five, the full-time part-time job hunt for the aged may have become the necessity which takes this service out of the "charitable" field.

Practical steps: A number of small steps reflect the new awareness that population changes will make permanent demands. A three-year study, for example, is planned by the New York Adult Education Council. It will try to determine how one hundred men and women in their forties and fifties can be helped to make realistic preparation for the 14.1 years, the 1953 expectation of life after age sixty-five. (7) One aspect will be how to earn supplementary income using old skills, or by learning less strenuous new ones.

Two versions of the same idea are already operating as pilot projects. They point to the same old story—older workers have diversified skills, knowledge, abilities, interests, and experience—and want to use them.

In Boston several industries have purchased a large building and have contracted for production of certain items at standard rates of pay. Only retired men will be employed. Part-time and split-shifts will be used, and job demands and older men's physical capacities will be watched.

In Wisconsin vocational schools are developing possibilities of part-time work in some seventeen different fields of employment. They range from lapidary work to furniture repair. The objective is to enable retired workers to augment their pension grants.

Also in Wisconsin, the "Homecrafters," originally organized for work with home-bound, severely handicapped clients, have gradually extended their program to include workers whose advanced years are accompanied by physical disabilities. Currently the oldest "pupil" is eighty-five. The training program runs from needlecraft, leathercraft, ceramics and metal working to the operation of small business enterprises in the home. Equipment and training materials are furnished through federal or state funds if the client is not able to meet the costs himself. Products are marketed at present through other organizations.

NEED FOR MORE RESEARCH

We need more information on specific jobs suitable for those whose chronological age is not a satisfactory method of determining their retirement. We need to learn the best ways to evaluate the productivity of older workers and the value of their experience to the labor market. Nevertheless, the question of job testing for older people is still in the area of controversy. Psychologists like Dr. Jacob Tuckerman of the Institute of Psychological Research think that tests which younger people take are not valid for older ones and that new methods can be standardized to determine capabilities of old people more fairly. On the whole industry is not convinced. (8)

What is clear is that if some or all of these problems are not solved, and soon, the plight of the old in 1975 will be considerably worse than in 1955. The remarks of Mrs. Geneva Mathiasen, the Executive Secretary of the National Committee on Aging (part of the National Social Welfare Assembly), are pertinent for all of us.

"Practically any community sufficiently interested," she says, "can secure regularly such information as the number of older workers seeking employment, their percentage in relation to other ages, current numbers of placements being made, the local situation in relation to other communities in the state and to the national picture. They can then judge trends and plan accordingly."

If you are concerned about the situation which confronts your own elderly and which may confront you in the next decade or two, the time to take action is *now*.

FINANCIAL SECURITY NEEDS

All the major industrial countries in the world have adopted some program for providing a supplementary income to aged persons when their regular income fails. Practically all of them also have adopted some plan to provide income for persons prematurely disabled who cannot work. In this last step we are still lagging behind.

One of the clichés of our time is that no person in our rich country ever need feel the pinch of want now that we have both private and governmental benevolent "assistance." That is true enough. We are caught, notwithstanding, on the horns of an Old

Age and Survivors Insurance law which was passed at a time when it was urgent to make more jobs go around for more people. Removing men and women past sixty-five from competition, and yet giving them a chance to reap a little from a lifetime of work, seemed in 1935 a good way out of some of the consequences of a national depression.

We are likely to go on arguing the pros and cons of extending or canceling that step for a long time. There is strong pressure from many quarters to make it possible for the old man or woman who has earned his federal-industrial pension to supplement it by his own labor for as high a price as he can get. As the Townsendites point out, that issue may be resolved by old people themselves. In a few years their voting block will be strong enough to get them practically anything they want.

Before that, if the back can be broken of the unwritten law which says a person of sixty-five *ought* to be willing to retire, we may all stay on a prosperity basis. Professor Sumner H. Slichter of Harvard University puts the arguments on a practical basis likely to appeal even to those who uphold the stand-pat attitude.(9) Dr. Slichter believes that if the retirement age were raised from sixty-five to seventy under the Old Age and Survivors Insurance law, that alone would add nearly one-sixtieth to the national wealth.

"In other words," he says, "they would increase it by almost four billion dollars a year. The whole community would benefit from this additional output of goods."

The revisions of the Social Security law in recent years to include more people in more liberal provisions, the increases in the number of industrial pensions and the genuine sense of responsibility which business on the whole is beginning to feel for its retiring workers, ought not to lull us into a sense of false security. No matter how far we go in making it possible for elderly men and women to work, there will always be large numbers not able to buffet competition or who are physically incapacitated. All our national programs to assure this last group a minimum of substance have scarcely kept up with changing price levels, and each of our programs of old age security is badly in need of improvement.

TRENDS IN HOUSING

Next to the money to pay for housing, there is no more urgent problem in the life of an old person than where he is to live. Fortunately, this is one area in which some of the most exciting developments are taking place.

The battle of whether or not older people are better off living with each other in special neighborhoods or special housing projects or "retirement villages" rages among housing experts and welfare workers. But old people serenely go on, following no norm. There is nothing more likely than that they will be as individual in their housing tastes and requirements in the year 1975 (or 2000) as in the present.

We have already made some progress in meeting the undeniable, great lacks in "sheltered care." How many of these interesting developments will be popular, or even practicable, years from now, no prophet has risen to say. The current trend leading away from institutional life in the old sense seems to be far beyond the trying-out stage. Homes for the aged will exist, but like the chronically ill hospital of the future, they are quite likely to be just one of the services for the aged, and not necessarily a permanent one, even for those who can no longer lead independent lives by themselves, or with their families.

There is genuine promise for any housing which offers permanent service geared to the physiologic and psychologic needs, health and safety of the old, and yet lacks the dehumanized, clinical atmosphere of an institution.

Apartment house projects: New York state led the way in a law which compels a small number of apartments in each public housing project to be set aside for elderly people of low income. Other states have followed with their own variations, sometimes under state or municipal auspices, more often privately endowed.

The central idea which planners recognize is to give old people a chance to have low rentals and new housing designs. The Commonwealth Housing Foundation of Boston, for instance, plans units which will include kitchenettes for those able to use them and a central cafeteria for those who cannot. Los Angeles County, which views its present population of 350,000 men and women over sixty-five merely as the vanguard of other elderly migrants, has a mutual financing plan for group living. Those able to pay annual dues will live in modern apartment houses especially designed for their needs. After the age of seventy members would move into a lodge which would provide complete care. (Whether vigorous "young" seventy year olds will like that remains to be known.)

Wherever they are, the new apartments have such features as electric instead of gas stoves, no thresholds to trip over, shelves and cabinets at low levels, casement windows that open and close mechanically, apartments on the sunny side of buildings, with provisions for extra heat for cold old bones, non-slip floors and square bathtubs with hand-grips—all the sensible factors to avoid accidents and forestall illness.

"Retirement villages": This is a popular term which has as wide a meaning as their geographical range is vast. New Jersey, for instance, has a cooperative colony composed of older people who live on tiny incomes in equally tiny houses near each other. Maine renovated an ex-CCC camp of the depression vintage, and turned it over to elderly ex-lumbermen. Florida, where already one out of twelve residents is over sixty-five, has plans for "satellite communities." The most elaborate union plan is that of the Upholsterers (AFL). They have purchased a site in Florida where housing units of three rooms and bath will be offered to retired members at a rental of approximately $40 per month.

Other states are still trying to find the answer to housing happiness for the old. The seriousness with which the problem is being tackled is indicated by Chicago's effort. There the Housing Authority, with the cooperation of the Welfare Council's Committee on the Aged, is trying to find out exactly what a suitable pattern of housing for the elderly ought to be. Its pioneer project is a seven-story elevator building where thirty-six one-bedroom units will be occupied by couples who are at least sixty years old. The rest of the project will house families in normally mixed age groups. Here at least the elderly will "retire" as they have lived, a part of the world around them.

INSTITUTIONAL LIFE IN FUTURE

There is one kind of housing which we do not need to guess about because its pattern is emerging more clearly every day. The fact that there will always be some people who need help even when their physical and emotional surroundings are reasonably adequate, calls for "substitute homes." They will be far removed from the old-time home for the aged, though they may preserve its shell. There will also have to be "home supplements," which means more visiting housekeepers, visiting nurses, even provision of special diets, and household instruction for those unskilled in home-making (both men and women), if we are to do our full duty. Nothing is more clear than the outline of the old age home of the future, whose skeleton is even now being clothed with fervor in some communities. Its various guises take these forms:

Residence clubs: These are already going concerns in California, Florida, New Jersey, New York, and certain other states. A life membership includes meals, a room or an apartment, and use of an infirmary. We need many more of them.

Congregate living: This term will certainly take on new meanings, judging by the fundamental changes already launched. The Methodist Home in Charlotte, North Carolina is an example of the trend to keep a main building for those least able to care for themselves, and add individual cottages on adjacent property where old couples may live and yet be serviced by the central resources. Some old age homes already maintain workshops where old people learn trades, sell products, and pay their entire way. Others have taken the last stigma out of the word "charity" by making an institution a home where people pay what they can, go and come as they please, yet have nursing and diet service they cannot get for themselves. Even the infirm can profit by this new idea of rehabilitation. Connecticut, for instance, has established a series of cottages for the aged on convalescent status in connection with its state hospital.

Whatever its physical setup, it is easily forseeable that the new-old age home will offer these services:

1) Individual counselling to all applicants, which will include placement in boarding or "foster homes," advice on financing, family relationships, recreation—even clothes.

2) Acceptance for care of those who ought to continue to live as a normal part of the community, yet are fearful. This can be done if we develop more health and recreational and housekeeping services. Many homes in large cities also are even now offering the use of their facilities—recreational, occupational, dining, etc.—to those who cannot or don't want to enter as permanent residents.

We need more of everything in every kind of housing. But at least we know the way we ought to go, so there is some hope of our arriving at our goal before it is too late.

RECREATION'S GROWING PLACE

There is one other field in which the "grass roots" approach has taken hold like the proverbial prairie fire. Cooking classes for bachelors, hobby classes for both sexes, orchestras made up of ex-musicians, current events courses and bridge lessons, and a spreading tendency to use children's camps in their off-season for adults—all these, and still others, attract old people of different abilities, tastes, and temperament. "Golden Age" clubs and town-wide "hobby shows" in which only the old participate are as common in towns the size of Hubbard, Iowa, as in great municipalities like New York.

The reason for all this organized recreational activity for old people is wholesome enough. But far too many communities establish a recreational once-a-week, or even a daily get-together center, and then consider all their responsibilities discharged.

Fortunately, there are sound reasons why recreation will play a more significant role not only for those who have abandoned the concept that complete leisure is the keystone to contentment, but in old age homes, in hospitals, and as a recognized part of the community welfare program. Medical science has definite proof that planned recreation, to fit the individual—not merely a means of getting old people off of young people's hands—can be as potent a weapon to fight deterioration as penicillin is in fighting pneumonia.

ADULT EDUCATION'S PROMISE

Such objectives ought not to be allowed, like "Topsy," merely to grow. They have to be thought out carefully on a community-wide basis and considerable education has to be done among old people themselves. We need many more vocational programs and many more cultural programs. Some have started in cities—where, it is sad to say, almost everything that is bright for the future of the old has to start becaues so many are involved—but there are also some promising beginnings in states with large rural and small-town populations. The prime purpose of all we do or should do has been well stated by Homer Kempfer of the U. S. Office of Education:

"The educational program for each individual should be focused primarily on the years immediately ahead to help him adapt his life to the biological changes and new human relationships that confront him. It should be concerned with what might be—not what might have been . . ."(10)

The most encouraging sign that this has been taken to heart lies in the extension of secondary education, particularly through extension courses and night schools, to adults late in life. But there are some other open doors which have never existed before, and some of these may be duplicated and triplicated before long:

The University of Chicago is making an attempt to reach people who are looking forward—not back—to their time of retirement. The University established the first correspondence course in the country for that purpose. It is addressed to the nearly aged; it includes counselling on health, employment, finances, use of leisure time, community and social participation, spiritual values, and understanding of the physical and psychologic changes which accompany aging.

At the University of Michigan extension of educational facilities has meant concentration on teaching older people how to solve their own problems through "demonstration projects," as well as formal instruction. The Michigan School of Social Work also established the nation's first college course in gerontology to serve two purposes. The first is to help people prepare for their own retirement; the second is to train them to work professionally with older citizens.

Other institutions have broken other new ground. The pioneering is not confined to any one section of the country. The Louisiana State University, for instance, now has an annual summer session course titled, "Needs and Problems of Aged Persons." The Adult Education Division of Brooklyn College, New York, boldly titles its course, "Planning for the Second Forty Years."

Education programs are not confined to colleges. They are now included as part of the programs of such groups as the American Association of University Women, the Business and Professional Women's Clubs, Federation of Women's Clubs, and so on.

Perhaps the most interesting experiment of all is being carried out on a sixty-acre estate at Cold Spring-on-Hudson, New York. There post-graduate courses are offered for college graduates who are at least sixty years old. In a year of living and working together it is hoped these re-educated persons will map out a formula for a contented and creative later life and return to their communities to lead in similar movements.

Whether such a bold step will be repeated elsewhere or not, at least it is further proof that older people themselves have begun to realize there should be no age limit to learning.

THE RESEARCH PATTERN

Of all the work, organized and voluntary, about and for old people, the most fundamental centers around the search for what the National Committee on Aging terms "the true nature of old age." It is comparable to the search during the first part of this century for the true nature of childhood, and is likely to be as far-reaching.

The list of research laboratories concerned not so much with prolonging life as making it more meaningful, is long. In many cases the work they are doing may not bear its ultimate fruit for this generation of old people, but will most certainly affect our own old age. At the University of Minnesota, for instance, a ten-year study is under way to determine whether regular exercise after forty is helpful or harmful. Three hundred businessmen, aged forty-five to fifty-four, are the "guinea pigs." The study will also attempt to determine whether eating habits and physical activity prevent or delay heart and blood-vessel diseases, and what are the effects of worry and tension.

In the East another long-time survey—several years—is under way at Cornell University. This one is to determine where physical infirmities of old age are related to psychological disturbances stemming from retirement and whether "persons who retire in good health at sixty-five do not live out their allotted years."

There is similar concern about the commonly held belief that old age is invariably accompanied by physical and mental decline. The Institute of Psychological Research at Columbia University is examining the attitudes of two hundred men and women between sixty and sixty-five over a term of years in the hope that the case-method study will get at the roots of this basic problem.

NO ROOM FOR COMPLACENCE

To its credit it can be said that our generation is fully aware it must find new ways to help older people adapt to the society in which they must live. Federal funds and private endowments have been tapped—many of them generously—to understand how this new being the twentieth century has produced can function best. In Cleveland, the Benjamin Rose Hospital, unique in all the country, is taking only sixty or so patients, though its equipment cost more than a million dollars. Its purpose is to study, treat and rehabilitate aged persons, not acutely ill.

The medical director of the research division says, "All our physiological and bio-chemical standards are based on young persons. And we don't know how they may differ in older people. . . .

We want to measure how older people differ from younger ones, even healthy older persons."

There is an urgent need for more understanding of the physiological changes during involution and senescence. The fact that many laboratories are working on the same problems is an encouraging sign. Baltimore City Hospital, working in cooperation with the U. S. Health Service, Goldwater Memorial Hospital in New York City, and Washington University in St. Louis, all are trying to solve the problem of deterioration of the circulatory system. At the College of Physicians and Surgeons in Columbia University researches are seeking more light on arteriosclerosis and kindred diseases. California has taken a way other states may learn to follow. The legislature granted financial aid to the University of California's Medical Center for research in arthritis, diseases of the liver, diabetes, and other afflictions that chiefly attack us late in life.

This by no means exhausts the list but it holds hope that the solution may be found to the question of how to delay or prevent the onset of the degenerative diseases, and defeat the word "incurable."

There is no dearth of specialized studies concerning many aspects of the old age problem. By 1946 the Social Science Research Council listed in its Research Planning Report a long bibliography dealing with social adjustment in the old. This is impressive, but it is still too early for us to realize fully the challenge an ever-growing older population will present, or what it means to be able to say that the average American who reaches the age of twenty-five has as many years of life before him as the average newly born baby did in 1900. (11)

We do know this. Our whole way of life—our work, our leisure, our family relationships—is bound to be altered by the fact that all of us have had our chances of survival to mid-life and even to the threshold of old age immensely improved.

For the old who are now among us we cannot do better than adopt the creed laid down by New York's State Joint Legislative Committee on Problems of the Aging. In itself it is a practical example of the kind of responsibility we shall need to assume if our own old age is to be something more than an affliction:

SENIOR CITIZENS' CREED

"Each of our Senior Citizens, regardless of race, color, or creed, is entitled to:

1. The right to an opportunity to continue to be useful.
2. The right to an equal opportunity to obtain employment based on merit, not birthdays.
3. The right to freedom from the spectre of want in old age and death in a pauper's grave.
4. The right to a fair share of the community's recreational, educational, and medical resources.
5. The right to obtain decent housing suited to the needs of later years.
6. The right to the respect of the community, based on service to the community.
7. The right to the support of one's family to an extent consonant with the best interest of the family.
8. The right to live independently, as one chooses.
9. The right to live with dignity as a free human being unfettered by antiquated concepts of the 'proper role of old people.'
10. The right of access to all available knowledge on how to make the later years happy years."

NOTES TO CHAPTER XV

(1) *Statistical Bulletin,* Metropolitan Life Insurance Company, Vol. 34, No. 7, July, 1953.

(2) Foreword and Summary of Report prepared in 1940 by the Welfare Council. Meeting of Welfare Council and Mayor's Advisory Committee for the Aged, New York, April 29-30, 1952.

(3) Third Annual Conference: "Living in the Later Years," University of Michigan, Ann Arbor, June 30, 1950.

(4) Scheele, Leonard A. "Current Experience in Multiphasic Health Examinations." *American Journal of Public Health,* Vol. 41, No. 6, June, 1951.

(5) *Newsletter,* New York State Joint Legislative Committee on Problems of the Aging, July, 1953.

(6) *Ibid.*

(7) *Statistical Bulletin,* Metropolitan Life Insurance Company, Vol. 34, No. 7, July, 1953.

(8) Clague, Ewan. "Labor Force Trends in the United States." *Journal of Gerontology,* Vol. 7, No. 1, Jan., 1952.

(9) Reported in *Christian Science Monitor,* Feb. 13, 1950.

(10) Kempfer, Homer. "Education for a Long and Useful Life," U.S. Office of Education pamphlet. Washington, D.C.: U.S. Government Printing Office, 1950.

(11) *Statistical Bulletin,* Metropolitan Life Insurance Company, July, 1952, and July, 1953.

APPENDICES

USEFUL SOURCES OF INFORMATION FOR SPECIAL PROBLEMS

In 1944, the year Dr. Ignatz Leo Nascher died, he read a paper on "The Aging Mind" at the second meeting of the American Geriatrics Society which he had helped to found. He was then eighty-one. This "father of modern geriatrics," as he is affectionately known, visited a Vienna institution in his youth. He was told casually that the inmates were suffering from "old age" and "nothing can be done about it." He took exception to the statement and spent a lifetime disproving it.

Today, the American Geriatrics Society is only one of a number of organizations trying in one way or another to find answers to the numerous problems still confronting older people. You will find listed in the following pages (under chapter headings to which they relate) names and addresses, of individuals, committees, and both national and local organizations concerned with the aged. Whether you need advice, instruction, or concrete aid, consult them freely.

Chapter I: Getting Along with Older People

TERMS USED IN THE MEDICAL PROFESSION AND SOCIAL WORK ABOUT THE AGING PROCESS AND THE AGING

Terms are bandied back and forth among medical men, social workers, and in newspaper and magazine articles which are not always clear to the rest of us. Here are some that are common today, and likely to remain so. Since 11% of us are expected to be in the "aged" category by 1975, it is in your interest to get acquainted with these concepts, and their definitions.

Aged: Present usage it to classify everyone sixty-five years old or over in this category. The aged, however, are those who show results of the aging process, and its symptoms usually appear from the fortieth year on. The term "aged family" means one with an aged head.

AGING: A normal, biologic process which begins at birth—or at conception—and continues with varying acceleration throughout life, ending only with death.

ALMSHOUSE: A generation or more ago this word denoted "a public institution for indoor relief of the poor." Since Social Security laws now enable many to live outside any institution, the term has dropped out of fashion. The institution still exists, sometimes under the name of "county farm" or "public home for the aged" (no longer called a "poorhouse"). It is generally reserved for the financially dependent too feeble to care for themselves.

BOARDING HOME: A legal definition, drawn up by welfare agencies (in a state where such institutions must be licensed and regularly inspected) is one "operated for profit and advertised, announced, or maintained for the express or implied purpose of providing care for three or more elderly people who are not acutely ill or in need of continuous nursing care."

CASEWORK: A profession unfortunately named, for it deals with people, not with "cases." A caseworker is equipped by special education and training to discern the underlying causes of difficulty more clearly than the person in trouble, enmeshed in his own problems.

CHRONIC DISEASE: Chronic comes from the Greek *chronikos,* "concerning time." A chronic disease is one that lasts a long time and involves an abnormal and persistent change in the structure or behavior of some part of the body. It is *not* necessarily confined to old people, nor always present in them.

CHRONIC ILLNESS: The American Red Cross uses this definition in one of its guides to instructors: "A disease or condition said to be progressive, with an indefinite period of recovery, frequently a complication of the aging process."

COUNSELLING SERVICE: This may be given by a psychologist, a psychiatrist, vocational counsellor, or psychiatric social worker, to a troubled individual. It may be, and frequently is, on a fee basis, often adjusted to the applicant's income. There are a few, very few, so-called geriatric clinics, where counselling of the old is included with other services.

CONSULTATION SERVICES: Usually this is applied to institutions—nursing homes, home for the aged, boarding home, convalescent home. It indicates that someone not on the day-by-day staff is called on to help the institution through advice on nutrition, on handling of patients, on methods of sanitation, etc.

DESIGNATED EXAMINER: The definition, given in the draft act governing hospitals for the mentally ill, prepared (1951) by the then Federal Security Agency and the National Institute of Mental Health, is: "A licensed physician registered by the state department of health, mental health commission, or department of mental hygiene, as especially qualified under standards established by it, in the diagnosis of mental or related illness."

DOTARD: An individual of advanced years, whose mental processes have been weakened or impaired but who shows no delusional formations, hallucinations, behavior, or emotional variations characteristic of mental illness. He is often found in mental institutions, not because he actually requires treatment given there, but through want of other facilities, or a family able or willing to care for him.

FAMILY: In legal or social work parlance, this means a group of two or more persons related by blood, marriage, or adoption, who reside together.

FAMILY CARE: Sometimes used interchangeably with "foster home care." It signifies a household which includes from one to three aged boarders, living in the familiar setting of a family.

FOSTER HOME CARE: A term originally employed in child care and now extended also to elderly persons. It signifies placement, usually by a welfare agency, of an individual in a home other than his own or his relatives'.

GERIATRICIAN: From the Greek, *geras,* old age, and *iatrikos,* healing. It signifies not only the physician who specializes in treating the elderly, but also all physicians who give aid in health and illness to the aged and the aging.

GERIATRICS: The study of old age and its diseases. The term was coined by Dr. I. L. Nascher, who wrote the first textbook on old age and its diseases, in 1904. He deserves credit for originating the conception of geriatrics as a major interest for a physician.

GERONTOLOGY: It is concerned with the scientific study of the aging process, its medical and sociological phenomena, and its end product, the aged individual. (From Greek, *geron,* an old man.)

HOME: A place that is familiar and secure, adequate for social and recreational activities, and preferably a center of family life.

HOME FOR THE AGED: An alternate term is "old people's home." An institution which gives an opportunity to elderly persons to live together. If private, it may be supported by contributions and endowments, and usually applicants pay an entrance fee, or board. If public, the home will be supported by taxes, the modern equivalent of the old-time "poorhouse" which puts its emphasis on the infirm indigent.

HOMEMAKER SERVICE: The supervised placement by a welfare agency, public or private, of a woman chosen for her household skills, and her ability to get along with people. She is placed in a home, most often on a temporary basis, where her services are needed to maintain and preserve the home as a unit.

HOUSEHOLD: It consists of all the persons who occupy a house, an apartment, or other group of rooms, or a room that constitutes separate living quarters. It includes the related family members, and also the unrelated persons, if any, such as lodgers or servants who share the dwelling unit.

INSANITY: A legal term, a finding of a court of competent jurisdiction for people whose behavior is such that society can no longer tolerate them in the community. Practically all those pronounced "insane" by a court have a psychosis that is the cause of the abnormal behavior, but a finding of insanity by a court is not *always* absolute evidence that the person is suffering from a mental illness.

MATURITY: According to a standard dictionary, maturity is a process brought about by completion and development for any function, appropriate to its kind. Aging is a phase in the life process which starts some time after maturity, beginning about the end of third decade or beginning of the fourth.

MENTAL HYGIENE: It seeks to prevent the development of mental disease, of feeble-mindedness, of epilepsy, and other mental factors which often lead to crime, dependency, and pauperism. Mental hygiene also concerns itself with conservation of mental health through improving human minds, developing better personalities, and increasing human happiness.

MENTALLY ILL: The National Institute of Mental Health defines the individual who is mentally ill as one who has a psychiatric or other disease which substantially impairs his mental health. A state law (New York's, for instance) may define him as one "afflicted with mental disease to such an extent that for his own welfare or that of the community he requires care and treatment."

NURSING HOME: A place where persons who are ill with disease, or who are crippled, infirm, or in any way afflicted, can have shelter, board, and essential nursing care. The law does not always provide for medical supervision, but usually requires licensing, which may imply regular inspection, a safeguard for the residents. A nursing home is not a hospital and cannot fulfill all the functions of one.

OCCUPATIONAL THERAPY: An activity, mental or physical, usually prescribed by a physician for its remedial or rehabilitation value.

PERSONALITY: The term used to describe the whole person, the way he reacts to outside influences and the way he thinks, feels, and behaves. Personality is made up of an inherited basic structure plus the effects of training, knowledge, experiences, and information, plus family and community relationships and experiences.

Psychiatric Clinic: A service for ambulatory patients with a psychiatrist in attendance at regularly scheduled hours. Available usually under the same conditions covering free or low-cost dispensary clinics.

Rehabilitation Center: A facility to prepare the disabled for more effective living. A center may utilize such services as diagnosis and counselling; physical medicine services for pre-vocational or conditioning therapy; testing, fitting, and training in the use of prosthetic devices; adjustment training; evaluation or control of special disabilities, and vocational training.

Residence Club: Usually a subsidized, or semi-subsidized attempt to meet housing problems; often operated on a cooperative basis. Usually open only to people with limited means, under supervision of church or welfare organization in a city. Its chief value for the aging is guarantee of privacy through living quarters in a room or small apartment, often with communal dining and recreational services. Sometimes medical and nursing care is available. The number of such apartments or buildings is extremely limited.

Retirement Communities: Several types, but all too few in number. In some, elderly couples have established themselves in small cottages, either under semi-supervision of the board of an adjacent home for the aged, or independently. Usually living arrangements are self-financed. design details for occupancy by older people wishing to live in a com-
In other places, real estate interests have erected houses incorporating munity with their contemporaries.

Senility: Feebleness of body and mind incident to old age; certain mental disorders may accompany the condition. Senility is *not* an absolute entity that comes at a given age. It is a state of being and *not* to be measured in years, but rather in the physiological state of the body. Senility is found in all degrees and at almost all ages and its problems may need remedies and understanding of varied kinds. A person may be senile at forty in his body tissues as well as his mental outlook; another may have the springy step and viewpoint of youth at seventy or eighty. (From Latin, *senex,* genitive, *senis,* old, an old man.)

Standard-Setting: The development of detailed standards for physical facilities, sanitation, record-keeping, personnel practices, etc., in convalescent and nursing homes, homes for the aged, public and private, and boarding homes of the "foster care" type.

Supervision: As used in state laws, this implies enforcement of requirements. It usually includes investigation for granting of a license to a boarding, convalescent, or nursing home, or home for the aged. It may include periodic inspection after licensing, though not always.

Waiting List: When used in connection with a privately supported home for the aged it includes the following persons: (*a*) those ready and anxious to accept the first opportunity to enter the home; (*b*) members of a particular church or organization who must wait for their turn until a vacancy occurs in the quota allowed their group; (*c*) those not yet ready to enter the home because they want to continue working as long as possible or remain in present living quarters as long as they can.

WITHDRAWAL: The removal of an applicant's name from the waiting list of a home for the aged at his own request, or through change of rules.

CHAPTER II: WHAT IS OLD AGE?

RED CROSS GUIDE TO CARE OF AGING

If you know what physical, mental, and psychological changes may occur, their effects, and what to do about them, you can help an older person develop his remaining capacities. The American Red Cross uses this outline as part of its instructors' guide, *Care of the Aging and Chronically Ill.* Remember that these changes do not occur invariably in the same way, or to the same extent in every person.

Changes that may occur	*Possible Effects*	*Points to Consider*
BODY TISSUE AND STRUCTURE		
Shift of mineral salts, particularly calcium, from bone to tissues and blood vessels. Retardation of cell division and of capacity for cell growth and tissue repair.	Bones more brittle, more easily broken. Blood vessels less elastic; heart must work harder to supply needed blood to organs.	1) Obtain periodic health examinations. 2) Avoid waxing floors. 3) Keep stairways and ramps uncluttered, well lighted, in good repair, and equipped with handrails to prevent tripping and possibility of breaking bones. 4) Provide well-constructed shoes for good support — broad, medium heel, ankle support if needed.

Changes that may occur	*Possible Effects*	*Points to Consider*
		5) Provide aids for circulation and muscle relaxation such as comfortable chairs and foot rests for frequent rest periods. Individuals should also rest lying down with legs and feet slightly elevated.
HEARING		
Possible progressive hearing loss—either unilateral or bilateral.	Individual may refuse to acknowledge handicap or be unaware of hearing loss; may get into embarrassing situations; may withdraw from group activities and feel lonely. Accidents may occur because of inability to hear warning signals.	1) Obtain medical care and treatment. 2) See that individual learns to use hearing aid, if recommended, or lip reading. 3) Help person gain an understanding of the situation and of his part in happy adjustment. 4) Promote family understanding and group participation. 5) Gain attention of listener, speak slowly and clearly, and avoid the confusion of many speaking at once.
CIRCULATION		
Adjusts more slowly to temperature and activity changes. Circulation in extremities, especially lower extremities, is poorer.	Narrowed and obstructed blood vessels result in slowing of blood flow, causing tendency for blood to clot. Any infection may tend to heal more slowly. When varicose veins	1) See that individual avoids contact with persons who have colds or other upper respiratory infection. What may be a mild infection for one may be severe for the one to whom transmitted. 2) Prevent body heat

Changes that may occur	*Possible Effects*	*Points to Consider*
	exist they may break down, resulting in ulcers. Individual needs more warm clothing than younger person.	loss; provide warm but lightweight clothing, such as sweaters, woolen underwear, bed socks as needed. 3) Keep floors and houses comfortably warm. 4) Keep individual reasonably active to promote circulation; if bedridden, provide mild active or passive exercise. 5) See that individual keeps skin clean and dry; provide easy and convenient bathing facilities, such as rubber suction mat in tub, hand-rails, stool, or seat on tub. 6) Provide elastic bandages as needed for varicose veins on legs; encourage patient to rest periodically, with legs elevated for muscle relaxation and to relieve feet and legs of weight.
NERVOUS SYSTEM		
Progressive degeneration and atrophy of the nervous system.	Sensory and motor impulses and reactions to external stimuli retarded—slower to react to dangers. Sensation is dulled—body responds slowly to heat or cold. Impaired memory and mental endurance.	1) Use caution when applying heat or cold to skin. 2) Be aware of tendency to forget present and remember incidents that happened long ago.

Changes that may occur	*Possible Effects*	*Points to Consider*
ELIMINATION		
Bowel is more sluggish, as result of reduced physical activity, dental and diet changes. Urine output may change.	Distention often present without discomfort; sensation dulled. Interference with usual hygiene of living—constipation, diarrhea. Tendency to overanxiety about daily bowel movements and inclination to develop the laxative habit. Scant or excessive amount of urine. Distress with urination; difficulty in retention resulting in dribbling, with discomfort, embarrassment, and inconvenience.	1) Develop regular toilet habits. 2) Provide mild exercise. 3) Select fruits and vegetables to provide roughage as allowed. 4) Avoid self-dosing with laxatives or taking unnecessary enemas. 5) Obtain medical treatment as needed. 6) Provide adequate protection for comfort. 7) Provide convenient toilet facilities.
VISION		
The lens and the blood vessels of the eye may change. Changes in ability to see near objects well.	Disturbed, blurred, and restricted field of vision. Glaucoma may occur. Interference with usual outlets of activity, such as reading, needlework, and other close eye work. May result in a variety of reactions; cheerful acceptance and adjustment or bitterness, moodiness, self-indulgence. Accidents may occur because of difficulty or inability to see.	1) Obtain medical care and treatment as needed, and promptly upon appearance of symptoms. 2) Provide adequate diet including vitamins, especially A and G. 3) Provide good lighting for any eyework. 4) Prevent prolonged or concentrated eyework. 5) Avoid cluttered floors or anything that may prove a hazard and cause stumbling. 6) Urge frequent rest perods for eyes. 7) Find suitable, satis-

Changes that may occur	*Possible Effects*	*Points to Consider*
		fying, and constructive work outlets, such as home responsibilites of own choosing, teaching cooking and needle craft, telling stories about historic events. 8) Teach children to be considerate, keep toys in proper place, read aloud, act as escorts, be helpful at all times.
SKIN		
Aging of other organs affects the skin both indirectly and directly. Circulation changes reduce blood supply to skin and retard transfer of sensory and motor impulses. Lessened action of the glands of the skin. Reduced amount of fatty tissue. Changes in mucous membranes of mouth; white cankers, eroded areas, inflamed and swollen.	Extremities, especially the feet, may be swollen, cold, burning, or otherwise uncomfortable. Skin bruises easily; less able to resist infection. Leg and foot infections are especially slow to heal. Danger of burning is increased. Skin may become uncomfortably dry and wrinkled; may have burning or itching sensations. Individual may feel less attractive and consequently tend to remain alone. Sores or irritations may result from infected, ragged teeth or from ill-fitting dentures. Mucous membranes may be sore and sensi-	1) Keep feet clean and dry; elevate feet if necessary, at frequent intervals. 2) Give special care to bony prominences when sitting or lying down—lower back, shoulders, heels, and elbows; prevent undue pressure that may lead to soreness. 4) Use caution when applying external heat or when feeding a helpless person hot fluids. 5) Obtain medical attention for excessive itching or burning sensation. 6) Report to the doctor any rash, unhealed sore, or change in a mole. 7) Lubricate skin with mild cold cream, hand lotion, or oil. 8) Use mild soap spar-

Changes that may occur	*Possible Effects*	*Points to Consider*
	tive (inadequate or improper diet).	ingly or not soap at all; bathe less frequently. 9) Handle skin with care. 10) Obtain dental care, clear mouth of infections, take care of broken teeth, provide well-fitting dentures. 11) Provide balanced diet.
HAIR		
Lessened gland activity and other aging factors may influence color, amount, and texture.	Hair may become gray, lessened in amount, and dry. Individual may resent these changes, feel less attractive, and become less tidy in appearance.	1) Brush hair gently, avoid bruising scalp, encourage new hair style. Keep hair clean. Provide shaving and haircut services for men and beauty aids for women as morale builders.
SLEEP		
Changes in routine of living produce sleep changes. Lessened activity lessens need for long periods of sleep; tendency to nap.	Increased free time encourages more frequent rest periods and napping. "Early to bed and early to rise" tends to be the order of the day. Individual may worry, feeling that early rising interferes with family regime, or may be inconsiderate and demanding.	1) Provide private room or opportunity for privacy if possible. 2) Provide convenient facilities for early morning tea or coffee if desired. 3) Keep individual up and about as long as permitted; encourage activity for the one who tends to be too inactive. 4) Provide couch, lounging chair, or other facility to encourage napping.

Chapter III: Old Age is Not a Disease

REHABILITATION CENTERS

If your elderly relative is disabled his case may not be hopeless. Rehabilitation centers are able to help older people as well as young men and women. They are growing in number and their services are expanding. The Office of Vocational Rehabilitation (Washington, D. C.) has a full-time consultant on its staff to coordinate the work of this federal agency with rehabilitation center personnel. Write the Office for information about where your elderly relatives can go to obtain the exact help they need, if it is not indicated in the list below.

The following directory represents only those centers which participated in a conference held under the sponsorship of the Office of Vocational Rehabilitation and the National Society for Crippled Children and Adults, December, 1952. Write the latter (11 South La Salle St., Chicago 3) for a booklet describing rehabilitation center programs.

Key to Symbols Used

PT	Physical Therapy	COUNS	Counseling
OT	Occupational Therapy	PSYCHO	Psychological services
SPEECH	Speech Therapy	SOC WORK	Social Work
IND FIT or MAT	Industrial Fitness or Manual Arts Therapy	VOC TNG	Vocational Training

ALABAMA

Tuskegee Rehabilitation Center, John A. Andrew Memorial Hospital, Tuskegee
Services: PT, OT, COUNS, PSYCHO, SOC WORK, VOC TNG

CALIFORNIA

Kabat-Kaiser Institute, 2600 Alameda St., Vallejo
Services: PT, OT, SPEECH, IND FIT or MAT, SOC WORK, COUNS, VOC TNG

May T. Morrison Center for Rehabilitation, 1680 Mission St., San Francisco
Services: PT, OT, SPEECH, IND FIT or MAT, SOC WORK

CONNECTICUT

The Hartford County Rehabilitation Workshop, Inc., 680 Franklin Ave., Hartford 6
Services: PT, OT, SPEECH, SOC WORK. Related Activities: SHELTERED WORKSHOP

Department of Physical Medicine and Rehabilitation, State Veterans Home and Hospital, Rocky Hill
Services: PT, OT, SPEECH, IND FIT or MAT, SOC WORK, VOC TNG

Rehabilitation Center for the Physically Handicapped, Inc., 20 Wall St., Stamford
Services: PT, OT, SPEECH, IND FIT or MAT, SOC WORK. Related Activities: Sheltered Workshop. (Local resources for counselling, psychological help, and vocational training are used when necessary.)

DELAWARE

Delaware Curative Workshop, Inc., 16th and Washington Sts., Wilmington
Services: PT, OT

ILLINOIS

The Rehabilitation Center, Liberty Mutual Insurance Company, 28 N. Franklin St., Chicago
Services: PT, OT, COUNS

INDIANA

Crossroads Rehabilitation Center, 3001 N. New Jersey St., Indianapolis
Services: PT, OT, COUNS, PSYCHO, SPEECH, SOC WORK, VOC TNG

IOWA

Iowa Vocational Rehabilitation Training Center, 1029 Des Moines St., Des Moines
Services: COUNS, CORRECTIVE THERAPY, OT

KENTUCKY

Curative Workshop, Kentucky Society for Crippled Children, Inc. 840 S. 3d St., Louisville, Ky.
Services: PT, OT

MASSACHUSETTS

The Rehabilitation Center of the Liberty Mutual Insurance Company, 691 Boylston St., Boston
Services: PT, OT, COUNS

Bay State Rehabilitation Center of Western Massachusetts, Springfield
Services: PT, OT, COUNS, PSYCHO, SPEECH, SOC WORK

Bay State Medical Rehabilitation Clinic, 225 Charles St., Boston
Services: PT, OT, SOC WORK

The Rehabilitation Center of Worcester, 30 Highland St., Worcester
Services: PT, OT, SPEECH, SOC WORK

MINNESOTA

Minneapolis Curative Workshop, 2515 Nicollet Ave., Minneapolis
Services: PT, OT, SPEECH, SOC WORK

St. Paul Rehabilitation Center, Inc., 319 Eagle St., St. Paul 2
Services: PT, OT, SPEECH, SOC WORK

MISSOURI

The Rehabilitation Institute, 3600 Troost St., Kansas City
Services: PT, OT, COUNS, PSYCHO, SPEECH

Miriam Convalescent Rehabilitation Hospital, 501 Bacon St., Webster Groves
Services: PT, OT, COUNS, PSYCHO, SPEECH, SOC WORK

NEW JERSEY

The Kessler Institute for Rehabilitation, Pleasant Valley Way, West Orange

NEW YORK

Department of Physical Medicine, University of Buffalo, Buffalo
Services: PT, OT, COUNS, PSYCHO, SPEECH, SOC WORK

The Institute of Physical Medicine and Rehabilitation, New York University-Bellevue Medical Center, 400 E. 34th St., New York
Services: PT, OT, COUNS, PSYCHO, SPEECH, SOC WORK

Mobility Incorporated, 10 Heatherbloom Rd., White Plains
Services: PT, OT, SPEECH, SOC WORK. Related Activities: WORKSHOP

Rochester Rehabilitation Center, Inc., 233 Alexander St., Rochester
Services: PT, OT, Work Evaluation

The Saranac Lake Rehabilitation Guild, Inc., 5 Franklin Ave., Saranac Lake

Services: EVALUATION, PT, OT, COUNS, IND FIT or MAT, SOC WORK, VOC TNG

New York State Rehabilitation Hospital, West Haverstraw
Services: PT, OT, COUNS, PSYCHO, SPEECH, SOC WORK

Institute for the Crippled and Disabled, 400 First Ave., New York
Services: MEDICAL EXAM AND CONSULTATION, PT, OT, COUNS, PSYCHO, ORTHOPEDIC AND PROSTHETIC APPLIANCES, SPEECH, IND FIT or MAT, SOC WORK, VOC TNG. Related Activities: SHELTERED WORKSHOP

Rehabilitation Services, Inc., 200 Court St., Binghamton
Services: PT, OT, SOC WORK

OHIO

Ohio State University Rehabilitation Center, Ohio State University, Columbus
Services: PT, OT, COUNS, PSYCHO, SPEECH, SOC WORK

The Cleveland Rehabilitation Center, 2239 E. 55th St., Cleveland
Services: PT, OT, COUNS, SPEECH, IND FIT or MAT, SOC WORK, VOC TNG. Related Activities: Sheltered Employment

Goodwill Industries of Cincinnati, 514 E. Pearl St., Cincinnati
Services: PT, OT, COUNS, SPEECH, IND FIT or MAT, VOC TNG, PSYCHO

OKLAHOMA

The Rehabilitation Center, Oklahoma A & M College, Okmulgee
Services: PT, COUNS, PSYCHO, VOC TNG

OREGON

Portland Rehabilitation Center, 1615 S. W. 14th Ave., Portland
Services: PT, OT, COUNS, SPEECH, IND FIT or MAT

PENNSYLVANIA

Philadelphia Society for Crippled Children and Adults, 2000 S. College Ave., Philadelphia
Services: PT. OT, PSYCHO, SPEECH, SOC WORK, VOC TNG

VIRGINIA

Woodrow Wilson Rehabilitation Center, Fishersville
Services: PT, OT, COUNS, PSYCHO, SPEECH, VOC TNG

WASHINGTON

Department of Labor and Industries Rehabilitation Center, 708 Fourth Ave., Seattle

Services: PT, OT, COUNS, AND PLACEMENT, PSYCHO (limited) IND FIT or MAT, SOC WORK

WISCONSIN

Curative Workshop of Milwaukee, Inc., 750 N. 18th St., Milwaukee
Services: PT, OT, SPEECH, IND FIT or MAT, SOC WORK, COUNS, PSYCHO and VOC TNG (available in community on referred basis)

The Curative Workshop of Racine, 2335 Northwestern Ave., Racine
Services: PT, OT

Curative Workshop of Green Bay, 1001 Cherry St., Green Bay

Lake Tomahawk State Camp, Lake Tomahawk
Services: COUNS, PSYCHO, VOC TNG

STATE MEDICAL ASSOCIATIONS

State medical societies have permanent offices through which you can obtain information on names and addresses of county medical societies (which can give you detailed information on physicians practicing in their area), hospitals, state laws, etc. The names and addresses of the executive secretaries of the state associations are published in every fourth issue of *The Journal of the American Medical Association* (535 North Dearborn Street, Chicago, 10, Ill.) The *Journal* is in all medical libraries and in major public ones.

ALABAMA

Medical Association, State of Alabama; Douglas L. Cannon, M.D., Executive Secretary, 537 Dexter Ave., Montgomery 4

ARIZONA

Arizona Medical Association, Inc., D. W. Melick, M.D., Executive Secretary, 541 Security Bldg., Phoenix

ARKANSAS

Arkansas Medical Society; Paul S. Schaefer, 215 Kelley Bldg., Fort Smith

CALIFORNIA

California Medical Association; Albert C. Daniels, M.D., Executive Secretary, 450 Sutter St., San Francisco

COLORADO

Colorado State Medical Society; Harvey T. Sethman, Executive Secretary, 835 Republic Bldg., Denver

CONNECTICUT

Connecticut State Medical Society; Greighton Barker, M.D., Executive Secretary, 160 St. Ronan St., New Haven 11

DELAWARE

Medical Society of Delaware; Andrew M. Gehret, M.D., Executive Secretary, 1007 Park Pl., Wilmington 7

DISTRICT OF COLUMBIA

Medical Society, District of Columbia; Theodore Wiprud, Executive Director and Secretary, 1718 M St., N.W., Washington 6

FLORIDA

Florida Medical Association; Samuel M. Day, M.D., 413 Professional Bldg., Jacksonville 1

GEORGIA

Medical Association of Georgia; Sid Wrightsman, Executive Secretary, 875 W. Peachtree St., N.E., Atlanta 3

IDAHO

Idaho State Medical Association; Robert S. McKean, M.D., Executive Secretary, 364 Sonna Bldg., Boise

ILLINOIS

Illinois State Medical Society; Harold M. Camp, M.D., Secretary, 224 S. Main St., Monmouth

INDIANA

Indiana State Medical Association; James A. Waggener, Executive Secretary, 23 E. Ohio St., Indianapolis

IOWA

Iowa State Medical Society; Allan B. Phillips, M.D., 529 36th St., Des Moines

KANSAS

Kansas Medical Society; D. D. Vermillion, M.D., Executive Secretary, 512 New England Bldg., Topeka

KENTUCKY

Kentucky State Medical Association; Bruce Underwood, M.D., Secretary, 620 S. Third St., Louisville

LOUISIANA

Louisiana State Medical Society; C. Grenes Cole, M.D., Secretary-Treasurer, 1430 Tulane Ave., New Orleans

MAINE

Maine Medical Association; W. Mayo Payson, Executive Secretary, 142 High St., Portland 3

MARYLAND

Medical and Chir. Faculty of Maryland; George H. Yeager, M.D., 1211 Cathedral St., Baltimore 1

MASSACHUSETTS

Massachusetts Medical Society; Robert W. Buck, M.D., Executive Secretary, 22 The Fenway, Boston 15

MICHIGAN

Michigan State Medical Society; L. F. Foster, M.D., 606 Townsend St., Lansing 15

MINNESOTA

Minnesota State Medical Association; B. B. Souster, M.D., Lowry Medical Arts Bldg., St. Paul 2

MISSISSIPPI

Mississippi State Medical Association; Rowland B. Kennedy, Executive Secretary, 507 First Federal Bldg., Jackson

MISSOURI

Missouri State Medical Association; H. E. Petersen, M.D., Executive Secretary, 634 North Grand Blvd., St. Louis 3

MONTANA

Montana Medical Association; L. R. Hegland, Executive Secretary, 104 N. Broadway, Billings

NEBRASKA

Nebraska State Medical Association; R. B. Adams, M.D., Executive Secretary, 1315 Sharp Bldg., Lincoln

NEVADA

Nevada State Medical Association; W. A. O'Brien, III, M.D., Secretary, 505 Chestnut St., Reno

NEW HAMPSHIRE
New Hampshire Medical Society; Deering G. Smith, M.D., Executive Secretary, 44 Chester St., Nashua

NEW JERSEY

Medical Society of New Jersey; M. H. Greifinger, M.D., Executive Officer, 315 W. State St., Trenton

NEW MEXICO

New Mexico Medical Society; Ralph R. Marshall, Executive Secretary, 221 W. Central Ave., Albuquerque

NEW YORK

Medical Society, State of New York; W. P. Anderton, M.D., Secretary, 386 Fourth Ave., New York

NORTH CAROLINA

Medical Society, State of North Carolina; James T. Barnes, Executive Secretary, 203 Capitol Club Bldg., Raleigh

NORTH DAKOTA

North Dakota State Medical Association; Lyle Limond, M.D., Box 1198, Bismarck

OHIO

Ohio State Medical Association; C. S. Nelson, Executive Secretary, 79 E. State St., Columbus

OKLAHOMA

Oklahoma State Medical Association; R. H. Graham, Executive Secretary, 1227 Classen St., Oklahoma City

OREGON

Oregon State Medical Society; C. E. Littlehales, M.D., Medical Dental Bldg., Portland 5

PENNSYLVANIA

Medical Society, State of Pennsylvania; H. B. Gardner, 230 State St., Harrisburg

RHODE ISLAND

Rhode Island Medical Society; Thomas Perry, Jr., M.D., 106 Francis St., Providence

SOUTH CAROLINA

South Carolina Medical Association; Robert L. Wilson, Jr., M.D., 120 W. Cheves St., Florence

SOUTH DAKOTA

South Dakota State Medical Association; John C. Foster, Executive Secretary, First National Bank Bldg., Sioux Falls

TENNESSEE

Tennessee State Medical Association; V. O. Foster, Executive Secretary, 706 Church St., Nashville

HAWAII

Hawaii Territorial Medical Association; Samuel L. Yee, M.D., Executive Secretary, 510 S. Beretania St., Honolulu

ISTHMIAN CANAL ZONE

Medical Association, Isthmian Canal Zone; 1 Robert Berger, M.D., Box "O," Ancon, Canal Zone

PUERTO RICO

Medical Association of Puerto Rico; L. R. Guzmán-López, Executive Secretary, Box 9111, Santurce, 29

CHAPTER IV: GETTING ON IN YEARS—SAFELY

FOOD FOR COMFORT AND GOOD DIGESTION

If an older person is coming to live with you, pin these "DO'S" and "DON'TS" up on your kitchen wall—or at least, keep them firmly in mind. They were summarized by the Division of Nutrition of Pennsylvania's Department of Health. They represent a generally accepted program for a normal older adult.

In general: Watch carbohydrates and fats, particularly animal fats such as egg yolk and butter, which increase blood cholesterol. High blood cholesterol is found in high blood pressure, hardening of the arteries, and nephritis. A well-rounded diet is the *best* source of needed vitamins. The foods most likely to cause distress are fatty rich foods, concentrated sweets and excessive amounts of tea and coffee. Advice for the older person:

He Should	He Should NOT
Have *regular* meals	*Skip* meals
Have *small* rather than large meals	*Overeat* at any one meal
Have heaviest meal at *noon*	Eat too heavily before *bedtime*
Have an *easily digested* evening meal	Eat rich, heavy food *at night*
Eat or drink something *hot* at each meal	Have meals of all *cold* foods
Have a *hot beverage* with evening meal	Take *strong* tea or coffee in evening
Take *hot* milk, cocoa or water	Drink too much *tea or coffee*
Include *milk* in some form each day	Forget *liquids,* especially water and milk
Include some *fruit* and *vegetables* daily	Take *fried, rich, spicy* foods often.
Chop, mince or *grind* foods hard to chew.	

THE RIGHT EXERCISE FOR THE AGING

Intelligent people know that doctors should prescribe exercises just as they prescribe drugs, and for the same reasons. In the thorough physical examination every older person ought to have at least annually, organs are given tests at the basal resting condition and stress tests with loads corresponding to what lies ahead in the years to come. In this way a doctor can measure any individual's tolerance for physical activity and plan for him a program of exercise that fits his condition.

Dr. C. Ward Crampton, a geriatrician, has been developing the following exercises over the many years he has studied elderly patients. He believes that they are safe enough for nearly everyone. However, before using them, he advises that the elderly check with their own physician.

"The Star Gazer": It will help posture. Clasp hands behind head—not neck—and pull head forward on count one. On count two the head is erect. On count three look up, and on count four push the head back as far as possible and try to look at the back of your neck. Hold this position, turning the head from side to side for four more slow counts with the chest high. Take two good long breaths and repeat slowly three times. This exercise strengthens the neck muscles, helps hold the head high all the time.

"Churning": This is practically perfect for toning up the vital organs.

Sit on the side of the bed or a chair, hands on knees. Then make the middle of the body describe a circle without moving the head. To learn this rolling, first try throwing the hips to the left and right, then front and back. This will help you get the feel of the circular motion. This churning massages your internal organs and helps prevent constipation. It is one of the oldest exercises in the world and one of the most valuable. Try it twenty times clockwise, then counter-clockwise.

"The Stretch": One of the wake-up routines that won't tire you out or strain your muscles, but will put them back in working order after their night's rest.

When you open your eyes in the morning, take a few minutes out to yawn and stretch. Flex and twist your body. Breathe deeply. Rest. Then stretch again. By doing this you are giving internal organs some massage, and circulation is being stepped up.

"Pumping": This is one of those exercises that are so simple they hardly seem like exercise because they've been right in front of you all your life.

After the stretch lie still and breathe a bit. Then make the chest big by pulling it up. This leaves the abdomen hollow. Count to six. On the seventh and eighth counts, make the chest small by pushing down. This makes the abdomen bulge. Repeat three times without breathing. Then take three long, slow breaths. Repeat the entire procedure three times.

"The Kick-up": This is part of the wake-up routine which ought to be done every day, because the only way to get results is through consistent performance. It is one of the simple, easy, rhythmic exercises which help keep organs working properly.

Lift the right knee to the chest then kick the bedclothes over the foot of the bed—with one kick. Do the same with the left knee. Kick the bedclothes over the footboard. Raise both legs up straight. If you wish to kick a few more times after the air has been cleared of flying covers, do so. Put some energy into it, but stop after half a dozen kicks.

Chapter V: Financing Old Age

COST OF HOSPITAL CARE

In the few hospitals in the country which have special chronic disease facilities, either separate wings or floors, special schedules of charges may be in force. In general, however, charges are customarily made according to accommodations and special services, whether for an elderly long-term patient or a short-term young one.

Since 1947 the American Hospital Association has made annual surveys of the entire hospital field. In its 1952 survey (*Hospital Rates 1952*), sixty-seven per cent of all general hospitals in the United States reported to the Association. They varied in their daily rates, depending on a number of factors such as standards, room location, type of services rendered, etc. You can get a fair idea of what your local situation is likely to be by the Association's rate study:

Hospital Room Rates: The Association found that "the most common daily room rates in 1952 in all U. S. general hospitals were as follows: single, $12.23; two-bed room, $9.68; and multi-bed room, $8.24. These rates are approximately seven per cent higher than in 1951 and over forty per cent higher than those obtaining in 1947. . . . Charges for operating rooms, diagnostic tests and therapeutic treatments are gradually increasing although the most frequent rate has remained fairly constant for the past six years . . ."

In regard to policies on such matters as anesthesia, laboratory tests, drugs, etc., the report states: "More than seventy per cent of the hospitals have only one rate on special services which applies to all patients irrespective of type of room occupied or financial status of the patients. Less than 10 per cent have two and three rates which are charged according to type of accommodation used by the patients. Compared with similar data five years ago, the one rate system seems to be gaining in practice."

No person can choose where he is going to fall ill; yet there is something to be said for selection of a hospital (for a non-acute stage, say, of a chronic illness) on the basis of rates. As the following table shows, room rates in general hospitals in 1952 varied considerably from one region of the country to another:

REGIONAL SUMMARY OF AVERAGE OF THE MOST COMMON DAILY ROOM RATES IN GENERAL HOSPITALS, 1952

Region	*One Person Room*	*Two-Person Room*	*Multi-Bed Room*
New England	$14.49	$11.44	$ 9.58
Middle Atlantic	13.56	10.76	8.26
South Atlantic	10.68	8.17	6.46
E.North Central	12.29	9.60	7.69
E.South Central	9.49	6.98	5.21
W.North Central	10.34	8.06	6.15
W.South Central	9.39	6.97	4.59
Mountain	11.29	8.95	7.99
Pacific	15.92	13.13	11.58
United States	12.23	9.68	8.24

FEES IN A HOME FOR THE AGED

St. Barnabas Hospital has a home for aged men and women on its grounds. The sums charged for admission to any home for old people, and the board rates, vary widely, not only in accordance with accommodations but with endowment or sponsorship. Nevertheless, the fees charged at the Braker Memorial Home will give you some idea of what to expect elsewhere in an institution which offers the same or similar services as this one in New York City.

NOTE: The Braker Home is primarily for persons between the ages of fifty-five to eighty years, in good health, who do not require medical or nursing care. Accommodations include room, board and laundry service, and medical and nursing care during any acute illness in the Braker Infirmary, at a charge of fifty cents per day above the board rate. All hospital and medical resources of St. Barnabas Hospital are available to the Braker guests when needed.

Admission Fee: $200, returnable if guest leaves at any time.

Application Fee: $7.50, payable at time of examination, not refunded, whether or not candidate is suitable for admission.

Daily Rates: $3 per day for a single room with running water; $3.50 to $4.50 per day for single room with interconnecting bath; $5 per day for double room with running water.

POSTSCRIPT: Though you may find fees lower or higher elsewhere, the waiting lists may be equally long. At Braker the wait is now four years, and additional applications have been refused.

NOTE: A staff physician examines the patient at home after his application forms are filled out, for which the fee is $5 to $30 depending on distance traveled. The fee is not refunded whether or not the patient is found suitable for admission.

BLUE CROSS AND BLUE SHIELD (NON-PROFIT) PLANS

Blue Cross Plans make it possible to prepay hospital bills. Each Plan is organized independently and is governed by a local board of trustees composed of community leaders, hospital representatives, and the medical profession, all of whom serve without pay. Eighty-four out of the eighty-seven Blue Cross Plans, through a coordinating organization, Blue Shield, offer protection against surgical and/or medical expense.

Since rates, benefits, and enrollment regulations are tailored to fit the local area, it will be necessary to query the community where your older friends and relatives live, to find out if they are eligible as subscribers, and for what length of time.

Code symbols in the following list: * Indicates non-profit medical and/or surgical plan available.

B means that subscribers of the Plan who have to be hospitalized in another area receive service benefits through participation in the Inter-Plan Service Benefit Bank.

T shows that the local Plan participates in the Inter-Plan Transfer Agreement. This reciprocal program permits subscribers moving to another area to transfer their membership to another participating Plan.

United States

ALABAMA

*Blue Cross-Blue Shield of Alabama; 2219 First Ave., N., Birmingham 3. *B, T*

ARIZONA

*Associated Hospital Service of Arizona; 605 N. Seventh Ave., P.O. Box 2710, Phoenix. *B, T*

ARKANSAS

*Arkansas Medical and Hospital Service, Inc., 1210 Main St., Little Rock. *B, T*

CALIFORNIA

*Hospital Service of Southern California, 3443 Wilshire Blvd., Los Angeles 5. *B, T*

(Blue Shield available through California Physicians' Service, 450 Mission St., San Francisco 5.)

*Hospital Service of California, 1919 Webster, Oakland 12. *T*

COLORADO

*Colorado Hospital Service, 1653 Lawrence St., Denver 2. *B, T*

(Blue Shield available through Colorado Medical Service, Inc.)

DELAWARE

*Group Hospital Service, Inc. 908 West St., Wilmington 99. *B, T*

DISTRICT OF COLUMBIA

*Group Hospitalization, Inc., Transportation Bldg., Washington 6. *B, T*

(Blue Shield available through Medical Service of District of Columbia, 825 Seventeenth St., N.W., Washington 6.)

FLORIDA

*Blue Cross of Florida, Inc., 532 Riverside Ave., P.O. Box 1798, Jacksonville. *B, T*

(Blue Shield available through Blue Shield of Florida, Inc., P.O. Box 1798, Jacksonville 1.)

GEORGIA

United Hospitals Service Association, 161 Spring St., N.W., Atlanta 3
*Georgia Hospital Service Association, Inc., Swift Bldg., Columbus. *B. T*
*Hospital Service Association of Savannah, Realty Bldg., Savannah. *B, T*

(Blue Shield available through Physicians Service, Inc., Swift Bldg., Columbus, and Physicians Service Association, Inc. of Savannah, Realty Bldg.)

IDAHO

*Idaho Hospital Service, 205 Jefferson Bldg., Boise. *B, T*

ILLINOIS

*Blue Cross Plan for Hospital Care, 425 N. Michigan Ave., Chicago 90. *B, T* and
*Illinois Hospital Service, Inc., 227 N. Wyman St., Rockford. *T*

(Blue Shield available through Medical-Surgical Service of Illinois, 303 First National Bank Bldg., Alton; Illinois Medical Service, 425 N. Michigan Ave., Chicago 90; Rock Island County Medical Service, 1630 Fifth Ave., Moline; Northern Illinois Medical Service Corporation, 227 North Wyman St., Rockford.)

INDIANA

*Blue Cross Hospital Service, 600 Terminal Bldg., 110 N. Illinois St., Indianapolis 9. *B, T*

(Blue Shield available through Mutual Medical Insurance, Inc., 110 N. Illinois St., Indianapolis 4.)

IOWA

*Hospital Service, Inc., of Iowa, Liberty Bldg., Des Moines 7. *B, T*
*Associated Hospitals Service, Inc., 522 Security Bldg., Sioux City 15. *B, T*

(Blue Shield available through Iowa Medical Service, 324 Liberty Bldg., Des Moines 9.)

KANSAS

*Kansas Hospital Service Association, Inc., 603 Topeka Blvd., Topeka. *B, T*
(Blue Shield available through Kansas Physicians' Service.)

KENTUCKY

*Blue Cross Hospital Plan, Inc., 231 W. Main St., Louisville 2. *B, T*
(Blue Shield available through Medical Service Mutual, Inc., Second National Bank Bldg., Ashland; and Kentucky Physicians Mutual, Inc., 231 W. Main St., Louisville.)

LOUISIANA

*Louisiana Hospital Service, 1006 Florida St., P.O. Box 1166, Baton Rouge. *B, T*
*Hospital Service Association of New Orleans, American Bank Bldg., New Orleans 12. *B, T*
(Blue Shield available through Louisiana Physicians Service, Inc., 119 North Galvez, New Orleans.)

MAINE

*Associated Hospital Service of Maine, 509 Forest Ave., Portland 5. *B, T*

MARYLAND

*Maryland Hospital Service, 200 W. Baltimore St., Baltimore 1. *B, T*
(Blue Shield available through Maryland Medical Service, Inc., 200 W. Baltimore St., Baltimore 1.)

MASSACHUSETTS

*Massachusetts Hospital Service, Inc., 38 Chauncy St., Boston 6. *T*

MICHIGAN

*Michigan Hospital Service, Washington Blvd. Bldg., Detroit 26. *B, T*

MINNESOTA

*Minnesota Hospital Service Association, 2610 University Ave., St. Paul 4. *B, T*
(Blue Shield available through Minnesota Medical Service, Inc.)

MISSISSIPPI

*Mississippi Hospital and Medical Service, 741 N. State St., P.O. Box 1043, Jackson 2. *B, T*

MISSOURI

*Group Hospital Service, Inc., 1021 McGee St., Kansas City 6. *B, T*
*Group Hospital Service, Inc., 4908 Delmar Blvd., St. Louis 8. *B, T*

(Blue Shield available through Surgical-Medical Care, 1021 McGee St., Kansas City 6; and Missouri Medical Service, 3615 Olive St., St. Louis 8.)

MONTANA

*Hospital Service Association of Montana, Rocky Mountain Bldg., P.O. Drawer BC, Great Falls. *B, T*

(Blue Shield available through Montana Physicians' Service, 3 N. Main St., P.O. Box 1677, Helena.)

NEBRASKA

*Nebraska Blue Cross Hospital Service Association, 518 Kilpatrick Bldg., Omaha 2. *B, T*

(Blue Shield available through Nebraska Medical Service, 518 Kilpatrick Bldg., Omaha 2.)

NEW HAMPSHIRE

*New Hampshire-Vermont Hospitalization, 6 Odd Fellows Ave., Concord, N. H. *B, T*

(Blue Shield available through New Hampshire-Vermont Physician Service, 6 Odd Fellows Ave., Concord.)

NEW JERSEY

*Hospital Service Plan of New Jersey, 790 Broad St., Newark 1. *B*

(Blue Shield available through Medical-Surgical Plan of New Jersey, 790 Broad St., Newark 1.)

NEW MEXICO

*Hospital Service, Inc., 207 Dartmouth Dr., N.E., Albuquerque. *B, T*

NEW YORK

*Associated Hospital Service of Capital District, 112 State St., Albany 7. *B, T*
*Hospital Service Corporation of Western New York, Blue Cross Bldg., 298 Main St., Buffalo 2. *B, T*
*Chautauqua Region Hospital Service Corporation, Wellman Bldg., Jamestown. *B, T*
*Associated Hospital Service of New York, 80 Lexington Ave., New York 16. *B, T*

*Rochester Hospital Service Corporation, 41 Chestnut St., Rochester 4. *B, T*
*Group Hospital Service, Inc., 407 S. State St., Syracuse 2. *B, T*
*Hospital Plan, Inc., 5 Hopper St., Utica. *T*
*Hospital Service Corporation of Jefferson County, Chamber of Commerce Bldg., Watertown. *B, T*
(Blue shield available through Northeastern New York Medical Service, Inc., 112 State St., Albany 7; Western New York Medical Plan, Inc., 298 Main St., Buffalo 2; Chautauqua Region Medical Service, Inc., Wellman Bldg., Jamestown; United Medical Service, Inc., 2 Park Ave., New York 16; Gennessee Valley Medical Care, Inc., 41 Chestnut St., Rochester 4; Central New York Medical Plan, Inc., 407 S. State St., Syracuse 2; Medical and Surgical Care, Inc., 5 Hopper St., Utica.)

NORTH CAROLINA

*Hospital Saving Association of North Carolina, Chapel Hill. *B, T*
*Hospital Care Association, Inc., Blue Cross Bldg., 410 W. Geer St., Durham. *B, T*
(Blue Shield available through Hospital Saving Association of North Carolina, Chapel Hill.)

NORTH DAKOTA

*North Dakota Hospital Service Association, 114½ Roberts St., Fargo. *B, T*
(Blue Shield available through North Dakota Physicians Service.)

OHIO

*Akron Hospital Service, 65 W. State St., Akron. *B, T*
*Hospital Service, Inc. of Stark County, 201 Ninth St., N.W., Canton 2. *B, T*
*Hospital Care Corporation, 1365 William Howard Taft Rd., Cincinnati 6. *B, T*
*Cleveland Hospital Service Association, 2060 E. 9th St., Cleveland 15. *B, T*
*Central Hospital Service, 79 E. State St., Columbia 15. *B, T*
*Hospital Service, Inc., 2nd Floor, Dauch Bldg., Lima. *B, T*
*Hospital Service Association of Toledo, 2139 Madison Ave., Toledo 2. *B, T*
*Associated Hospital Service, Inc., Realty Bldg., Youngstown 3. *B, T*
(Blue Shield available through Ohio Medical Indemnity, Inc., 925 Beggs Bldg., 21 E. State St., Columbus 15.)

OKLAHOMA

*Group Hospital Service, 315 S. Denver, Tulsa. *B, T*

(Blue Shield available through Oklahoma Physicians Service.)

OREGON

*Northwest Hospital Service, 1320 S.W. Broadway, P.O. Box 1271, Portland 7. *B, T*

(Blue Shield available through Coos Bay Hospital Association, 218 Hall Bldg., Coos Bay; Pacific Hospital Association, 343 Eugene Medical Center, Eugene; Klamath Medical Service Bureau, 405 Pine St., Klamath Falls; Physicians Association of Clackamas County, Barclay Bldg., Oregon City; Oregon Physicians' Service, 619 S.W. Eleventh Ave., Portland 5.)

PENNSYLVANIA

*Hospital Service Plan of Lehigh Valley, 201 Hunsicker Bldg., Allentown. *B, T*

*Capital Hospital Service, Inc. 116 Pine St., Harrisburg. *B, T*

*Associated Hospital Service of Philadelphia, 112 S. 16th St., Philadelphia 2. *B, T*

*Hospital Service Association of Pittsburgh, Union Trust Bldg., Pittsburgh 19. *B, T*

*Hospital Service Association of Northeastern Pennsylvania, Bennett Bldg., Wilkes-Barre. *B, T*

(Blue Shield available through Medical Service Association of Pennsylvania, 2521 Front St., Harrisburg.)

RHODE ISLAND

*Hospital Service Corporation of Rhode Island, 31 Canal St., Providence 2. *T*

SOUTH CAROLINA

*South Carolina Hospital Service Plan, 309 E. McBee Ave., Greenville. *B, T*

(Blue Shield available through South Carolina Medical Care Plan.)

SOUTH DAKOTA

Served by Sioux City, Iowa

TENNESSEE

*Tennessee Hospital Service Association, Blue Cross Bldg., 707 Chestnut St., Chattanooga 2. *B, T*

*Community Hospital Service, Holston Valley Community Hospital, Kingsport. *B, T*
*Memphis Hospital Service and Surgical Association, 1006 Dermon Bldg., Third and Court Sts., Memphis. *B, T*
(Blue Shield available through Tennessee Hospital Service Association; Community Medical Service, Inc., 145 Commerce St., Kingsport; Memphis Hospital Service and Surgical Association.)

TEXAS

*Group Hospital Service, 2208 Main St., Dallas 1. *B, T*
(Blue Shield available through The Dallas County Medical Plan, 433 Medical Arts Bldg., Dallas 1; and Group Medical and Surgical Service, 2208 Main St., Dallas 1.)

UTAH

*Intermountain Hospital Service, 24½ E. First South, P.O. Box 270, Salt Lake City. *B, T*
(Blue Shield available through Medical Service Bureau of the Utah State Medical Association, Inc.)

VERMONT

(Served by Concord, New Hampshire)

VIRGINIA

*Piedmont Hospital Service Association, Peoplès National Bank Bldg., Lynchburg. *B, T*
*Tidewater Hospital Service Association, 269 Boush St., Norfolk. *B, T*
*Virginia Hospital Service Association, 207 East Franklin St., Richmond 19.
*Hospital Service Association of Roanoke, Colonial-American Bank Bldg., Roanoke 8. *B, T*
(Blue Shield available through Virginia Medical Service Association, 207 E. Franklin St., Richmond 19; and Surgical Care, Inc., Colonial-American Bank Bldg., Roanoke 8.)

WASHINGTON

*Washington Hospital Service, 2121 Third Ave., Seattle 1. *B, T*

WEST VIRGINIA

*Associated Hospitals, Inc., 404 Bland St., Bluefield. *B, T*
*Hospital Service, Inc., 203 Atlas Bldg., Charleston. *B, T*
*Marion County Hospital Service, Inc., 201 Masonic Bldg., Fairmont. *B, T*

*Blue Cross Hospital Service, Inc., Hotel Prichard Bldg., P.O. Box 238, Huntington 9.

*Parkersburg Hospital Service, Inc., 202 Union Trust Bldg., Parkersburg. *B, T*

*West Virginia Hospital Service, Inc., Peoples Federal Savings Bldg., Wheeling. *B, T*

(Blue Shield available through Surgical Service, Inc., 404 Bland St., Bluefield; Medical Service, Inc., Atlas Bldg., Charleston; Medical-Surgical Service, Inc., Empire National Bank Bldg., Clarksburg; Marion County Medical Service, Inc., 201 Masonic Bldg., Fairmont; Medical Care, Inc., Hotel Prichard Bldg., Huntington 9; Medical-Surgical Service, Inc., 265 High St., Morgantown; Medical-Surgical Care, Inc., 202 Union Trust Bldg., Parkersburg; West Virginia Medical Service, Inc., Peoples Federal Savings Bldg., Wheeling.)

WISCONSIN

*Associated Hospital Service, Inc., 826 N. Plankinton Ave., Milwaukee 3. *B, T*

(Blue Shield available through Wisconsin Physicians Service of the State Medical Society of Wisconsin, 704 E. Gorham St., Madison 3; and Surgical Care, 208 E. Wisconsin Ave., Milwaukee 2.)

WYOMING

*Wyoming Hospital Service, Read Bldg., P.O. Box 1252, Cheyenne. *B, T*

(Blue Shield available through Wyoming Medical Service.)

TERRITORIES

HAWAII

Hawaii Medical Service Association, 1154 Bishop St., Honolulu 8.

(Blue Shield Plan; non-profit hospital plan also available.)

PUERTO RICO

*Puerto Rico Hospital Service Association, Diario de Puerto Rico Bldg., Ponce de Leon Ave., Santurce. *B, T*

CANADA

ALBERTA

Alberta Blue Cross Plan, 10124 101st St., P.O. Box 610, Edmonton. *B, T*

BRITISH COLUMBIA

Medical Services Association, 423 West Broadway, Vancouver. (Blue Shield Plan)

MANITOBA

Manitoba Hospital Service Association, 116 Edmonton St., P.O. Box 2885, Winnipeg. *B, T*

(Blue Shield Plan available through Manitoba Medical Service, 149 Portage Ave., East Winnipeg.)

NEW BRUNSWICK

*Maritime Hospital Service Association, 560 Main St., Moncton.

(Blue Shield Plan; non-profit hospital plan also available.)

PRINCE EDWARD ISLAND

*Maritime Hospital Service Association, 560 Main St., Moncton, N.B. *B, T*

ONTARIO

*Blue Cross Plan for Hospital Care, 135 S. Clair Ave., W., Toronto 5. *B, T*

(Blue Shield available through Physicians' Services, Inc., 25 Bloor St., W., Toronto 5.)

QUEBEC

*Quebec Hospital Service Association, 1200 S. Alexandre St., Montreal 2. *B, T*

SASKATCHEWAN

Group Medical Services, 1843 Broad St., Regina. (Blue Shield Plan available.)

Medical Services, Inc., 201 Standard Bldg., Saskatoon.

CHAPTER VI: TO WORK OR NOT TO WORK

POSSIBLE JOB OPENINGS

The Vocational Guidance Bureau of Cleveland, Ohio, which maintains a Counsellor for Older Workers, has made a list of suitable occupations for the elderly. As the Bureau points out, any Counsellor can only help a man or woman analyze his own situation, and suggest possible occupations for which he seems fitted by ability, temperament, education, experience, interest, or special aptitude. His job is to get in touch with sources for such openings, and "to persevere to the point of job realization." These are the occupations which may not be glamorous but do hold out possibilities:

For Men Well Over Fifty	For Not-So-Young Women
Hotel Clerk	Cashier or Checker
Auto Salesman	File Clerk
Insurance Salesman	Dormitory Supervisor
Real Estate Salesman	Laundry Worker
Retail Clerk—Store Walker	Information Clerk
Messenger or Office Clerk	P.B.X. Operator
Tool or Stock Room Clerk	Bakery Clerk or Worker
Coal Office Clerk	Demonstrator
Contact Man or Survey Worker	Packer or Wrapper
Recreation Parlor Attendant	Nurse Attendant
Filling Station Attendant	Housekeeper or Companion
Elevator Operator	Rest Room Attendant
Maintenance Worker	Kitchen Helper
Night Watchman	Linen Room Attendant
Mail Room Clerk	Seamstress or Alteration Worker
Custodian or Caretaker	Retail Clerk
Gardener or Groundskeeper	Canvasser or Saleswoman
Cigar Counter Clerk	Charwoman or Custodian
Candy-Tobacco-Food Broker	Baby Sitter
Blueprint Machine Operator	Private Tutor
Manufacturer's Representative	Cook or Cafeteria Worker
Museum or Plant Guard	Survey Worker
Tailor or Presser	Religious Worker
Weigh Master	Telephone Solicitor
Check Room Attendant	Receptionist
Sweeper or Clean-Up Man	Dispensary Aide
Parking Lot Attendant	Bookbindery Worker
Lumberyard Utility Man	Protective Service Worker
Route Man or Canvasser	Hemstitcher & Buttonmaker
Telephone Solicitor	Carpet Sewer and Binder
Building Lobby Receptionist	Tearoom Hostess
Furniture Repairman	Millinery Shopworker
Shipping & Receiving Clerk	Assembler
Electrical Appliance Repairman	Mailing Service Worker
Shoe Cobbler	Merchandise Marker
Gunsmith	Corsetier

The Vocational Guidance Bureau offers these suggestions for home industries and small business for the golden years, with the advice that "there is no age limit for the exercise of perseverance, ingenuity, and skill."

Upholsterer
Neighborhood Handyman
Weaver
Basket Maker
Doll Hospital
Fixit Shop
Key Shop
Flower Shop
Furniture Refinisher
Chair Caner
Fish-lure Maker
Income Tax Expert
Notary Service
Accountant Service (Small Accts.)
Telephone Solicitor
Costume Jewelry Maker
Leather Worker
Metal Craft Worker
Valet Service
Window Curtain Service
Toy Maker
Model Builder
Saw and Tool Sharpening
Specialty Food Shop
Bicycle Repair Shop
Card Shop
Used Clothing Shop
Cabinet Making Shop
Shoe Repair Shop
Concession Stand
Dry Cleaning & Laundry Agency
Hobby Shop
Confectionery
Souvenir Shop
Newsstand
Gift Shop
Toy Repair Shop

VOCATIONAL REHABILITATION OFFICES

Each of the forty-eight states, the District of Columbia, Alaska, Puerto Rico, and Hawaii, operate vocational rehabilitation programs. Thirty-five states are authorized to provide separate and distinct services for the blind. In most cases, the Division of Vocational Rehabilitation is listed in the telephone directory under "State Department of Education." The main office of the state programs are listed here; that office will give you the address of its branches and the agency, if one exists, which deals with the visually handicapped, irrespective of age.

ALABAMA

501 Dexter Ave., Montgomery (nine local offices)

ALASKA

P.O. Box 2688, Juneau

ARIZONA

13 S. Seventeenth Ave., Phoenix (two local offices)

ARKANSAS

1811 Spring St., Little Rock (five local offices)

CALIFORNIA

705 California St., Sacramento (21 local offices)

COLORADO

210 State Office Bldg., Denver (four local offices and one for the blind)

CONNECTICUT

156 Capitol Ave., Hartford (five local offices and one for the blind)

DELAWARE

11 Concord Ave., Wilmington (and an office for the blind)

DISTRICT OF COLUMBIA

Federal Security Bldg., Fourth St. and Independence Ave.

FLORIDA

Capitol Bldg., Tallahassee (seven local offices and one for the blind)

GEORGIA

State Office Bldg., Atlanta (sixteen local offices)

HAWAII

P.O. Box 2360, Honolulu (one local office and another for the blind)

IDAHO

308 State House, Boise (and an office for the blind)

ILLINOIS

700 East Adams St., Springfield (twenty-eight local offices)

INDIANA

701 Board of Trade Bldg., Indianapolis (fourteen local offices and one for the blind)

IOWA

415 Bankers Trust Bldg., Des Moines (and an office for the blind)

KANSAS

1001 Harrison St., Topeka (six local offices and two for the blind)

KENTUCKY

State Capitol, Frankfort (twelve local offices)

LOUISIANA

State Capitol, Baton Rouge (thirteen local offices)

MAINE

32 Winthrop St., Augusta (four local offices and two for the blind)

MARYLAND

1111 Lexington Bldg., Baltimore (four local offices)

MASSACHUSETTS

200 Newbury St., Boston (six local offices)

MICHIGAN

900 Bauch Bldg., Lansing (eight local offices and three for the blind)

MINNESOTA

State Office Bldg., St. Paul (six local offices and one for the blind)

MISSISSIPPI

120 N. Congress St., Jackson (nine local offices and four for the blind)

MISSOURI

Governor Hotel, Jefferson City (eight local offices and four for the blind)

MONTANA

508 Power Block, Helena (two local offices, one for the blind)

NEBRASKA

Capitol Bldg., Lincoln (four local offices, one for the blind)

NEVADA

Capitol Bldg., Carson City

NEW HAMPSHIRE

State Capitol, Concord (and one office for the blind)

NEW JERSEY

38 S. Clinton Ave., Trenton (eight local offices and one for the blind)

NEW YORK

Education Bldg. (nine local offices, and five for blind)

NORTH CAROLINA

Education Bldg., Raleigh (ten local offices, one for the blind)

NORTH DAKOTA

University Station, Grand Forks

OHIO

83 S. High St., Columbus (ten local offices, and eleven for blind)

OKLAHOMA

708 Midwest Bldg., Oklahoma City (six local offices)

OREGON

103 State Library Bldg., Salem (four local offices and five for the blind)

PENNSYLVANIA

Blackstone Bldg., 112 Market St., Harrisburg (nine local offices and nine for blind)

PUERTO RICO

Medical Arts Bldg., San Juan (five local offices)

RHODE ISLAND

205 Benefit St., Providence (and one for blind)

SOUTH CAROLINA

425 Calhoun Office Bldg., Columbia (fifteen local offices and one for blind)

SOUTH DAKOTA

State Capitol, Pierre (and office for blind)

TENNESSEE

411 Seventh Ave., North Nashville (twelve local offices and five for blind)

TEXAS

302 Walton Bldg., Austin (seventeen local offices and seven for blind)

UTAH

Capitol Bldg., Salt Lake City (three local offices)

VERMONT

84 State St., Montpelier (and office for blind)

VIRGINIA

State Department of Education, Richmond (ten local offices and one for blind)

WASHINGTON

Old Capitol Bldg., Olympia (five local offices and one for blind)

WEST VIRGINIA

Capital City Bldg., Charleston (ten local offices)

WISCONSIN

State Office Bldg., Madison (nine local offices and one for blind)

WYOMING

State Capitol Bldg., Cheyenne (two local offices)

FORTY PLUS CLUBS FOR MEN WITHOUT JOBS

As the name implies, Forty Plus Club members are in their middle years, or beyond. They are men who are temporarily out of employment. They have previously held executive positions where they have earned more than $5,000 a year. The Forty Plus Clubs are independently organized, as cooperative, non-profit organizations in which members do all the work of getting jobs for fellow-members. They have been in operation about fifteen years; their constant turn-over of enrollment proves the idea is successful. If your relative lives in one of the communities where such a club exists, and can qualify for it, urge him to use it as a means of re-entering employment.

Forty Plus Club of New England, 120 Milk St., Boston, Mass.
Forty Plus Club of New York, Inc., 220 Broadway, New York 38, N. Y.
Men Over Forty, 8 S. Dearborn St., Chicago 3, Ill.
Forty Plus Club of Philadelphia, 1714 Chestnut St., Philadelphia 3, Pa.
Forty Plus, Inc., Transportation Bldg., Detroit 26, Mich.

Forty Plus Executives of Western New York, 203 Chamber of Commerce Bldg., Buffalo 2, N. Y.

Forty Plus Association of Northern California, Inc., 170 Tenth St., San Francisco, Calif.

Forty Plus Association of Southern California, 525 Flower St., Los Angeles 13, Calif.

Forty Plus of Greater Kansas City Area, 218 YMCA Bldg., 404 E. 10th St., Kansas City 6, Mo.

Chapter VII: Active Leisure: New Ways for Old

ORGANIZING A CLUB FOR OLDER PEOPLE

The Philadelphia program of organizing clubs for older people on a city-wide basis is said to be the first in this country. The plan of organization formulated there can be applied in any community, large or small, and does not necessarily require professional leadership. The following *"Salient Points on Organization of Clubs for Older People"* by Georgene E. Bowen, Director of Recreation for Philadelphia's Older People, will show you what is necessary to organize and make a club successful.

Facilities

Convenient to transportation
Near ground level
Atmosphere attractive, warm and friendly
Cooking and toilet facilities on same floor, if possible
Good lighting in room and passages
Piano, folding tables, radio, if possible

Sponsoring Agency or Committee

Provides facilities
Gives financial backing (see "Member Participation")
Secures experienced leader
Acts as guardian and protector of club from exploitation
Makes certain decisions in advance:

1. Size of club-group to be accommodated
2. Boundaries from which members will be accepted
3. Eligibility of members—age, sex, race
4. Time of day meeting

Financial Backing

Facilities provided without cost
Provision of a leader, preferable staff member or other paid person
Simple refreshments at each meeting
Supplies for activities—crafts, games, art, music, etc.

Club Leader

Should be experienced in recreation
Have ability in one or more skills, such as:
 music, arts, crafts, games, party-planning,
 dancing, simple dramatics, discussion-leading
Be familiar with skills, other than own, and have a knowledge of persons who might supply them if need arises
Keep club democratic, giving every member opportunity to take part, express his opinion
Plan program club chooses
Frequently introduce new ideas, but not urge them
A leader who is staff member or other paid person:
 Assures continuity of the program
 Keeps personal contact with members
 Is responsible for important details
 Can be controlled or replaced by sponsoring organization

Use of Volunteers

Raise money for club supplies
Help recruit club members
Visit in illness
Car service for trips or special occasions
Help leader at club meetings
Accompany new members, first time
Interpret project to community at large

Recruitment of Members

Family Society
Department of Public Assistance, local representative
Visiting Nurse Society
Neighborhood churches, synagogues, hospitals, rooming houses, homes for aged
Ask neighborhood groups of parents, children
Ask members to bring members
Keep on alert as you walk about streets, parks, public places
Notices to: Community newspaper and community councils
Posters: In neighborhood grocery, bakery, at place where club meets, etc.

Member Participation

Encourage participation of any kind, on any level. At least three ways for members to contribute:

1. *Financial contributions*

Since many members may be able to pay very little, or nothing at all, it seems wise not to ask for money from members. If, however, the club votes to collect money, it could be done by using a box with a slot, into which voluntary contributions can be placed inconspicuously.

2. *Making something to sell*

In craft groups, extra articles could be made or brought in from home for sale. The money could thus be used for the benefit of the club.

3. *Help with all kinds of club jobs* (see Delegating Responsibility)

Delegating Responsibility

Best way to draw members out, encourage them to help, find out where their talents lie, is to give them almost immediately a special volunteer job to do, such as:

Sending out notices
Preparing refreshments
Serving refreshments
Washing dishes and cleaning up
Setting up chairs and tables
Arranging flowers
Writing letters, birthday cards
Use members who are musicians, artists, writers, etc.
Welcoming members at door
Librarian—care of books, magazines, etc.
Secretary—keep attendance records
Treasurers—2 or 3 to count contributions, keep records, expend money
Rotate jobs frequently, giving all opportunity
Keep in touch with absent members

Encourage Group Decision

Allow frequent opportunity for group to informally decide problems of interest to them, such as:

Shall we have a picnic? Where?
Shall we take up contributions? What for?
What program next month?
Thanksgiving party? Members volunteer for committee?
Choose a name for club

This may lead into a decision for a regular business meeting and simple organization, or it may not. After six months or a year of association, members will know better what they want to do and to whom to delegate responsibility as officers.

It is recommended that formal organization as a club, with officers, business meetings and constitution, be postponed. Give members full opportunity to feel at home and become acquainted with each other. This is best done in a relaxed, unhurried atmosphere, where problems can be discussed and decisions reached with deliberation.

The Club Meeting

The club meeting may take any number of forms and have any one content or combinations thereof. Two aims, if kept in mind by the leader, will help bring satisfaction to every member. These aims:

1. To give the fullest opportunity for active participation rather than passive entertainment.
2. To offer as wide a variety of content as possible, so that any handicapped person can participate, at some point in the program.

The Club Meeting Program

1. Free time for greetings, introductions, chatting
2. Music, business
3. Activity: One or two elements, such as:
   Party and table games Discussion Writing Poetry Vocal and instrumental music Rhythm band Painting Ceramics Dramatics Dancing Crafts Picture appreciation Parties Trips Movies Lectures
4. Refreshments
5. Announcements
6. Clearing up

Hazards for Leader and Volunteers

1. Referral of material needs.

If your function is recreation for older people, then it is *not* old-age counselling, relief, visiting nurse, clinics, adjustment of relief grants, or individual services, such as securing glasses, etc. Know the referral agencies of your community and have this information available before the first meeting of the group.

2. Referral of spiritual needs:

Since the purpose is recreation, it is recommended that older people be referred to the church of their choice for worship.

If the religious element is generally requested by club members, better provide a time for it, *not* within the recreation period, so that attendance can be voluntary.

3. If the club is intended for community participation, try to avoid controversial issues; political, religious, other.
4. Do not wait on members too much.
5. Do not show favoritism.

6. Avoid urgency and pressure or soliciting untimely decisions and action. Let older people proceed at their own pace.

7. Guard against saying, "They want this," or "They will not do that," unless the statement be proven beyond question. Not the leader's opinion, but the oldsters', should be sought and ultimately followed as far as practicable.

Dictatorship Should Be Avoided at All Costs

This seems to be the greatest hazard of all. Lonely older persons, who come from comparative seclusion or inactivity into an unfamiliar group, tend to be too amenable to domination. Try to prevent outspoken or aggressive members from dictating group thinking and action. This policy applies also to leader and volunteers.

Through a long period of becoming acquainted naturally, each member of the group can be drawn out more easily to self-expression and individual activity. The project of bringing satisfaction and happiness to every person will thus be more nearly achieved.

(NOTE: The foregoing outline is intended to be suggestive rather than comprehensive. You can alter it to fitting dimensions in your own community.)

COMMUNITY BUREAUS FOR VOLUNTEERS

Many cities and a number of small towns have a "volunteer bureau" where older people can make good use of their increased leisure to make life better and happier for their neighbors. Older men and women, especially lonely ones, find this useful service gratifying. They still have a great deal to contribute if they "can knit, crochet, or sew, play games, read aloud, write letters, speak another language, sketch, paint or woodcarve, sing or play an instrument, offer escort service, or be otherwise helpful." This is the appeal by the Senior Citizens' Service Corps in New York City. There is urgent need elsewhere in hospitals, clinics, nursing and boarding homes, and in civil defense activities, for volunteer service. Introduce your elderly friends and relatives to it.

The following list was compiled by Community Chests and Councils of America, Inc. (345 East 46th Street, New York City). If no volunteer bureau exists where your elderly live, any local welfare organization, or the Red Cross, will suggest avenues to explore.

ARKANSAS

Texarkana. Volunteer Service Bureau, 212 Miller County Court House

CALIFORNIA

Burbank. Volunteer Service Bureau, 228 E. Angelo Ave.
Glendale. Volunteer Service Bureau, 515 N. Central Ave.
Long Beach. Community Volunteer Office, 1213 Cedar Ave.
Los Angeles. Volunteer Bureau, 729 S. Figueroa St.
Oakland. Volunteer Bureau, 337 13th St.
Pasadena. Volunteer Placement Bureau, 118 S. Oak Knoll Ave.
Sacramento. Volunteer Bureau, 11th and J Sts., P.O. Box 805
San Diego. Volunteer Bureau, 645 A St.
San Francisco. Volunteer Bureau, Galileo High School, Rm. 253
San Jose. Community Welfare Council Volunteer Bureau, 325 Security Bldg.
Santa Barbara. Volunteer Bureau, 802 Santa Barbara St.

CANADA

Edmonton. Central Volunteer Bureau, Reynolds Bldg., 102nd St.
London. Central Volunteer Bureau, 255 Queens Ave.
Montreal. Women's Voluntary Services, Sun Life Bldg., Rm. 150
Toronto. Volunteer Department. 100 Adelaide St., W.
Vancouver. Volunteer Bureau of Greater Vancouver, 415 W. Cordova St.
Winnipeg. Central Volunteer Bureau, 460 Main St.

COLORADO

Denver. Volunteer Community Services, 314 Fourteenth St.
Pueblo. Volunteer Service Bureau, 322 W. 5th St.

CONNECTICUT

Bridgeport. The Volunteer Bureau, 105 Bank St.
Hartford. Volunteer Bureau of Greater Hartford, 315 Pearl St.
New Britain. Volunteer Bureau of New Britain, 33 Court St.

DELAWARE

Wilmington. Volunteer Bureau, 1404 N. Franklin St.

DISTRICT OF COLUMBIA

Washington. Volunteer Services Department, 1101 M St. N.W.

FLORIDA

Jacksonville. Community Volunteer Office, 1203 Davis St.
Orlando. Volunteer Service Bureau, 122 Wall St.

HAWAII

Honolulu. Volunteer Placement Bureau, 420 S. Hotel St.

ILLINOIS

Aurora. Volunteer Service Bureau, 37 S. River St.
Chicago. Volunteer Bureau, 123 W. Madison St.
Evanston. Volunteer Service Committee, 614 Davis St.
Peoria. Central Volunteer Bureau, 832 Main St.
Rockford. Committee on Volunteers, 202 News Tower Bldg., 99 E. State St.

INDIANA

Evansville. Volunteer Services, 206 Southeast First St.
Gary. Volunteer Committee, 935 Gary National Bank Bldg.
Indianapolis. Volunteer Service Department, 901 Lemcke Bldg.

KENTUCKY

Louisville. Volunteers' Bureau, 431 W. Liberty St.

LOUISIANA

Baton Rouge. Community Volunteer Service, Florida and 19th Sts.
New Orleans. Community Volunteer Service, 211 Camp St.

MARYLAND

Silver Spring. Volunteer Referral Bureau, 911 Pershing Dr. P.O. Box 7

MASSACHUSETTS

Boston. Volunteer Service Bureau, 14 Somerset St.
Cambridge. Volunteer Service Bureau, 53 Church St.
Springfield. Citizen Participation Committee, 184 Mill St.

MICHIGAN

Battle Creek. Volunteer Bureau, 20 Kingman Bldg.
Detroit. Central Volunteer Bureau, 51 West Warren Ave.
Grand Rapids. Central Volunteer Service, 305 Association of Commerce Bldg.
Jackson. Volunteer Service Bureau, 405 Security Bldg.
Lansing. Volunteer Bureau, 615 N. Capitol Ave.

MINNESOTA

Minneapolis. Volunteer Service Bureau, 317 Citizens Aid Bldg.
St. Paul. The Volunteer Bureau, Inc., 306 Minnesota Bldg.

MISSOURI

Kansas City. Volunteer Service Bureau, 1020 McGee St.
St. Louis. Volunteer Service Bureau, 505 N. 7th St.

NEW JERSEY

Newark. Volunteer Bureau, 1004 Broad St.

NEW MEXICO

Albuquerque. Volunteer Placement Bureau, 1020½ W. Gold Ave.

NEW YORK

New Rochelle. Volunteer Referral Committee, 272 North Ave.
Rochester. Department of Volunteers, 70 N. Water St.
Syracuse. Volunteer Center, Inc., 612 Loew Bldg.
White Plains. Volunteer Service Department, County Office Bldg.
Volunteer Service Bureau, 149 Grand St.

NORTH CAROLINA

Charlotte. Volunteer Bureau, 121 E. 3rd St.
Wilmington. Volunteer Service Bureau, 211 Insurance Bldg.
Winston-Salem. Community Volunteer Office, City National Bank Bldg.

OHIO

Akron. Volunteer Service Bureau, 160 Perkins St.
Cincinnati. Central Volunteer Bureau, 312 W. 9th St.
Cleveland. Central Volunteer Bureau, 1001 Huron Rd.
Columbus. Volunteer Service Bureau, 137 E. State St.
Dayton. Volunteer Service Bureau, 225 N. Jefferson St.
Toledo. Volunteer Bureau of Toledo, Memorial Hall, 805 Adams St.

OKLAHOMA

Tulsa. Volunteer Service Bureau, 602 South Cheyenne

PENNSYLVANIA

Bradford. Volunteer Service Bureau, 200 Pleasant St.
Philadelphia. Council of Volunteers, Rm. 903, 3115 Juniper St.
Pittsburgh, 19. Volunteer Bureau of Health & Welfare, 200 Ross St.

RHODE ISLAND

Providence. Volunteer Bureau, 100 N. Main St.

TEXAS

Dallas. Volunteer Service Bureau, 426 S. Akard St.
El Paso. Volunteer Service Bureau, 303 N. Oregon St.

Fort Worth. Volunteer Center, 315 Danciger Bldg.
Galveston. Galveston Volunteer Service Bureau, 1802 Market St.
Houston. Volunteer Community Service, 1209½ Capitol Ave.

VIRGINIA

Alexandria. Volunteer Service Bureau, 110 N. St. Asaph St.
Arlington. Volunteer and Information Center, 3151 N. Washington Blvd.
Lynchburg. Volunteer Service Bureau, 214-15 Young Bldg., Church St.
Richmond. Volunteer Service Bureau, Allison Bldg.

WEST VIRGINIA

Charleston. Volunteer Service Bureau, 108½ Capitol St.

WISCONSIN

Milwaukee. Citizens Service Department, 797 N. Van Buren St.

CHAPTER VIII: LEAVING THE WELL-ENOUGH ALONE

HOMEMAKER SERVICE FOR THE AGED

Visiting housekeepers are available chiefly in urban centers. No place has a sufficient number to meet the need for any type of situation. However, Homemaker Service, as it is known nationally, is available in all but fifteen states, and in Puerto Rico, and some Provinces in Canada. Not all the Services can give help to the old. The following list of those which do is compiled from records maintained by the parent body, the National Homemaker Service (composed of representatives from welfare organizations, public and private), and the U. S. Children's Bureau.

This is a growing development. If you want to know whether there is likelihood of its reaching the community where your elderly relatives live, if their home town is not listed here, write the Division of Social Services, Children's Bureau, Washington, 25, D. C.

CALIFORNIA

Oakland: Jewish Welfare Federation, 724 14th St.

COLORADO

Denver: Family Welfare Service, 314 14th St.

Connecticut

Hartford: Family Service Society, 36 Trumbull St.

District of Columbia

Washington: Health Department Hospital Permit Bureau, Municipal Center Bldg.

Illinois

Chicago: Department of Welfare, 25 S. Damen Ave.
Jewish Family and Community Service, 231 S. Wells St.

Indiana

Elkhart: Family Service Association, 241-43 Equity Bldg.
Fort Wayne: Family and Children's Service, Inc., 346 W. Jefferson St.
Indianapolis: Jewish Social Services, Inc., 1915 N. Meridian St.

Kentucky

Louisville: Department of Public Welfare, 621 W. Jefferson St.

Massachusetts

Boston: Provident Association, 7 Water St.
Swampscott: Swampscott Community Service, Inc., 73 Pine St.
Worcester: Board of Public Welfare, 74 Front St.

Michigan

Detroit: Jewish Social Service Bureau, 5737 Second St.
Visiting Housekeeper Association of Metropolitan Detroit, 51 W. Warren Ave.
Lansing: Family Service Agency, 615 N. Capitol Ave.

Minnesota

Duluth: Bureau of Catholic Charities, Rm. 310, Moore Memorial Bldg.
Minneapolis: Family and Children's Service, 404 S. 8th St.
St. Paul: Family Service Society, 104 Wilder Bldg.

Missouri

Kansas City: United Jewish Social Service, 1000 Admiral Bldg.
St. Louis: Family and Children's Service, 4643 Lindell Blvd.

Nebraska

Omaha: Visiting Nurse Association, 2101 Cuming St.

NEW JERSEY

Newark: Essex County Service for the Chronically Ill, Inc., 1004 Broad St.

NEW YORK

Albany: Visiting Nurse Association of Albany Inc., 245 Lark St.
Brooklyn: Catholic Charities Diocese of Brooklyn, 191 Joralemon St.
Jamaica: Jewish Community Services of Long Island, 89-31 161 St.
New York: Community Service Society of New York, 105 E. 22nd St.
Department of Welfare, 601 E. 9th St.
Jewish Family Service, 113 W. 57th St.
White Plains: Westchester Jewish Community Services, 116 Main St.

OHIO

Cleveland: Cleveland Housekeeper Service for Older Persons, 1001 Huron Rd.
County Welfare Department, 914 Huron Rd.
Jewish Family Service Association, 2073 E. 9th St.

PENNSYLVANIA

Philadelphia: Jewish Family Service, 1619 Spruce St.
Pittsburgh: Family and Children's Service, 519 Smithfield St.
Jewish Social Service, 15 Fernando St.

PUERTO RICO

Santurce: Child Welfare Bureau, Division of Public Welfare

RHODE ISLAND

Providence: Family Service, Inc., 100 N. Main St.

TENNESSEE

Memphis: Family Service of Memphis, 910 Falls Bldg.
Oak Ridge: National Council of Jewish Women, Oak Ridge Section

TEXAS

Houston: Sheltering Arms, 2809 Leeland St.

WISCONSIN

Madison: Family Service, 22 N. Hancock St.
Milwaukee: Family Service, 1243 N. Van Buren St.
Society of St. Vincent de Paul, 1624 N. 7th St.

VIRGINIA

Richmond: Family Service Society, 221 Governor St.

CANADA

Montreal: Family Welfare Association, 1646 Dorchester St., W.
Family Welfare Department, Baron de Hirsch Institute, 493 Sherbrooke St., W.

Hamilton: Visiting Homemakers' Association, 72 Main St., W.

CHAPTER IX: PREPARING THE OLD FOR CHANGE

INFORMATION AND REFERRAL CENTERS

Community Welfare Councils have various titles—Councils of Social Agencies, Red Feather Service, Health and Welfare Council, etc.—but their purpose is the same. They are formed by citizens and organizations of a community to deal with social problems which affect *all* citizens. Many maintain special information services, available without charge, an excellent place to ask for advice when older people have to resettle themselves.

The national organization, Community Chests and Councils of America, Inc. (345 East 46th Street, New York City) publishes a directory which gives names and address of member agencies. Information services are growing; if your community does not appear in the following list, ask the national organization for the address of the one nearest to it, for a local source of help.

Atlanta, Ga.: Social Service Information Center, Community Planning Council of Metropolitan Atlanta, 167 Walton St., N. W., 3

Boston, Mass.: Red Feather Information Service, United Community Services of Metropolitan Boston, 14 Somerset St., 8

Chicago, Ill.: Community Referral Service, Welfare Council of Metropolitan Chicago, 123 W. Madison St., 2

Cincinnati, Ohio: Information Service, Council of Social Agencies, 312 W. 9th St., 2

Cleveland, Ohio: Community Information Service, Welfare Federation of Cleveland, 1001 Huron Rd., 15

Columbus, Ohio: Department of Information and Community Services, Community Chest and Council of Franklin County, 137 E. State St., 15

Denver, Colorado.: Information Service, Denver Area Welfare Council, Inc., 314 Fourteenth St., 2

Detroit, Mich.: Community Information Service, United Community Services of Metropolitan Detroit, 51 W. Warren Ave., 1

Flint, Mich.: Information and Referral Service, Flint Council of Social Agencies, 200 E. Kearsley St., 3

Grand Rapids, Mich.: Council of Social Agencies of Grand Rapids, 5-7 Lyon St., N. W., 2

Hartford, Conn.: Red Feather Information Service of the Volunteer Bureau, Rm. 205, 315 Pearl St.

Indianapolis, Ind.: Health and Welfare Council of Indianapolis, 106 E. Market St., 4

Los Angeles, Calif.: Welfare Information Service, Welfare Council of Metropolitan Los Angeles, 729 S. Figueroa St., 17

Memphis, Tenn.: Central Welfare Information Bureau, Community Council of Memphis-Shelby County, 210 Madison Ave., 3

Minneapolis, Minn.: Community Information Center, Community Chest and Council of Hennepin County, 404 S. 8th St., 4

Milwaukee, Wis.: Community and Veterans Information Service, Community Welfare Council of Milwaukee County, 797 N. Van Buren St., 2

Newark, N. J.: Information and Referral Services, Council of Social Agencies of Newark, 1004 Broad St., 2

New Haven, Conn.: Information and Referral Service, New Haven Council of Social Agencies, 397 Temple St., 10

New Orleans, La.: Information Service, Council of Social Agencies of New Orleans, 211 Camp St., 12

New York City: Information Bureau, Welfare and Health Council of New York City, 44 E. 23rd St., 10

Norfolk, Va.: Community Information and Service Center, Norfolk Council of Social Agencies, 22 Monticello Ave., 10

Oakland, Calif.: Information Service, Community Welfare Council, 337 Thirteenth St., 12

Oklahoma City, Okla.: Welfare Information and Referral Center, Community Council of Oklahoma City, 208 N. Broadway, P.O. Box 1474, 2

Philadelphia, Pa.: Information and Referral Service, Health and Welfare Council, 311 S. Juniper St., 7

Pittsburgh, Pa.: Information Service of the Community Chest and Health and Welfare Federation, 200 Ross St., 19

Portland, Oregon: Information Service Section, Portland Council of Social Agencies, 1220 S. W. Morrison St., 5

Rochester, New York: Service Department, Council of Social Agencies, Inc., 70 N. Water St., 4

San Francisco, Calif.: Information and Referral Service, Community Chest of San Francisco, 2015 Steiner St., 15

Seattle, Wash.: Information and Referral Service, Health and Welfare Council of Seattle, 1535 Summit Ave., 22

Trenton, New Jersey: Information Service, Delaware Valley United Fund, 1 W. State St., 8

Washington, D. C.: Information and Referral Service, United Community Services of Washington, 1101 M St., N.W., 5

White Plains, N. Y.: Information Services, Westchester County, Council of Social Agencies, Inc., 709 County Office Building.

CANADA

Toronto: Information and Referral Service, Welfare Council of Toronto and District, 100 Adelaide St., W., 1

Chapter X: Homes for the Aged: Pros and Cons

PHYSICAL ELIGIBILITY FOR ADMISSION

It is impossible to lay down arbitrary rules about medical suitability of applicants because there is no set pattern through the country. However, The Welfare Council of New York, in its "*Suggested Standards for Homes for the Aged*" (Sixth Edition), makes these recommendations which many homes follow.

A. Applicants with the following types of disease, the Council states, should not be admitted:

Active pulmonary tuberculosis

Cancer, of inoperable type or requiring constant care

Mental disease or personality problems which prevent adjustment to group living

Decompensated heart disease (where constant medical supervision is required)

B. Diseases which should NOT necessarily preclude admission:

Arrested pulmonary tuberculosis

Syphilis that has had adequate treatment

Mental conditions which do not interfere with group living

Arteriosclerosis . . . unless there are focal symptoms of a serious nature such as those related to the heart, brain, kidney or extremities, where hospital care is indicated.

High blood pressure (over 160 systolic, 90 diastolic) unless there is serious kidney involvement and disability resulting from hypertension. Many aged persons with high blood pressure do very well in an institutional home because they are relieved of nervous strain and worry which frequently contribute to elevated blood pressure.

Mild diabetes which can usually be handled with minimum medical supervision and can be well controlled through simple diets of a special nature. . . . However, diabetics who are uncooperative and difficult to control as to diet and those who may require insulin injections may constitute a special problem which might preclude admission depending upon the type of medical service available within the given home.

Arthritis in the aged should be evaluated as to its severity and crippling effects relative to whether or not the applicant can be appropriately cared for within the given home. . . .

STANDARDS FOR EXTERIORS AND INTERIORS

Good planning and contruction of buildings is a factor in bringing comfort to residents of old age homes. A number of denominations are deeply concerned about this and other problems of the old. The Methodist Church Board of Hospitals and Homes publishes "Approved Standards and Suggestions for Homes for the Aged," based on recommendations of the Welfare Council of New York and the California State Department of Social Welfare.

The following excerpt is a gauge to judge how far a particular home, regardless of auspices, has been able to meet desirable standards in this aspect of care.

Fire Protection: The building should be fireproof and should conform to the regulations of fire insurance underwriters and local ordinances as to construction, equipment and alarms. Employees should have fire drills and assigned stations. Fire doors, automatic sprinklers and other fire-retarding construction are mandatory. . . .

Elevators: Any building more than one story high should have some type of elevator. For homes having a capacity of approximately fifty or more residents, there should be at least two elevators, so that one will always be in running order in case of fire or other emergency. One should be large enough to admit stretchers or beds. The automatic type, with quiet, easy operation of elevator and doors and automatic leveling apparatus is desirable.

Halls: These should be well lighted day and night and provided with outlets for vacuum cleaners, scrubbing or buffing machines, etc. Halls should be a minimum of six feet, preferably seven feet, in width.

Hand-rails on side walls are a comfort to the feeble and provide added safety. Lights on baseboards are recommended.

Walls: Sound-proofed walls are essential between bedrooms and lavatories or service rooms.

Floors: Fireproof concrete, covered or treated according to type of space, is important. Wax with turpentine base should not be used on floors on account of danger of slipping. . . . Terrazzo and marble floors tire the feet of employees and residents and are not sound-absorbent. . . .

Doors: Bedroom doors should be a minimum width of forty-two inches. They should be so built as to be easy to open and close. Louvres in doors aid in ventilation. Card plates for residents' names on bedroom doors are helpful. Special consideration should be given to the type of locks which can be operated by a single master key and locked or unlocked from both sides.

Windows: Double-hung windows are preferable to casement windows in bedrooms. Small panes make window washing more difficult. Windows should be screened full length on the outside for protection from bugs and flies. Provision either through special screens or other devices should be provided where protection of residents is a factor. Sills should be high enough for safety and low enough for good visibility. Interlocking weather strips make for comfort and save heat. Windows should not be so large that they are heavy to open. Storm windows and screens are needed for their usual purposes. . . .

Heating Plant: Types of heating plant and fuel should be governed by local conditions. The aged require an indoor temperature of 72 degrees at the floor. Thus in rooms where they sit around, a floor-heating system may be desirable. . . .

Lighting: Bedrooms and public rooms should be centrally lighted and have base plugs for lamps and electric appliances. Halls and infirmary should be provided with nightlights; the types which are installed near the floor are satisfactory. Indirect lighting is desirable in the infirmary. Floor plugs should be numerous throughout the building, for light and labor-saving devices. . . .

LIVING ACCOMMODATIONS

NOTE: The recommendations for administrative offices, the workrooms for housekeeping, etc., are equally important, but usually these will not be open for inspection. If accommodations for residents meet these minimal standards, you can be fairly certain that the behind-the-scenes quarters are also.

Resident Rooms: Single rooms make most residents happier and eliminate friction. Rooms should be as nearly alike in size as possible.

Eight hundred cubic feet of air space per person is a minimum requirement for bedroom space. . . .

a) A *signal system,* either light or bell, is usually advisable, particularly in separate rooms.

b) *Closets* should be built in walls of all bedrooms, having shelves within easy reach, clothes pole and hooks. They should have sliding doors. There should be a light in each closet.

c) *Running water* is desirable in each room. . . .

Bathrooms, Washrooms, and Toilets: Bathrooms should be located so as to be easily accessible on each sleeping floor and have painted or tiled (preferably tiled) walls. Tubs should be of medium size with rolled rims—at least one tub to each ten residents. Rubber mat in tub and on floor, and handles on wall reduce danger of slipping. Intake should be above rim of tub in order to avoid possibility of syphoning.

a) *Washrooms* should be adjacent to bathrooms rather than a part of them, if wash basins are not installed in bedrooms; the latter is preferable.

b) *Toilets* should be in separate room adjoining bath; one toilet for each six guests. One basin is necessary in room with toilets.

c) *Showers* with side sprays, stools, and hand-railing are recommended for persons unable to get in and out of tubs with ease. Showers alone are not adequate equipment for an institution for aged.

d) *All doors* to toilet and bath compartments should open out and be easily opened from outside in emergency.

e) *Button signals* for emergency help in bathrooms (either light system or bell) should be considered.

Living Rooms: These should be large and airy with ceiling lights and base plugs. A few small sitting rooms where residents may receive personal callers are desirable and useful. Where there is no auditorium, the living room should be so constructed that it can be used for general gatherings. While fireplaces add to the attractiveness and are often desired by old persons, they are not recommended because of the hazards involved.

Sun Parlors and Screened Porches: These are highly desirable; one should be accessible to each floor. . . .

Library: A library should be provided and preferably should be located in a separate room. If this is not possible, a living or recreation room or sun parlor may be used, provided that quiet, which is usually required in a library, is not required in such recreation rooms.

Dining Rooms: The dining rooms should be large enough to meet the needs of the population. They should be clean, cheerful, well ventilated and lighted. The equipment and furnishings should be attractive and comfortable. Tables seating four to eight, with some tables for two for married couples, are advisable. Chairs should be sturdy and well balanced, some with arms, if necessary or desired by residents, to assist in rising. Table linen, silverware, and attractive dishes are recommended. Doilies or place mats may be used on well-finished surfaces. . . .

Auditorium: This may be provided with chapel facilities. Where there must be economy of space, sliding partitions may convert the recreation, game, radio, living rooms and library into one large room. In arranging seating, the needs of those with crutches or wooden legs or in wheel-chairs should be kept in mind. . . .

Chapter XI: Substitute Homes for the Well

MINIMUM STANDARDS FOR A BOARDING HOME

Practical, minimum standards for commercial boarding homes for the aged were set up by the Health and Welfare Council of Delaware, Montgomery, and Philadelphia Counties, Pennsylvania. Its goal was a licensure law (achieved in 1951). Many provisions in this guide should be considered as essential whether the law elsewhere demands them or not. A number would apply equally well to a foster home, or any other type of housing an aged person may seek when he is in a fair state of health.

Minimum Standards for Commercially Operated Boarding Homes

(The Pennsylvania pattern)

I. *Requirements for Applicant and Personnel*

1. The applicant for a license shall be a person of integrity and shall provide satisfactory references.

2. The person in charge, who may or may not be the applicant, shall be physically and temperamentally qualified and have capabilities for this kind of work.

3. According to the size of the boarding home, sufficient personnel shall be provided to insure adequate care of the boarders. The minimum number of personnel shall be determined by the licensing agency.

4. A complete physical examination, including chest X-ray and Wassermann test shall be required for the person in charge prior to the granting of the license and annually thereafter. Employees shall meet the same requirements prior to employment and annually. State and local "Food Handlers' Requirements" shall be met.

Family members of owner.

Composition of family members of the person in charge who will live in the home shall be taken into consideration; such matters as relationship, age range, health and quarters to be occupied.

II. *Boarders*

A. Eligibility Requirements

Boarders shall be limited to adults who meet the following requirements:

1. Ambulatory, including housebound persons, but no roombound or wheel-chair cases permitted;
2. Those who regularly require only limited personal services, such as bathing and personal cleanliness, but no feeding cases;
3. The blind who are capable of getting around and caring for self.
4. Senile cases not to be admitted.

B. Health

1. A health statement signed by a physician licensed in Pennsylvania or a hospital interne shall be presented on admission, showing eligibility as previously listed in this section.
2. It is advisable that each boarder on admission designate the name and address of a physician or physicians licensed in Pennsylvania to be called at the onset of any illness, injury, or increase in physical disability.
3. Boarders shall submit the name of a responsible person and/or agency who should be contacted in case of an emergency.

C. Finances

1. No operator shall be permitted to accept a sum of money from a boarder to pay for his care for life.
2. All boarders whose income is minimal, regardless of source, shall retain some of their money for clothing and incidentals.

D. Grouping of Boarders

It is of advantage to the blind person to be in a room with a sighted person.

E. Number of Boarders

The maximum number of boarders for each home shall be stipulated by the licensing agency.

F. Removal of Boarder

1. As soon as a boarder no longer meets the eligibility requirements as previously listed in this section, the responsible person, the

sponsoring health or welfare agency, or the licensing agency shall be required to remove the boarder.

2. No operator shall transfer a boarder from one boarding home to another nor to any other place without permission of the boarder and/or before informing the responsible person, the responsible health or welfare agency or the licensing agency.

III. *Building, Equipment, and Sanitation*

A. Building

1. All commercial boarding homes covered in these regulations must be approved in writing by the responsible bureaus or agencies for
   a. Building construction
   b. Sanitation
   c. Fire protection

Note: Specific information covering all requirements of the local law enforcement agencies shall be made available by the licensing agency to the applicant.

2. No part of the building shall be used for any other commercial purpose.

B. Bedroom

1. Bedrooms shall be of sufficient size to allow not less than 700 cubic feet of air space and 70 square feet of floor space per boarder. They shall be outside rooms and the window space shall be not less than ⅛ of the floor space. There shall be provision for unobstructed natural light and adequate ventilation.

2. A separate bed shall be provided for each boarder. Not less than three feet shall be allowed between beds. Beds shall be equipped with mattresses of cotton, felt, fiber, or better material, and shall be supplied with a pillow and adequate blankets. Change of linen weekly, and more frequently when necessary, shall be required.

3. An individual cabinet or separate drawer space with a lock, and adequate closet space, with hangers, shall be provided for each boarder.

4. Each room shall be equipped with a bell for summoning assistance in case of need.

5. No boarder shall be housed, or required to use any facilities, above the third floor, unless there is elevator service. No boarder shall be housed in the basement.

C. Bathroom

1. There shall be a bathroom with toilet and washbasin in the ratio of one to eight persons (boarders, employees, and family) on each sleeping floor used by the boarders.

2. There shall be tubs or showers in the ratio of one to every ten residents (boarders, employees and family). The bathtubs shall be equipped with strong handles for support and rubber mats for safety.

3. Night lights shall be provided in the bathrooms at night time.

D. Living-Dining Room

A well-lighted and ventilated living-dining room shall be provided for boarders. At least one meal a day shall be served in this room.

E. Halls and Stairways

All halls and stairways shall be well lighted at all times. Stairways shall be equipped with hand-rails and supplied with a collapsible gate at the top, to be kept closed at night.

F. Heating and Screens

1. Outside doors, windows, and openings shall be protected by the seasonal use of screens.

2. There shall be a central heating system that will maintain a minimum temperature of 70 to 74 degrees Fahrenheit from 7 A.M. to 10 P.M.

G. Food Service and Sanitation

1. Three nutritionally adequate meals a day shall be served.

2. There shall be adequate facilities for the proper storage, preparation, and serving of food for boarders and personnel.

3. All perishable foods, including milk, shall be adequately refrigerated. There shall be a reliable thermometer in each refrigerator and storeroom for perishable foods.

4. All utensils used for eating, drinking, and in preparation or serving of food and drink shall be washed after each use in a manner approved by the local health authorities.

5. There shall be adequate hand-washing facilities with soap, running hot and cold water and an adequate supply of individual paper towels in all kitchens and in washrooms and toilets used by individuals preparing or serving food.

IV. *Program*

A. Personal care of Boarder:

The operator shall provide the following services:

1. Assistance with bathing and personal cleanliness as required.

2. Personal laundry.

3. Tray service for those temporarily unable to go to the dining room.

4. Person in charge or responsible substitute shall sleep in the same house with boarders to be available for an emergency at night.

5. Supervision of boarders to insure that proper clothing is worn in accordance with the weather.

B. Fire Prevention Program

1. Fire drills shall be held periodically, at least every 60 days.

2. Doors shall be unlocked at all times in the bedrooms and bathrooms. To insure privacy in the bathrooms, occupancy signs shall be available.

3. Indoor smoking shall be permitted in the community room only.

4. In addition to the above, all requirements of the local Fire Marshal shall be followed.

C. Recreation

1. There shall be a community room for the use of residents for reading and other recreational purposes. This room may be the living-dining room previously described. It shall be equipped with comfortable chairs, reading lights, card tables, and if suitable, with a radio, books, and periodicals, table games, etc.

2. The proprietor shall make such regulations as he deems necessary to prevent one boarder's recreational activities from annoying any other boarder.

3. The proprietor shall encourage the boarders to use initiative in entertaining themselves.

D. Personal Life of Boarder

1. Boarders shall be free to come and go as desired. If they plan to be away overnight they should inform the proprietor where they can be reached.

2. Boarders shall be permitted to receive visitors with reasonable privacy in the community room at stated visiting hours. These should be as frequent as possible.

V. *Records*

A. All records shall be permanent, either typewritten or legibly written with pen and ink.

B. The following data shall be recorded for each boarder:

1. Name, address, date of admission
2. Age, sex, date of birth

3. Name, address, and telephone number of nearest relative or friend, and/or referring agency.

4. Name, address, and telephone number of family physician(s).

C. Special Reports

1. Statement of health as noted in item II B.

2. Epidemic diseases, poisoning (food and other), and major injuries, shall be reported by the patient's physician to the licensing agency and the local bureau of health. It is mandatory to report certain diseases and poisoning to the local bureau of health.

Chapter XII: Community Care for the Sick

HOSPITAL BEDS FOR CHRONICALLY ILL

In 1951 the Commission on Chronic Illness circularized 2,400 general hospitals to find out if a special ward, wing, or building had been set aside for sufferers from chronic diseases. Those listed below replied that they did have some facilities. If you want to know whether they are available for people over sixty-five, query the hospital you are interested in, for the Commission issues this caution:

"Not all hospitals with special facilities for the chronic or long-term patient devote them to the aged. Some hospitals which reported they cared for the chronically ill have wards for polio patients (children and young adults); some accommodate tuberculosis patients (primarily young and middle-aged adults); some have wards for rheumatic fever patients (primarily children); some are children's orthopedic hospitals."

NON-PROFIT (VOLUNTARY) HOSPITALS

An encouraging note: Few, if any, limit admissions to residents of a particular area. If there is a short supply of beds, local residents probably would get preference. If you have difficulty finding an immediate place for your relative, remember every fifth person in the United States has a chronic disease, and it has been estimated that an additional 300,000 beds in hospitals are needed to take care of those who belong there.

State	*City*	*Name of Hospital*	*Bed Capacity* Total	Special Ward for chronic patients	*Type of Service* American Medical Association Registration
ALABAMA	Selma	Good Samaritan	85	13	Not registered
	Tuskegee Institute	Andrew Memorial*	145	25 (polio)	General
ARIZONA	Phoenix	St. Monica's	230	16 (polio)	General
	Tucson	Tucson Medical Center	225	36	General
		St. Mary's*	300	27	General-Tuberculosis
CALIFORNIA	Los Angeles	Mount Sinai**	80	80	Chronic, long term
COLORADO	Boulder	Boulder-Col. Sanitarium and Hospital	101	40	General
CONNECTICUT	Hartford	St. Francis	535	15	General
	Manchester	Manchester Memorial	155	45	General
	New Haven	Grace-New Haven Community*	491	?	General
	Stamford	Stamford*	232	30	General
FLORIDA	Miami	Variety Children's	97	27	Children's
IDAHO	Nampa	Samaritan	50	?	General
ILLINOIS	Chicago	Bethany Methodist*	100	50	General
	Lincoln	Evangelical Deaconess	75	16	General
	Peoria	St. Francis	530	111	General
INDIANA	La Porte	Fairview	76	12	General
IOWA	Centerville	St. Joseph's Mercy	50	6	General
KANSAS	Dodge City	Trinity	55	8	General
	Hutchinson	Grace	145	15	General
	Kansas City	St. Margaret's	196	8	General
	Wichita	St. Joseph's	145	15	General
KENTUCKY	Louisville	Norton Memorial	280	11	
LOUISIANA	Baton Rouge	Baton Rouge General*	250	40	General
MARYLAND	Baltimore	Sinai	309	11	General
MASSACHUSETTS	Boston	Robert Breck Brigham	103	66	General (average stay 29.9 days)
		Massachusetts General	930	? (arthritis)	General
	Fall River	Truesdale	169	16	General
	Lowell	Lowell General	183	?	General
	Springfield	Springfield	281	51	General

State	*City*	*Name of Hospital*	*Bed Capacity* Total	Special Ward for chronic patients	*Type of Service* American Medical Association Registration
MICHIGAN	Battle Creek	Battle Creek Sanatorium	307	35	General
	Detroit	Henry Ford	600	36 (tuberculosis)	General
	St. John's	Clinton Memorial	75	10	General
MINNESOTA	Bemidji	Lutheran	75	?	General
	Fairmont	Fairmont Community	50	6	General
	Marshall	Weiner Memorial	56	25	General
	Red Wing	St. John's	95	13	General
	Wabasha	St. Elizabeth's	74	20	General
MISSOURI	Kansas City	Menorah	280	50	General
	St. Louis	St. Mary's*	740	16	General-Tuberculosis
	Springfield	Burge Hospital*	131	25	General
MONTANA	Bozeman	Bozeman Deaconess	82	18	General
NEBRASKA	Omaha	Immanuel Deaconess	123	60	General
NEW JERSEY	Long Branch	Dr. E. C. Hazard*	50	?	General
NEW MEXICO	Albuquerque	St. Joseph's Sanitarium and Hospital	241	50	General-Tuberculosis
NEW YORK	Albany	Albany	541	56	General-Tuberculosis
	Olean	Olean General	126	24	General
	Staten Island	Sailor's Snug Harbor**	165	106	***
	Utica	Masonic Soldiers & Sailors**	170	162	General-Long term
	Yonkers	St. Joseph's	195	22	General
NORTH DAKOTA	Minot	Trinity	188	12	General
OHIO	Columbus	St. Anthony	200	?	General
	Elyria	Elyria Memorial	142	50	General
	Hamilton	Mercy	300	24	General
	Springfield	Mercy	219	16	General
PENNSYLVANIA	Allentown	Allentown	417	?	General
	Philadelphia	Episcopal*	495	82	General
	Scranton	West Side	85	12	General
RHODE ISLAND	Providence	Rhode Island Hospital*	569	50 (children)	General
SOUTH CAROLINA	Charleston	St. Francis Xavier	111	10	General
TEXAS	Temple	Gulf, Colorado & Santa Fe	135	18	Industrial

State	City	Name of Hospital	Bed Capacity Total	Special Ward for chronic patients	Type of Service American Medical Association Registration
UTAH	Ogden	Dee Memorial	281	?	General
VIRGINIA	Norfolk	Leigh Memorial	173	29	General
	Roanoke	Memorial & Crippled Children	150	28 (crippled children)	General-Orthopedic
WASHINGTON	Bremerton	Puget Sound Naval Memorial	90	30	General
	Tacoma	St. Joseph's*	279	34	General
	Wenatchee	Central Washington Deaconess	100	16	General
WISCONSIN	Dodgeville	St. Joseph's	61	16	General
	La Crosse	Grandview	87	16	General
	Milwaukee	Milwaukee Hospital	263	?	General

* Has an organized rehabilitation service.

** Long-term general hospital.

NOTE: Many governmental hospitals which take chronically ill patients are also "related institutions," that is, they give care of a nursing or custodial nature, rather than that of a hospital. Since many of them accept only dependent persons or persons who cannot afford to pay for hospital care, a state department of welfare or health can supply you with local lists.

COST OF CHRONIC ILLNESS IN A HOSPITAL

It may help you understand why hospital care has to be high for those who can afford it, and what happens if they cannot, if you look at the situation at St. Barnabas Hospital for Chronic Diseases in New York City. (The fact that this institution till recent years carried the words "for incurables" in its name reflects today's hopeful medical outlook.)

This is a hospital of the voluntary (non-profit) type. Like others, it meets expenses by patients' fees, plus contributions, payment from public or welfare agencies, or private philanthropic sources, or from its own endowment funds, for those who cannot pay. One third of its four hundred beds are occupied by patients who pay full costs of care; one third, partial cost; one third are free patients. No one, least of all the hospital authorities, "looks down" on this last group; few people are able to meet the full cost of care which long periods of chronic illness require.

The 1953 rates are as follows:

12 and 16 bed wards	$50 per week
6 and 8 bed wards	$55-60 per week
4-bed rooms	$60-65 per week
3-bed rooms	$65-70 per week
2-bed rooms	$70-75 per week
Private rooms	$80-130 per week

Kane Cancer Pavilion

4-bed room	$70 per week
Semi-private rooms	$75-80 per week
Private rooms	$85-130 per week

CAUTION: Rates in hospitals, as in homes for the aged, and nursing homes, vary through the country, depending on standards and service. Also, rates sometimes change from year to year, according to the nation's economic state.

HOME CARE MEDICAL PLANS

The Commission on Chronic Illness, together with the U. S. Public Health Service engaged in a nation-wide study in 1953 to determine strengths and weaknesses of home medical care plans. This is a device originated by Montefiore Hospital in New York City to bring hospital services to the patient in his own home. The program has not yet spread widely, but it is expanding. The Commission on Chronic Illness (615 North Wolfe Street, Baltimore 5, Md.) can tell you what the possibilities are of its reaching the community where your elderly are living.

A partial list of hospitals and other agencies which offer a program modeled on the Montefiore plan include the city hospitals in New York City (in addition to Montefiore, supported by voluntary contributions); Massachusetts Memorial Hospital in Boston; Michael Reese Hospital, Chicago; the Public Health Department of Richmond, Va.; Gallinger Hospital, Washington, D. C., and the Visiting Nurse Society of Philadelphia, Pa.

The manner in which this Society has organized its service will show you how it might be done with local variations, elsewhere.

INTENSIVE HOME CARE PLAN: PHILADELPHIA

What it is: Under the direction of the patient's own doctor and with consultation from the Intensive Home Care Plan Medical Director of the Visiting Nurse Society, all necessary medical, nursing, social, and domestic services are offered, such as:

(*a*) Skilled nursing care; (*b*) physical therapy; (*c*) occupational therapy; (*d*) speech therapy; (*e*) nutrition, social service, mental hygiene, or other desired consultation; (*f*) diagnostic and laboratory facilities (through local hospitals); (*g*) help in solving housekeeping problems; (*h*) help in getting supplies and equipment, such as wheelchairs, hospital beds, etc.

Who gives the service: The Visiting Nurse Society of Philadelphia, in conjunction with the Starr Centre Association. The staff includes a medical consultant, registered nurses and specialists.

Who can use the service: Available to a limited group of patients who need this intensive care, and whose doctors request it.

How it is paid for: All the services are offered at cost; nursing service for instance, is $3 for the first hour, but any patient who cannot meet the full cost pays as much as he can afford; the rest is met through funds granted to the Intensive Home Care Plan.

SOURCE LISTS FOR NURSING HOMES

To investigate nursing homes in a particular vicinity, you will need a list of those for which an ailing, elderly person is eligible. You can secure this, as well as information about licensing and other legal regulations in any state by consulting one of the two national organizations of nursing homes.

The American Association of Nursing Homes: Executive Secretary, 1970 Union Ave., Memphis, Tenn.

This organization is composed of state associations of nursing home operators. An inquiry will give you the name and address of a secretary of the state association, if there is one, or a list of nursing homes in any area.

National Association of Registered Nursing Homes, Inc., Executive Secretary, 25 Ridgeview Ave., White Plains, N.Y.

An annual directory of nursing homes is published. The homes listed are those registered with the National Association, which was chartered in 1946. The directory is free to any inquirer.

Chapter XIII: What to Do with the Mentally Ill

MENTAL ILLNESS—DIRECTORY OF RESOURCES

The 1952 *Directory of Psychiatric Clinics and Other Resources in the United States,* the tenth of its kind, is a valuable reference book. It is published by the National Association for Mental Health, Inc. (1790 Broadway, New York 19), and can be purchased directly, for $1.25. Or you can consult it in any large library. It contains a listing of the psychiatric clinics in this country (defined as "a service for ambulatory patients which has a psychiatrist in attendance at regularly scheduled hours"), the numerous mental health associations, state institutions, state governmental departments dealing with mental health, federal mental hospitals, etc.

STATE MENTAL HEALTH DEPARTMENTS

If you want to know what kind of care your, or another, state gives to its mentally ill, get in touch with the department which has been designated as the Mental Health Authority. The following list includes also the division or bureau, if any, which supervises or conducts community clinics in a particular state.

Alabama

Mental Health Authority: State Department of Public Health, Montgomery 4. Division of Mental Hygiene, Birmingham
Mental Hospital Authority: Alabama State Hospitals, Tuscaloosa

Arizona

Mental Health Authority: State Department of Public Health, Phoenix

Arkansas

Mental Health Authority: State Board of Health, Little Rock

California

Mental Health and Hospital Authority: State Department of Mental Hygiene, 1320 K St., Sacramento

COLORADO

Mental Health Authority: State Department of Public Health, State Office Bldg., Denver 2
Mental Hospital Authority: State Department of Public Health (licensing of private psychiatric facilities) and Director of State Institutions, Capitol Bldg., Denver 2

CONNECTICUT

Mental Health Authority: State Department of Health, Hartford 6. Bureau of Mental Hygiene.

DELAWARE

Mental Health and Hospital Authority: State Board of Trustees, Delaware State Hospital, Farnhurst

DISTRICT OF COLUMBIA

Mental Health Authority: District of Columbia Health Department, Washington. Bureau of Mental Hygiene

FLORIDA

Mental Health Authority: State Board of Health, Jacksonville 1
Mental Hospital Authority: Board of Commissioners of State Institutions, Tallahassee.

GEORGIA

Mental Health Authority: State Department of Public Health, Atlanta. Division of Mental Hygiene.
Mental Hospital Authority: Department of Public Welfare, State Office Bldg., Atlanta

IDAHO

Mental Health Authority: State Department of Public Health, Boise. Mental Health Section.
Mental Hospital Authority: State Hospitals Board, Boise

ILLINOIS

Mental Health and Hospital Authority: State Department of Public Welfare, Springfield. Mental Health Service.

INDIANA

Mental Health and Hospital Authority: Indiana Council for Mental Health, 1315 W. 10th St., Indianapolis 7

IOWA

Mental Health Authority: Psychopathic Hospital, State University of Iowa
Mental Hospital Administration: Board of Control of State Institutions, Des Moines. (Exception: Psychopathic Hospital is under the State Board of Education.)

KANSAS

Mental Health Authority: State Board of Social Welfare, Topeka

KENTUCKY

Mental Health Authority: State Department of Health, 620 S. 3rd St., Louisville.
Mental Hospital Authority: Department of Mental Health, 620 S. 3rd St., Louisville.

LOUISIANA

Mental Health and Hospital Authority: Department of Institutions, Baton Rouge

MAINE

Mental Health Authority: State Department of Health and Welfare. Division of Mental Health
Mental Hospital Authority: State Department of Institutional Service, Augusta

MARYLAND

Mental Health Authority: State Board of Health, State Department of Health, 2411 N. Charles St., Baltimore 18
Mental Hospital Authority: State Department of Mental Hygiene, 2218 N. Charles St., Baltimore 18

MASSACHUSETTS

Mental Health and Hospital Authority: Department of Mental Health, 15 Ashburton Pl., Boston

MICHIGAN

Mental Health and Hospital Authority: State Department of Mental Health, Bank of Lansing Bldg., Lansing 16

MINNESOTA

Mental Health and Hospital Authority: Division of Public Institutions, 410 Globe Bldg., 4th and Cedar Sts., St. Paul

MISSISSIPPI

Mental Health Authority: State Board of Health, Jackson, 113
Mental Hospital Authority: Board of Trustees of Mental Institutions, 2550 N. State St., Jackson 14

MISSOURI

Mental Health and Hospital Authority: State Department of Public Health and Welfare, State Office Bldg., Jefferson City. Division of Mental Diseases

MONTANA

Mental Health Authority: Montana State Hospital, Warm Springs
Mental Hospital Authority: State Department of Public Welfare, Board of Commissioners for the Insane, Helena

NEBRASKA

Mental Health Authority: State Department of Health, Lincoln. Division of Mental Health
Mental Hospital Authority: State Board of Control of State Institutions, Lincoln

NEVADA

Mental Health Authority: State Department of Health, Carson City.

NEW HAMPSHIRE

Mental Health and Hospital Authority: New Hampshire Commission of Mental Health, Concord

NEW JERSEY

Mental Health and Hospital Authority: State Department of Institutions and Agencies, Trenton 7

NEW MEXICO

Mental Health Authority: State Department of Mental Health, Santa Fe. Division of Mental Health.

NEW YORK

Mental Health and Hospital Authority: State Department of Mental Hygiene, State Office Bldg., Albany 1

NORTH CAROLINA

Mental Health Authority: State Board of Health, Raleigh
Mental Hospital Authority: North Carolina Hospitals Board of Control, 357 Revenue Bldg. Annex, Raleigh

North Dakota

Mental Health Authority: State Department of Health, Bismarck. Division of Mental Health
Mental Hospital Authority: State Board of Administration, Bismarck

Ohio

Mental Health and Hospital Authority: Division of Mental Hygiene, State Department of Public Welfare, State Office Bldg., Columbus

Oklahoma

Mental Health Authority: State Department of Health, 3400 North Eastern, Oklahoma City 5
Mental Hospital Authority: Department of Mental Health, Oklahoma City

Oregon

Mental Health Authority: State Board of Health, 1400 S.W. 5th St., Portland 1. Mental Hygiene Section.
Mental Hospital Authority: State Board of Control, Salem

Pennsylvania

Mental Health Authority: Commonwealth of Pennsylvania Department of Welfare, Harrisburg.
Mental Hospital Authority: Bureau of Mental Health, Department of Welfare, Harrisburg

Rhode Island

Mental Health and Hospital Authority: State Department of Social Welfare, 40 Fountain St., Providence

South Carolina

Mental Health Authority: South Carolina State Hospital, Columbia. Department of Mental Hygiene

South Dakota

Mental Health Authority: State Department of Health, Pierre
Mental Hospital Authority: State Board of Charities and Corrections, Huron

Tennessee

Mental Health Authority: State Department of Public Health, Nashville
Mental Hospital Authority: State Department of Institutions, Nashville

TEXAS

Mental Health Authority: State Department of Health, Austin 2. Division of Mental Health.
Mental Hospital Authority: Board of Texas State Hospitals and Special Schools, Capitol Station, Austin

UTAH

Mental Health Authority: State Department of Health, 130 State Capitol, Salt Lake City 1
Mental Hospital Authority. State Department of Public Welfare, 220 State Capitol, Salt Lake City 1

VERMONT

Mental Health Authority: State Department of Health, Burlington
Mental Hospital Authority: State Department of Institutions and Corrections, Burlington

VIRGINIA

Mental Health Authority: State Department of Mental Hygiene and Hospitals, 9 N. 12th St., Richmond 19

WASHINGTON

Mental Health Authority: State Department of Health, Smith Tower, Seattle 4. Mental Health Section.
Mental Hospital Authority: Department of State Institutions

WEST VIRGINIA

Mental Health Authority: State Department of Health, Charleston. Bureau of Mental Hygiene.

WISCONSIN

Mental Health and Hospital Authority: State Department of Public Welfare, Capitol Bldg., 128 South, Madison 2. Division of Mental Health.

WYOMING

Mental Health Authority: State Department of Health, Cheyenne
Mental Hospital Authority: State Board of Charities and Reform, Cheyenne

ALASKA

Mental Health Authority: Alaska Department of Health, Territorial Bldg., Juneau

HAWAII

Mental Health Authority: Territory of Hawaii Department of Health, Honolulu. Bureau of Mental Hygiene.

PUERTO RICO

Mental Health and Hospital Authority: Department of Health, Santurce

VIRGIN ISLANDS

Mental Health Authority: Department of Health, Charlotte Amalie

WHAT TO LOOK FOR IN A MENTAL HOSPITAL

"A mental illness may be as minor as a cold . . . or as serious as cancer." This is the word of the National Institute of Mental Health, which is part of our Federal Public Health Service. (Single copies of informative publications, such Dr. Robert H. Felix's "Mental Health Needs of the Aged" are free. Write the Institute at Bethesda 14, Maryland.)

If your older relative or a friend is one of the 665,000 people who will occupy a hospital bed because he has a serious mental illness, you will want to know how to judge whether a mental hospital is going to help him. The National Association for Mental Health, Inc. (1790 Broadway, New York 19) thinks you should keep these and related questions in mind and ask them when you visit any sanitarium, public or private. The best way to find out about conditions to to get your information first hand.

ASK THE SUPERINTENDENT

1. *How many doctors on his staff are members of the American Psychiatric Association?* Practically all trained psychiatrists belong to the APA. The answer will help you form an opinion as to how competent the medical staff is.

2. *How many patients is each doctor responsible for?* On the average, there should be one full-time doctor for every 150 patients.

ASK TO SEE THE "BACK" WARDS AS WELL AS GOOD WARDS

Here are some things to observe:

1. *The condition of the buildings:* Are they run down and in need of repair?
2. *The toilet facilities:* Are they adequate and clean?
3. *Appearance of buildings:* Do they seem like a prison or a modern hospital?
4. *The wards:* Do they smell bad?
5. *The patients:* Are they reasonably neat and properly clothed?
6. *Attendants and nurses:* Do they show an understanding and sympathetic attitude toward the patients?

ASK THE NURSE

1. *How many patients are in her ward?* Find out how many patients the ward was built for to judge congestion.
2. *How many patients does she take care of?* On wards where active treatment is necessary, there should be at least one nurse for every thirty patients. Every ward should have at least one graduate nurse, preferably with training in psychiatric nursing.

ASK THE ATTENDANT

1. *How many patients has he under his supervision?* There should be at least one attendant to every twenty patients on the average ward.
2. *What kind of instruction has the attendant received in caring for patients after he came to the hospital?* Does he feel the training was as helpful as it should be?
3. *What does he do when patients become disturbed and overactive?* Does he have to have the doctor's order for putting a patient in restraint?
4. *Does he have an opportunity to talk with the doctor and nurse about his patients' welfare?*

VISIT THE KITCHEN AND DINING ROOM

1. *Are they clean and sanitary?*
2. *Are precautions taken against contamination?* This includes refrigeration, screens, good health of kitchen workers, etc.
3. *Ask the dietician how much is spent per day per patient for food.*

Request a menu. Then compare it with what is actually served the patients.

VISIT OCCUPATIONAL THERAPY DEPARTMENT

1. *Find out what percentage of patients get occupational therapy.* How many are left to sit idle on the wards?

2. *Are worker patients—those who do cleaning and maintenance work—given due consideration?* Such as days off, and a reasonable amount of free time?

RECREATION AND RELIGIOUS ACTIVITY

1. *What is being done to provide recreational activity for patients?*
2. *Are religious counsellors and religious services available?*

BEFORE YOU LEAVE

1. *Find out whether the institution has an out-patient clinic where people can come for treatment.*

2. *Ask whether it has an adequate staff of social workers to help patients with their problems when they leave the hospital.* There should be one social worker for every hundred patients admitted to the hospital in one year.

3. *Find out what percentage of patients are discharged each year.* Try to compare this (if possible enlist your doctor's aid) with the rate of discharge in other mental hospitals.

VISITORS' CHECK LIST

A simple method to help you decide what kind of care the mentally sick are given in a particular hospital or sanitarium is to jot down your impressions. Then talk them over with a qualified physician, before you make up your mind for or against placing your relative there. The following "Visitor's Check List" is approved by the National Association for Mental Health, Inc. It is incorporated in their publication, *The Mental Hospital,* by Edith M. Stern, one of a number of simply stated, informative booklets you can obtain free, or at a small charge.

	Satisfactory	*Unsatisfactory*
Grounds		
Exterior of Buildings		
General Impression		
Maintenance		
Barred windows		
Interior of Buildings		
Cleanliness		
Orderliness		
Odors		
Ventilation		
Screens		
Fire Extinguishers		
Porches		
Location of senile (old people's) wards		
Admission building		
Segregated tuberculous wards		
Day rooms		
Spaciousness		
Decoration		
Furniture		
Facilities for diversion		
Lighting		
Dormitories and bed space		
Toilets		
Number		
Privacy		
Washrooms		
Kitchens and pantries		
Sanitation		
Equipment		
Dining Rooms		
Number of seats at a table		
Decoration		
Operating Room		
Dental Office		
Therapy Rooms		
Shock		
Hydrotherapy		
Physiotherapy		
Gymnasium		
Bowling alleys		
Occupational therapy workshop		

	Satisfactory	*Unsatisfactory*
Chapel		
Library		
Barber Shop		
Beauty parlor		
Auditorium		
Staff living quarters		
Doctors		
Nurses		
Attendants		
Food Service		
Food: quality and abundance		
Utensils		
Crockery		
Service		
Bed trays		
Staff		
Superintendent		
Medical staff		
Psychiatric training facilities		
Dentist		
Ward Personnel		
Graduate nurses		
Nursing training facilities		
Attendant training facilities		
Occupational therapists		
Recreation Director		
Director of Music		
Dieticians		
Pharmacist		
Librarian		
Chiropodist		
Barbers		
Beauty Parlor Operator		
Fire marshal		
Patients		
Appearance		
Attitude toward visitors		
General manner		
Restraint		
Seclusion		
Indications of neglect		
Classification		

Chapter XIV: Where to Turn for Help

DIRECTORY: WELFARE COUNSELLING SERVICES

There are approximately two hundred and fifty welfare agencies affiliated with the Family Service Association of America (192 Lexington Ave., New York 16, N. Y.). All of them are able to give professional counselling on family problems, but some of them charge a fee to those who can afford it. The following list are agencies which reported to the national organization in 1950 that they were offering counselling services on a fee basis. However, this is an expanding practice. If your community is not listed here, write the national organization to find out whom you should approach locally. Or you can inquire at a Red Cross Chapter, the Salvation Army, the Welfare Department, or any other organization whose purpose is to help all citizens and non-citizens of this country.

Note: While the following charge fees (often on a sliding scale), they never refuse services to those without the funds to pay for counselling.

California

Los Angeles. Family Service, 355 S. Broadway
Oakland. Family Service Bureau, 121 E. 11th St.
Pasadena. Family Service, 118 S. Oak Knoll Ave.
San Bernardino. Family and Child Service Agency, 546 Sixth St.
San Diego. Family Service Association, 645 A St.
San Francisco. Family and Children's Agency, 1010 Gough St.
Jewish Family Service Agency, 1600 Scott St.
San Jose. Family Service Association, 148 W. San Carlos St.
Santa Barbara. Neighborhood House, 800 Santa Barbara St.

Connecticut

Bridgeport. Family Service, 1074 Iranistan Ave.
Greenwich. Greenwich Center for Child & Family Service, 40 Arch St.
Hartford. Family Service Society, 36 Trumbull St.
New Haven. Family Service, 484 Orange St.
Stamford. Family and Children's Center, 79 Worth St.

District of Columbia

Washington. Family and Child Services, 1022 11th St., N.W.

FLORIDA

Miami. Family Service, 127 N.W. Second St.

ILLINOIS

Aurora. Family Service Association, 32 S. River St.
Chicago. Family Service Bureau, United Charities, 123 W. Madison St.
Jewish Family and Community Service, 231 S. Wells St.
Oak Park, Family Service Association, 1103 Westgate

INDIANA

Indianapolis. Family Service Association, 1003 N. Meridian St.

IOWA

Des Moines. Family Society, 625 Flynn Bldg.

KENTUCKY

Louisville. Family Service Organization, 215 E. Walnut St.

MAINE

Portland. Child and Family Service, 187 Middle St.

MASSACHUSETTS

Boston. Family Service, 10 Derne St.
Brookline, Family Service, 10 Walter Ave.
Newton, Family Service Bureau, 74 Walnut Park

MICHIGAN

Detroit. Family Service Society, 51 Warren Ave., W.
Wyandotte, Down River Consultation Service, 2824 First St.

MINNESOTA

Minneapolis. Family and Children's Service, 404 S. 8th St.
Jewish Family and Children's Service, 404 S. 8th St.

MISSOURI

Clayton. Family Service Society, 107 S. Meramec Ave.
Kansas City. Family Service, 113 Railway Exchange Bldg.
St. Louis. Jewish Family Service Agency, 5654 Easton Ave.

NEBRASKA

Omaha. Family Service, 1504 Dodge St.

New Jersey

Montclair. Family and Children's Society, 213 Glenridge Ave.
Paterson. Family Service, 136 Washington St.
Princeton. Social Service Bureau, 120 John St.

New York

Brooklyn. Bureau of Social Service & Children's Aid Society, 285 Schermerhorn St.
Buffalo. Family Service Society, 181 Franklin St.
New York. Community Service Society, 105 E. 22nd St.
Jewish Family Service, 113 W. 57th St.
Rochester. Family Service, 31 Gibbs St.
Scarsdale. Family Service, 403 Harwood Bldg.
Staten Island. Social Service, Inc., 42 Richmond Terrace
Tuckahoe. Family Consultation Service, 62 Main St.

Ohio

Cincinnatti. Family Service, 2343 Auburn Ave.
Jewish Family Service Bureau, 1430 Central Parkway
Cleveland. Family Service Association, 1001 Huron Rd.
Jewish Family Service Association, 2073 E. 9th St.

Pennsylvania

Ardmore. Family Service of the Main Line Federation of Churches, 18 Simpson Rd.
Philadelphia. Family Service, 311 S. Juniper St.
Jewish Family Service, 1610 Spruce St.
Wayne. Family Service Division, Neighborhood League, 119 W. Wayne Ave.

Tennessee

Memphis. Family Service, 910 Falls Bldg.

Texas

Dallas. Family Service, 409 N. Akard
Houston. Jewish Family Service, 4015 San Jacinto
Family Service Bureau, 403 Gray Ave.

Washington

Spokane. Family Society, 309 City Hall
Tacoma. Family and Child Service, 222 Provident Bldg.

West Virginia

Charleston. Family Service, 1121 Quarrier St.

APPROVED NURSES' REGISTRIES

Nurses' registries have to meet the high standards established by state nurses' associations before they are approved. (*Note:* There may be other registries in any community which are entirely adequate but which, for one reason or another, have not qualified as nurses' professional registries.) The list of approved registries is published semi-annually in the May and November issues of the *American Journal of Nursing*. You can secure a copy by writing to the *Journal's* offices, 2 Park Ave., New York 16, N. Y., or you can probably consult it in a local medical or nursing school library. Some public libraries will also have it.

The following list gives only the addresses of the current approved registries, since names vary from time to time.

ALABAMA

Birmingham, 420-21 Brown Marx Bldg.
Mobile, 705 Ruth St.

ARIZONA

Phoenix, 711 E. Monroe St.
Tucson, 734 N. Euclid Ave.

ARKANSAS

Fort Smith, 1322 N. 36th St.
North Little Rock, 2601 E. Washington Ave.

CALIFORNIA

Bakersfield, 2019 18th St.
Fresno, 550 N. Van Ness Ave.
Glendale, Rm. 204, 203 E. Broadway
Huntington Park, South Gate, 8631 California Ave.
Long Beach, Rm. 331, 141 W. Ocean Blvd.
Los Angeles, Rm. 419, 1052 W. 6th St.
Orange County, 58 Plaza, Orange
Palo Alto, Palo Alto Hospital
Pasadena, Rm. D, 924 E. Green St.
Sacramento, Rm. 11, Sacramento Hotel, 10th and K Sts.
San Bernardino, 1997 D St.

San Francisco, 1155 Pine St.
San Jose, 311 Twohy Bldg.
San Mateo, 77 San Mateo Dr.
Santa Barbara, 25 W. Anapamu St.
Santa Monica, 406 Wilshire Blvd.
Santa Rosa, 313½ Mendocino Ave.
Stockton, 134 E. Weber Ave.

COLORADO

Denver, Rm. 55, Argonaut Hotel

CONNECTICUT

New Haven, 1150 Chapel St.

DELAWARE

Wilmington, 607 N. Broom St.

DISTRICT OF COLUMBIA

Washington, 1720 M St., N.W.

FLORIDA

Daytona Beach, 610 Fifth Ave.
Jacksonville, 28 E. Bay St.
Miami, Rm. 315, 10 N. East Third Ave.
Orlando, 112 Jefferson Court Hotel
St. Petersburg, 307 Empire Bldg.
Tampa, Rm. 250, Hillsboro Hotel
West Palm Beach, 438 16th St.

GEORGIA

Atlanta, 446 Henry Grady Hotel
Macon, 163 College St.
Savannah, 10 E. Macon St.

HAWAII

Honolulu, 510 S. Beretania St.

ILLINOIS

Chicago, Rms. 1511-20, 8 S. Michigan Ave.

INDIANA

Fort Wayne, 1017 Northwood Blvd.
Gary, Rm. 728, 504 Broadway
Indianapolis, 1012 Chamber of Commerce

South Bend, 319 S. Main St.
Terre Haute, 420 S. 22nd St.

IOWA

Council Bluffs, 324 S. First
Davenport, 1516 Farnam St.
Des Moines, Rm. 96, 917 Locust St.
Dubuque, 1168 Center Pl.
Fort Dodge, 1209 Second Ave., N.
Sioux City, 525 10th St.
Waterloo, 220 Locust St.

KANSAS

Topeka, 305 Greenwood St.
Wichita, 329 S. Chautauqua St.

LOUISIANA

Alexandria, 53 Mary St.
Baton Rouge, 3004 Fairfield Ave.
Lake Charles, Route 3, Box 21
Monroe, 110 Hilton St.
New Orleans, 2605 Prytania St.
Shreveport, 172 Patton St.

MAINE

Portland, 91 Fessenden St.

MARYLAND

Baltimore, 1217 Cathedral St.

MASSACHUSETTS

Boston, Rm. 711, 14 Somerset St.
New Bedford, 80 W. Trinity St.
Northampton, 14 Arlington St.
Worcester, 10 Walnut St.

MICHIGAN

Ann Arbor, 401 Thompson St.
Battle Creek, 182 W. Van Buren St.
Gay City, 243 N. Jefferson St.
Detroit, 51 W. Warren Ave.
Flint, 816 E. Wood St.
Grand Rapids, 621 Atwoods St., N.E.

Jackson, 317 W. Mason St.
Kalamazoo, 102 Pratt Bldg.
Lansing, 615 N. Capitol Ave.
Muskegon, 189 Strong Ave.
Pontiac, 75 Delaware Dr.
Saginaw, Rm. 701, 1501 N. Michigan Ave.

MINNESOTA

Duluth, 302 Board of Trade Bldg.
Minneapolis, 1750 Hennepin Ave.
St. Paul, 484 Lowry Bldg.

MISSOURI

Kansas City, 1210 Waldheim Bldg.
Springfield, Route 5, Box 69
St. Joseph, 1414 N. 2nd St.
St. Louis, Rm. 702, 3615 Olive St.

NEBRASKA

North Platte, 1724 W. 2nd St.
Ohama, 301 Merchants National Bldg.

NEW HAMPSHIRE

Manchester, 257 Myrtle St.

NEW JERSEY

Camden, 725 Federal St.
Plainfield, 745 Watchung Ave.
Trenton, 235 E. State St.

NEW MEXICO

Albuquerque, 1516 E. Gold

NEW YORK

Brooklyn, 542 Carlton Ave.
Freeport, Long Island, 115 N. Bergen Pl.
Ithaca, 103 Hudson St.
New York City, 200 W. 57th St.
Ogdensburg, 928 Caroline St.
Potsdam, Charlebois Nursing Home
Rochester, 714 Powers Bldg.
Staten Island, 100 Central Ave. St. George
Syracuse, 704 E. Jefferson St.
Watertown, 1029 Madison Ave.
White Plains, 108 Grand St.

North Carolina

Asheville, 144 Cumberland Ave.
Charlotte, 1217 Elizabeth Ave.
Concord, 375 S. Spring St.
Greensboro, 700 Chestnut St.
Raleigh, 709 Hillsboro St.
Salisbury, Box 26, E. Spencer
Wilmington, 507 N. Fifth Ave.
Winston-Salem, 801 Belleview Dr.

Ohio

Akron, 42 Hawthorne Ave.
Cincinnati, Apt. 26, 2651 Gilbero Ave.
Cleveland, 807 Carnegie Hall
Columbus, Rm. 202, Southern Hotel
Dayton, Rm. 270, 211 S. Main St.
Marion, 199 Olney Ave.
Toledo, 412-413 Colton Bldg.
Youngstown, 1316 Mahoning Bank Bldg.

Oklahoma

Ponca City, 1015 S. 7th St.
Tulsa, Apartment 324, 9 W. 9th St.

Oregon

Eugene, 115 Eleventh Ave.
Portland, 419 Pittock Block

Pennsylvania

Philadelphia, 311 S. Juniper St.
Pittsburgh, Rm. 607, 119 Fifth Ave.

Rhode Island

Providence, Rm. 707, 49 Westminster St.

South Carolina

Charleston, 17-A College St.
Columbia, 1510 Barnwell St.

Tennessee

Chattanooga, Medical Arts Bldg.
Knoxville, 510 Hamilton Bank Bldg.
Memphis, Rm. 232 Medical Arts Bldg.
Nashville, 607 Employment Security Bldg.

TEXAS

Amarillo, 2306 W. 6th St.
Austin, 2612 Bridle Path
Beaumont, 4715 Kenneth St.
Corpus Christi, 4101 Quaile Dr.
Dallas, 201 Medical Arts Bldg.
Fort Worth, 1968 Alston Ave.
Houston, 924 Southern Standard Bldg.
Longview, 805 Travis St.
Port Arthur, 724 Memphis Ave.
San Angelo, 1230 Preusser St.
San Antonio, 105 Howard St.
Tyler, 520 S. Banner St.
Waco, 3309 N. 24th St.
Wichita Falls, 2511 Holiday St.

UTAH

Ogden, 1369 28th St.
Salt Lake City, 112 S. State St.

VERMONT

Burlington, 16 Colchester Ave.

VIRGINIA

Falls Church, 525 Meadow Lane
Newport News, 2314 Oak Ave.
Norfolk, 4400 E. Princess Anne Rd.

WASHINGTON

Longview, 1203 22nd Ave.
Seattle, 6619 White Bldg.
Spokane, W. 819½ First Ave.
Tacoma, 240 Perkins Bldg.
Walla Walla, 511 Locust St.

WEST VIRGINIA

Charleston, 207 Noyes Bldg.
Huntington, 1226 Sixth Ave.
Parkersburg, 215 11th St.

WISCONSIN

Madison, Tenney Bldg.
Milwaukee, 622 N. Water St.

WYOMING

Cheyenne, 2814 Dillon St.

CHAPTER XV: WHAT'S NEW FOR THE OLD

DIRECTORY: NATIONAL ORGANIZATIONS

There is a national organization or committee on education, health, recreation, welfare, and every other phase of importance in our lives. Most of the national sources of information can direct you to their nearest branch agency. In this, the century of the old, all in the following list have work which in some aspects touches the lives of the aged. When in doubt, call on them.

Adult Education Association of the United States, 1201 16th St., N.W., Washington, D. C.

American Association of Social Workers, 1 Park Ave., New York City

American Association of Nursing Homes, 1970 Union Ave., Memphis, Tenn.

American Cancer Society, 47 Beaver St., New York City

American Diabetes Association, 1790 Broadway, New York City

American Foundation for the Blind, 15 W. 16th St., New York City

American Heart Association, 1775 Broadway, New York City

American Hearing Society, 817 14th St., N. W., Washington, D. C.

American Hospital Association, 18 E. Division St., Chicago, Ill.

American Medical Association, 535 N. Dearborn St., Chicago, Ill.

American National Red Cross, Red Cross Headquarters, Washington, D. C.

American Nurses Association, 2 Park Ave., New York City

American Public Health Association, 1790 Broadway, New York City

American Public Welfare Association, 1313 E. 60th St., Chicago 37

American Social Hygiene Association, 1790 Broadway, New York City

Arthritis and Rheumatism Foundation, 23 W. 45th St., New York City

Boards of Hospitals and Homes of Methodist Church, 740 Rush St., Chicago, Ill.

Canadian Welfare Council, 245 Cooper St., Ottawa, Ontario, Canada

Commission on Chronic Illness, 615 N. Wolfe St., Baltimore, Md.

Committee on Aging and Geriatrics, U. S. Department of Health, Education, and Welfare, Washington, D. C.

Community Chests and Councils of America, Inc., 345 E. 46th St., New York City

Family Service Association of America, 192 Lexington Ave., New York City

Health Information Foundation, 420 Lexington Ave., New York City

Joint Commission on Accreditation of Hospitals, 660 N. Rush St., Chicago, Ill.

National Association for the Advancement of Colored People, 20 W. 40th St., New York City

National Association of Goodwill Industries, 744 N. 4th St., Milwaukee, Wis.

National Association for Mental Health, 1790 Broadway, New York City

National Association of Registered Nursing Homes, 25 Ridgeview Ave., White Plains, N. Y.

National Committee on the Aging, 345 E. 46th St., New York City

National Conference of Christians and Jews, 381 Fourth Ave., New York City

National Council of Churches of Christ, 297 Fourth Ave., New York City

National Conference of Social Work, 22 W. Gay St., Columbus, Ohio

National Health Council, 1790 Broadway, New York City

National Information Bureau, 205 E. 42nd St., New York City

National Institutes of Health, Section on Gerontology, Bethesda, Md.

National League for Nursing, 2 Park Ave., New York City

National Legal Aid Association, 328 Main St., Rochester, N. Y.

National Lutheran Council, Division of Welfare, 50 Madison Ave., New York City

National Multiple Sclerosis Society, 270 Park Ave., New York City

National Recreation Association, 315 Fourth Ave., New York City

National Safety Council, 425 N. Michigan Ave., Chicago, Ill.

National Social Welfare Assembly, 345 E. 46th St., New York City

National Society for the Prevention of Blindness, 1790 Broadway, New York City

National Tuberculosis Association, 1790 Broadway, New York City

National Urban League, 1133 Broadway, New York City

Salvation Army, 120 W. 14th St., New York City

Shut-in-Society, 221 Lexington Ave., New York City

U. S. Public Health Service, 4th and Independence Ave., S.W., Washington, D. C.

EXHIBITS, MOTION PICTURES, RECORDINGS

There are now coming on the market visual and auditory materials which endeavor to make old people and their worries "come alive." They are useful in round-table discussions with your neighbors, your clubs, or to arouse your whole community. Sometimes they can give you a better understanding of the human factors involved in aging than can printed media. Because exhibits and motion pictures and recordings are more difficult and expensive to produce than the spoken or printed word, the supply is limited. Also, "where-to-get-it" information is not always locally accessible.

To fill the need, the national Committee on Aging and Geriatrics tries to keep a list of current materials which are useful and interesting. Write the Chairman, Washington 25, D. C., or ask one of the Regional Offices of the Department of Health, Education and Welfare, of which the Committee is a part. If you want to see the exhibits the Committee has prepared, or find out where to listen to the recordings, write the national office for the address of the nearest Regional Office.

EXHIBITS

The Committee has prepared two exhibits, suitable for display at conferences, community meetings, university round-tables, and in prominent public places, such as a "main-street" store-window. Table-models, small-size replicas of these exhibits, portable, and easy to set up as a "one-man show," can also be borrowed.

Exhibit 1. "Living in the Later Years"

Theme: To stimulate community action programs looking toward improving services for older people. Six large panels tell the story in photographs, with brief descriptive captions.

Exhibit 2. "What's New in the Challenge of Aging"

Theme: To portray this inescapable personal and local problem in its national proportions—what older people need, what communities want to do about it, what the federal government can do to help states and communities meet the needs of health, useful employment, financial security, living arrangements, and art of living.

MOTION PICTURES

Most of the following are available on loan, a few are distributed on a rental basis. Consult the distributor for cost and other arrangements. Unless otherwise indicated, all films are 16 mm. black and white prints with sound. This list is not all-inclusive but is representative of the lengthening number which appear annually.

TITLE: *Be Your Age*. STORY: How a middle-aged man recovers from a heart attack and learns to adjust himself to living with a handicapped heart. DISTRIBUTORS: Metropolitan Life Insurance Co., 1 Madison Ave., New York 10, N. Y.; New York State Department of Health Film Library, 18 Dove St., Albany, N. Y.

TITLE: *Date of Birth*. STORY: Plays up the older worker's high standard of dependability and productivity and stresses the importance of giving him a fair chance. Gives actual record of older workers. DISTRIBUTOR: National Film Board of Canada, 1270 Avenue of the Americas, New York 20, N. Y.

TITLE: *Life Begins Again*. STORY: Problems of deafness presented as the cause of many accidents and social difficulties; points out the value of a hearing aid. DISTRIBUTOR: New York State Department of Health Film Library, 18 Dove St., Albany, N. Y.

TITLE: *Life with Grandpa*. STORY: Discusses the problems of old age, including ill health and economic insecurity. Various ways are suggested to meet typical problems, including the feeling of loneliness and uselessness in the later years. DISTRIBUTORS: Columbia University Educational Films, 431 W. 117 St., New York 27, N. Y.; Ideal Films, 207 E. 37th St., New York 16, N. Y.; New York University Film Library, 26 Washington Pl., New York 3, N. Y.

TITLE: *Looking Aheaa*. STORY: How a sixty-eight-year-old industrial worker faces retirement and begins to learn about his Social Security protection. The services of an Old Age and Survivors Insurance Field Office. DISTRIBUTOR: Regional Offices, U. S. Department of Health, Education, and Welfare. Available in both 35 and 16 mm. prints.

TITLE: *Retire to Life*. STORY: Deals with the emotional problems of older persons after retirement from active employment. DISTRIBUTORS: Some State Health Departments; Mental Health Division,

Oklahoma State Department of Health, 3400 Northeastern St., Oklahoma City, Okla.; International Film Bureau, 57 E. Jackson Blvd., Chicago 4, Ill.

TITLE: *Steps of Age.* STORY: How a sensitive elderly widow adjusts to later years. DISTRIBUTOR: State Mental Health Agencies. Available in both 16 and 35 mm. prints.

TITLE: *Where Life Begins Again.* STORY: The story of an elderly man who, despite misfortune, finds comfort and happiness at the Moosehaven Home for the Aged in Florida. DISTRIBUTOR: Earle W. Horton, Loyal Order of Moose, Mooseheart, Illinois.

TITLE: *Your Social Security.* STORY: Shows the objectives of Social Security insurance and how to become eligible for it. DISTRIBUTOR: Regional Offices, U. S. Department of Health, Education, and Welfare.

TAPE-RECORDINGS AND RECORDS

Tape-recordings require a special machine which may often be rented, or borrowed. Good sources of inquiry are local radio stations, boards of education, or welfare agencies. The usual type has two speeds (3¾″ and 7½″ per second) so that if you are borrowing or renting tape-recordings, check on their speed.

This is also a factor in phonograph records but all the newer machines accommodate three speeds 33⅓, 45, and 78 rpm (revolutions per minute). Electrical transcriptions are suitable for radio stations, a good thing to remember if you are interested in making your community aware of old age problems and solutions. Note the various distributors in this sample list of both tape-recordings and phonograph records.

TITLE: *Looking Ahead:* A series of four informal round-table discussions. SUBJECTS: "Adjustment to Retirement"; "Education for Longer Living"; "Employment and Retirement for Older Workers"; "Problems in the Field of Aging." DISTRIBUTORS: Local field offices of the Department of Health, Education, and Welfare. (Records).

TITLE: *Humanizing the Aged:* Two interviews in which older citizens talk over their problems, in one transcription with an employment counsellor, in the other with a social worker. DISTRIBUTOR: New York State Joint Legislative Committee on Problems of the Aging, 94 Broadway, Newburgh, N. Y. (Tape-recordings.)

TITLE: *The People Act in Syracuse:* How an industrial city organized to meet the needs of its older citizens. DISTRIBUTOR: The People Act Center, State College, Pa. (12 inch, 1. p. disc, 33⅓ rpm.)

TITLE: *Silver Threads Among the Gold:* Discusses the use of leisure-time in old age, and the preparations which ought to be made.

DISTRIBUTOR: New York State College of Agriculture, Ithaca, N. Y. (Recording.)

TITLE: *Learning for Living Longer:* A series of recorded lectures by national experts with Dr. Wilma T. Donahue, Psychologist, of the Institute for Human Adjustment, University of Michigan, as Moderator. They parallel the lectures in the course by a similar name, offered in Ann Arbor and other Michigan centers for a number of years. (These are tape-recordings which can be purchased or rented.)

SUBJECTS:

1. *Aging in American Life.* Charles Kidd, Executive Director, Research and Planning Council, Office of the Surgeon General, U. S. Public Health Service, Washington, D. C. and Clark Tibbitts, Chairman, Committee on Aging and Geriatrics.
2. *Psychological Aspects of Growing Older.* Wilma T. Donahue, Institute for Human Adjustment, University of Michigan.
3. *Physical Health and Care in the Later Years.* Martin Gumpert, M.D., geriatrician, Goldwater Memorial Hospital, New York City.
4. *Nutritional Needs of Older People.* Clyde McCay, Professor of Nutrition, Cornell University.
5. *Maintenance of Mental Health Through the Years.* Moses M. Frohlich, M.D., Associate Professor of Psychiatry; in charge of the Veterans Readjustment Center, University of Michigan.
6. *Family Life, Living Arrangements, and Housing for Older People.* Ollie Randall, Consultant, Community Service Society, New York City.
7. *Financing the Older Years.* Robert Ball, Assistant Director, Bureau of Old Age and Survivors Insurance, Washington, D. C.
8. *Opportunities in Retirement as One Grows Older.* Alexander G. Ruthven, President, University of Michigan.
9. *Creative and Recreational Activities for Older People.* Helen Laue, Assistant Director, Community Project for the Aged, Welfare Council of Metropolitan Chicago.
10. *Alternatives in Later Maturity.* Bonaro Wilkinson Overstreet, lecturer, author of *How to Think About Ourselves,* etc., and Harry A. Overstreet, lecturer, educator, author of *The Mature Mind,* etc.

SUGGESTIONS FOR HELPFUL READING

As yet, there are no quick and ready reference books to which we can turn when we want to know more about what we can or cannot do, or what we should or must do in a particular situation where aging people are concerned.

Much valuable information is buried in medical journals or scientific or technical magazines. Usually, only workers in the vineyard of old age see them. However, since many of the articles can be understood with ease, and read with pleasure and profit by any of us, a number are listed in the following pages, together with books on special aspects of the aging process. Practically any good public library will have them, or tell you where you can find them.

If the number of so-called "popular" books in this list seems scanty, it is because most of us in the past have been much more concerned in having wise men tell us what we can do to keep young than help us find the best ways to grow old.

Chapter I: Getting Along with Older People

Aging. Issued bi-monthly by the Committee on Aging and Geriatrics of the U. S. Department of Health, Education, and Welfare. It is a medium through which agencies, organizations, and individuals exchange information about programs and activities and trends affecting the old. Available through the Superintendent of Documents, U. S. Government Printing Office, Washington, D. C.

Geriatrics. Official journal of the American Geriatrics Society. It reports research and clinical studies of the diseases of the aged and processes of aging. Bi-monthly. Publication office, 84 South Tenth Street, Minneapolis, Minnesota.

Journal of Gerontology. Official magazine of the Gerontological Society, Inc. It publishes manuscripts dealing with problems of the aging from the fields of natural and social sciences and the humanities, review articles, and selected abstracts from current literature in the field. Quarterly. Publication office, 10 North Howard Street, Baltimore, Maryland.

Journal of Living. This lively and informative magazine was established in 1936. Published monthly in pocket-size format, it places its chief emphasis on matters of interest to older people. Publication office is at 1819 Broadway, New York City.

Lifetime Living, whose sub-title is "The magazine for people who plan ahead." First published June, 1952. Monthly. It carries a wide range of feature articles on health, retirement planning, recreation, sports. Publication office is at 22 East 38th Street, New York City.

Acquaintance with any of these periodicals, which will be found in most large public libraries, may help you over a family hurdle, and are indispensable for up-to-date news affecting the old.

Chapter II: What is Normal Old Age?

Behrens, H. D. and Nester, R. F. "Intellectual Changes during Maturity and Old Age." *Review of Educational Research,* Vol. 20: 361-366, December, 1950.

Blair, Glenn M. "Personality and Social Development." *Review of Educational Research,* Vol. 20:375-389, December, 1950.

De Gruchy, Clare. *Creative Old Age.* San Francisco: Old Age Counselling Center, 1946.

Fox, Charlotte and Birren, J. E. "Intellectual Deterioration in the Aged." *Journal of Consulting Psychology,* Vol. 14:305-310, August, 1950.

Fox, Charlotte. "Vocational Ability in Later Maturity." *Journal of Educational Psychology,* Vol. 38:482-492, December, 1947.

Johnson, Wingate M., M.D. *The Years After Fifty.* New York: Whittlesey House, 1947.

Lawton, George. *Aging Successfully.* New York: Columbia University Press, 1946.

Lawton, George. *New Goals for Old Age.* New York: Columbia University Press, 1943.

Schilder, Paul. "Psychiatric Aspects of Old Age and Aging." *American Journal of Orthopsychiatry,* Vol. 10, January, 1940; 62-72.

Todd, Arthur T. *Medical Aspects of Growing Old.* Baltimore: Williams & Wilkins Company, 1946.

Tyson, R. C. "Adjusting to Old Age." *Journal of Clinical Psychology,* Vol. 7, January, 1951; 79-86.

Chapter III: Old Age Is not a Disease

1. *Aging.* New York: Community Service Society, Department of Educational Nursing. Family Health Series, No. 8, 1948.

2. *American Red Cross Home Nursing Textbook.* Philadelphia: The Blakiston Company, 1950.

3. Armstrong, Donald, M.D., and Hallock, Grace T. *What to Do Till the Doctor Comes.* New York: Simon & Schuster, 1943.

4. Boas, Ernst P., M.D. *Treatment of the Patient Past Fifty.* Chicago: The Year Book Publishers, Inc., 1947. (Third edition)

5. Cowdry, Edmund V., M.D., Editor. *Problems of Aging: Biological and Medical Aspects.* Baltimore: Williams & Wilkins Company, 1949. (Second edition)

6. Crampton, C. Ward., M.D. *Live Long and Like It.* New York: Public Affairs Committee, Inc., 1948. Pamphlet No. 139.

7. Diehl, Harold S., M.D. *Textbook of Healthful Living,* Chapter XXI, "Health Problems of Advancing Years." New York: McGraw-Hill Book Co., 1950.

8. Gelbach, Sarah B. "Nursing Care of the Aged." *American Journal of Nursing,* Vol. 43: 1112-1114, December, 1943.

9. Johnson, Wingate, M.D. *The Years After Fifty.* New York: Whittlesey House, 1947.

10. Kessler, Henry H., M.D. *Rehabilitation of the Physically Handicapped*. New York: Columbia University Press, 1947.

11. *Resistance and the Aging Process*. New York: The Metropolitan Life Insurance Company, Health Bulletin for Teachers, Vol. 18: May, 1947.

12. Stieglitz, Edward J., M.D. *The Second Forty Years*. Philadelphia: J. B. Lippincott Company, 1946.

13. Turner, Violet. *Chronic Illness*. Washington, D. C.: Superintendent of Documents, Government Printing Office, Public Health Bibliography Series, No. 1, 1951.

Chapter IV: Getting on in Years—Safely

Adequate Low-Calorie Diet. Chicago: The American Dietetic Association, 1952.

Allergy Recipes. Chicago: The American Dietetic Association, 1945.

Bayles, S. and Ebaugh, F. G. *Emotional Factors in Eating and Obesity*. Chicago: The American Dietetic Association, June, 1950.

Care of the Aging and Chronically Ill. Washington, D. C.: American Red Cross, ARC 1615, 1950. Pp. 65-66.

Crampton, C. Ward, M.D. "Dietary Aids and Dangers for the Aging." *Public Health Nursing,* June, 1949.

Donahue, Wilma T. *Psychologic Aspects of Feeding the Aged*. Chicago: The American Dietetic Association, June, 1951.

Eating for Health in Later Life. Chicago: Evaporated Milk Association, February, 1950.

Eating Is Fun—for Older People, Too. Chicago: The American Dietetic Association, June, 1950.

Food for Your Heart. New York: New York Heart Association, 1953.

Food Guide for Older Folks. Washington, D. C.: Superintendent of Documents, 1952. Catalog No. Al.77:17.

Getting On—Safely. Chicago: National Safety Council. (No date)

Meyer, Jacob, M.D. "Diet for the Aged." *Geriatrics,* May-June, 1947.

Ohlson, Margaret A. "The Dietary Requirements of Aging Women," *American Journal of Nursing,* November, 1948.

Payne, Alma Smith and Callahan, Dorothy. *The Low Sodium Cook Book*. Boston: Little, Brown Co., 1953.

Zeman, Frederic D., M.D. "The Functional Capacity of the Aged." New York: Columbia University Press, 1945 (In *Proceedings of the Natl. Conference of Social Work*).

Zeman, Frederic D., M.D. "Accident Hazards of Old Age; the

Physician's Role in a Program of Prevention," *Geriatrics,* Jan.-Feb., 1948.

CHAPTER V: FINANCING OLD AGE

"A Budget for an Elderly Couple." *Social Security Bulletin,* Volume 11, Feb., 1948. Pp. 4-12.

Ford, Norman D. *Where to Retire on a Small Income.* Greenlawn, N. Y.: Harian Publications, 1951.

Graham, Benjamin. *The Intelligent Investor.* New York: Harper & Bros., 1949.

Greenough, William C. *A New Approach to Retirement Income.* New York: Teachers Insurance and Annuity Association of America, 1951.

Kidd, Charles V. "Economic Security for Older Persons." In *Living Through the Older Years.* Tibbitts, Clark, Editor. Ann Arbor: University of Michigan Press, 1949.

O'Neill, Hugh. *Modern Pension Plans: Principles and Practices.* New York: Prentice-Hall, Inc., 1947.

Pogge, Oscar C. "Family Relationships and Old-Age and Survivors Insurance." *Social Security Bulletin,* July, 1945.

Steinhaus, Henry W. *Financing Old Age.* New York: National Industrial Conference Board, 1948.

Stewart, Maxwell S. *Women and Their Money.* New York: Public Affairs Committe, Inc., 1949.

Stewart, Maxwell S. *How to Buy Life Insurance.* New York: Public Affairs Committee, Inc., 1946.

Washington, Lawrence. *How to Plan Your Financial Security.* New York: Whittlesey House, McGraw-Hill Book Co., 1949.

CHAPTER VI: TO WORK OR NOT TO WORK

Abrams, Albert J. "Barriers to the Employment of Older Workers." *The Annals of the American Academy of Political and Social Sciences.* January, 1952. Pp. 62-71.

Arthur, Julietta K. *Jobs for Women Over Thirty-Five.* New York: Prentice-Hall, Inc., 1947.

Clague, Ewan. "Aging and Employability." *Living Through the Older Years.* Tibbitts, Clark, Editor. Ann Arbor: University of Michigan Press, 1949.

Close, Kathryn. *Getting Ready to Retire.* New York: Public Affairs Committee, Inc. Pamphlet No. 182, 1952.

Never too Old. Albany, N. Y.: Desmond Report. New York State Joint Legislative Committee on Problems of the Aging, Document 32, 1949.

Klumpp, Theodore G. "Future of the Older Worker." *Geriatrics,* May-June, 1947.

Kossoris, Max D. "Relation of Age to Industrial Injuries." *Monthly Labor Review.* Vol. 51: 789-804, 1940.

Kuh, Clifford. "Selective Placement of Older Workers." *Journal of Gerontology,* Vol. 1: 313-318, 1946.

McFarland, Ross A. "The Older Worker in Industry." *Harvard Business Review,* Summer, 1943.

Miles, Walter R. "Performance in Relation to Age." *Mental Health in Later Maturity.* Supplement 168, Public Health Reports, U. S. Public Health Service, U. S. Government Printing Office, Washington, D. C., 1942.

Shock, Nathan W. "Older People and Their Potentialities for Gainful Employment." *Journal of Gerontology,* April, 1947.

CHAPTER VII: ACTIVE LEISURE: NEW WAYS FOR OLD

"Aging and Retirement" (12 articles). *The American Journal of Sociology,* Jan., 1954.

Brown, Giles T. "Never Too Old to Learn." *School and Society.* Vol. 74, Nov. 3, 1951. Pp. 279-281.

Brungardt, Theresa S. "Fun for the Older Person in the Country." In *Proceedings of the National Conference of Social Work.* New York: Columbia University Press, 1946. Pp. 219-227.

Bunker, Ruth. "Creative Activities Through Handcrafts." *Annals of the American Academy of Political and Social Science,* Vol. 279, Jan., 1952. Pp. 93-97.

Donahue, Wilma. "Experiments in the Education of Older Adults." *Adult Education,* Vol. 2, Dec., 1951. Pp. 49-59.

Fuchs, Dora and Levine, Harry. "The Hodson Community Center: An Experiment in Preservation of Personality." *Journal of Gerontology,* January, 1946.

Giles, Ray. *How to Retire—and Enjoy It.* New York: Whittlesey House, McGraw-Hill Book Company, 1949.

Griffin, John J. "Recreation for the Aged." *Public Welfare,* December, 1944. Also in *Recreation,* September, 1945.

Hall, Edward T. "The Creative Urge in Older People." In *New Goals for Old Age,* Lawton, George, Editor. New York: Columbia University Press, 1943.

Havighurst, Robert J. "Life Begins Again at Sixty-Five." *Nation's Schools.* Vol. 46, July, 1950. Pp. 23-25.

Strong, E. K. *Change of Interests with Age.* Stanford University, Calif.: Stanford University Press, 1931.

Thorndike, Edward L. *Adult Interests.* New York: The Macmillan Company, 1935.

Woods, James H. "Camping for Oldsters." *Recreation,* March, 1950.

CHAPTER VIII: LEAVING THE WELL-ENOUGH ALONE

Carson, J. J. "How Do We Aged Get Along?" *Survey Graphic,* Vol. 33:16, January, 1944.

Corliss, Ray J. "You Can Live in Paradise for $125 a Month." *Lifetime Living,* Vol. 1:24-6, July, 1952.

Davis, Gertrude R. "Visiting Housekeeper Service for the Aged." *Journal of Social Casework,* Vol. 29:22-27, 1948.

Fraenkel, Marta. "Housekeeping Service for Chronic Patients." New York: Welfare Council Research Bureau, 1942.

Graham, Lee E. "Old Folks at Home—Their Own." New York: *Times Magazine,* Nov. 9, 1952. P. 53.

Gumpert, Martin, M.D. and others. "Where and with Whom Should Older People Live?" Chicago: University of Chicago Round Table, No. 703.

Hill, Ruth. "Old Age at the Crossroads. Patterns of Living in the Community." In *New Goals for Old Age,* Lawton, George, Editor. New York: Columbia University Press, 1943.

Johnson, Ralph J. and Pond, M. Allen. "Health Standards of Housing for the Aging Population." *Journal of Gerontology,* Vol. 7, No. 2, April, 1952.

Laverty, Ruth. "Nonresident Aid—Community vs. Institutional Care for Older People." *Journal of Gerontology,* Vol. 5, August, 1950. Pp. 370-374.

Pemberton, Annie May. "Services to the Aged through Public Welfare." *Public Welfare,* Vol. 6:153-154, 1948.

CHAPTER IX: PREPARING THE OLD FOR CHANGE

Cavan, Ruth S. "Family Life and Family Substitutes in Old Age." *American Sociological Review,* Vol. 14:81-83, February, 1949.

Cavan, Ruth S., Burgess, Ernest W., Havighurst, Robert J. and Goldhamer, Herbert. *Personal Adjustment in Old Age.* Chicago: Science Research Associates, 1949.

Hill, Ruth. "Understanding the Problems of Older People." *The Family,* January, 1938.

Lawton, George and Stewart, Maxwell S. *When You Grow Older.* New York: Public Affairs Committee, 1947. Pamphlet 131.

Lemkau, Paul V., M.D. "The Period of Old Age." In his *Mental Hygiene in Public Health.* New York: McGraw-Hill Company, 1949. Pp. 205-318.

Pollak, Otto. "Conservatism in Later Maturity and Old Age." *American Sociological Review,* April, 1943. Pp. 175-179.

Vischer, A. L., M.D. *Old Age, Its Compensations and Rewards.* London: George Allen & Unwin, Ltd., 1947.

Wagner, Margaret W. "Meet Yourself at Sixty-Five." *Survey Midmonthly,* April, 1946.

Williams, C. L. "The Mental Hygiene of Aging." *Geriatrics,* Vol. 1:361-368, Sept.-Oct., 1946.

Chapter X: Homes for the Aged: Pros and Cons

"Care of Aged in Old People's Homes." *Monthly Labor Review,* Vol. 50, May, 1940. Pp. 1043-61.

Cooper, Frank A. "Wanted: A New Kind of Old People's Home." *American Home Magazine,* Vol. 47, January, 1952.

Dean, John P. "Public Housing for the Aged." *Proceedings of the National Conference of Social Work.* New York: Columbia University Press, 1946. Pp. 491-97.

Griffin, John J. "Institutional Facilities for Care of the Aged." *Catholic Action,* Vol. 29, No. 3., April, 1948.

Hathaway, Victoria. "Our Homes for the Aged." *Today's Health,* Vol. 29, March, 1951. Pp. 16-17.

Homes for the Aged in the United States. (Includes a directory.) Washington: U. S. Bureau of Labor Statistics, Bulletin No. 677, 1941.

"I Moved to an Old Ladies' Home." *American Mercury,* February, 1938.

Moore, E. H. "Homes, Hostels, and Other Institutions for the Aged." *Journal of Gerontology,* July, 1948. Pp. 207-214.

Report on National Conference on Protestant Homes for the Aged. New York: Federal Council of the Churches of Christ in America, 1948.

Suggested Standards for Homes for the Aged. New York: Welfare Council of New York City, 1948. (Sixth Edition)

Zeman, Frederic D., M.D. "The Medical Organization of the Modern Home for the Aged." *Journal of Gerontology,* Vol. 5, July, 1950. Pp. 262-65.

Chapter XI: Substitute Homes for the Well

Griffin, John J. "The Sheltering of the Aged; a Thorough Analysis of the Living Arrangements of 1900 Old Age Assistance Recipients." *Journal of Gerontology,* Vol. 5, January, 1950. Pp. 30-43.

Kraus, Hertha. "Housing Our Older Citizens." *Annals of the American Academy of Political and Social Sciences,* January, 1952.

Kasius, Peter. "Services Offered Older People." (In *National Conference of Social Work, Selected Papers. Social Work in the Current Scene, 1950*). New York: Columbia University Press, 1950.

Lewi, Emma Weil. "A Home of Their Own. A description of an apartment-house project connected with the Home for Aged and Infirm Hebrews, New York." *Better Times,* March 21, 1947.

Nicholson, Edna, and Nairne, Lillie H. "Private Living Arrangements for Elderly People." In *Proceedings of the National Conference of Social Work.* New York: Columbia University Press, 1947. Pp. 477-90.

Powell, Amy S. "Community Planning for the Aged." *Geriatrics,* Vol. 5, Sept.-Oct., 1950. Pp. 288-91.

Randall, Ollie A. "Somewhere to Live—in One's Later Years." *Public Aid in Illinois,* May, 1949.

Silk, Leonard S. "The Housing Circumstances of the Aged in the United States." *Journal of Gerontology,* Vol. 7, January, 1952. Pp. 87-91.

Wagner, Margaret W. "Foster Home Care for the Aged." *Journal of Social Casework,* October, 1946.

CHAPTER XII: COMMUNITY CARE FOR THE SICK

Bluestone, E. M., M.D. "Home Care: An Extramural Hospital Function." *Survey Midmonthly,* April, 1948.

Bluestone, E. M., M.D. "Medical Care—A Community Plan." *The Survey,* March, 1949.

Bourke, John J. and Wagner, Hildegarde. "State Planning for the Chronically Ill." *Proceedings of the National Conference of Social Work.* New York: Columbia University Press, 1948.

Dublin, Louis I. *The Facts of Life from Birth to Death.* New York: The Macmillan Company, 1951.

Freeman, Lucy. *It's Your Hospital and Your Life.* New York: Public Affairs Pamphlets, No. 187, 1952.

Mountin, Joseph W. "Community Health Services for Older People." In *Growing in the Older Years.* Ann Arbor: University of Michigan Press, 1951. Pp. 71-83.

Mulaney, Gertrude S. and Waterman, Theda L. "A Community Plans for Its Aged and Chronically Ill." *Public Health Nursing,* Vol. 42, October, 1950. Pp. 568-73.

"Planning for the Chronically Ill." Report of American Public Health Association and American Medical Association. *The Journal of the American Medical Association.* October 11, 1947. Vol. 135, Part I, pp. 343-47.

Rapp, Sarah S. "Boarding Care for the Aged Sick." *The Family,* July, 1946. Vol. 27, No. 5, pp. 192-96.

Terris, Milton. "National Planning for the Chronically Ill." *Proceedings of the National Conference of Social Work.* New York: Columbia University Press, 1948.

Chapter XIII: What to Do with the Mentally Ill

Clow, Hillis, M.D. "The Outlook for Patients Admitted to a Mental Hospital After the Age of Sixty." *New York State Journal of Medicine,* Nov. 1, 1948.

Crutcher, Hester B. *Family Care of the Mentally Ill.* New York: The New York State Society for Mental Health, 1952-53. (Reprint from American Association for Advancement of Science)

Doyle, Kathleen. *When Mental Illness Strikes Your Family.* New York: Public Affairs Pamphlets, No. 172, May, 1951.

Hartwell, Samuel W., M.D. "Mental Diseases of the Aged." In *New Goals for Old Age,* Lawton, George, Editor. New York: Columbia University Press, 1943.

Kaplan, Oscar J., M.D., Editor. *Mental Disorders in Later Life.* Stanford: Stanford University Press, 1945.

Kennedy, Foster, M.D. "Borderline Mental Problems in Late Maturity." In *Mental Health in Later Maturity.* Washington: U. S. Government Printing Office, Public Health Reports, Supplement No. 168, 1943.

MacCurdy, Frederick. "The Aged in Our Mental Institutions." In *Birthdays Don't Count.* Albany: New York State Joint Legislative Committee on Problems of the Aging, Legislative Document 61, 1948.

Stieglitz, Edward J., M.D. "Factors Contributing to Mental Disease in the Aged." *Journal of Gerontology,* October, 1947.

Wagner, Margaret W. "Mental Hazards in Old Age." *The Family,* June, 1944.

Chapter XIV: Where to Turn for Help

1. De Gruchy, Clare. *Creative Old Age.* San Francisco: Old Age Counselling Center, 1946.

2. Donahue, Wilma, "Age with a Future." *Proceedings, National Conference of Social Work.* New York: Columbia University Press. Pp. 70-86.

3. McFarland, Joseph. *How to Choose a Doctor.* Chicago: American Medical Association, Bureau of Health Education. Pamphlet, 1943. (Fifth Printing)

4. Maves, Paul B. "The Church in Community Planning for the Aged." *Geriatrics,* Vol. 5, Nov.-Dec. 1950. Pp. 339-42.

5. Maves, Paul B. and Cedarleaf, J. Lennart. *Older People and the Church.* New York: Abingdon-Cokesbury Press, 1949.

6. Martin, Lilien J. and De Gruchy, Clare. *Salvaging Old Age.* New York: The Macmillan Company, 1930.

7. Randall, Ollie A. "Meeting the Discouragements of Elderly People." *Proceedings, National Conference of Social Work.* New York: Columbia University Press, 1937.

8. Schifferes, Justus. *How to Live Longer.* New York: Dutton & Company, 1949.

9. Waterman, Le Roy. "Religion and Religious Observance in Old Age." In Tibbitts, Clark, Editor. *Living Through the Older Years.* Ann Arbor: University of Michigan Press, 1949.

10. Zeman, Frederic D., M.D. "Constructive Programs for the Mental Health of the Elderly." *Mental Hygiene,* Vol. 35, April, 1951. Pp. 221-34.

Chapter XV: What's New for the Old

A Classified Bibliography on Gerontology and Geriatrics. The 18,000 listings in this monumental compendium are likely to touch on any aspect of old age in which you may be interested. The author, Dr. Nathan W. Shock, Director of the Gerontology Research Unit, National Heart Institute, keeps it current through a bibliography section in each issue of the *Journal of Gerontology.* (Both Bibliography and Journal available in most large libraries.)

Making the Most of Maturity. A home study course, first of its kind, available through University of Chicago. Course includes ten lessons, dealing with social and personal attitudes toward aging; physical and health problems; financial and employment problems; living arrangements for older people; use of leisure time; and a philosophy for the later years. Course is available to individuals, and recommended as basis for group discussion. The text, *Good Living After Fifty,* may be purchased separately without enrollment in course. Address Home-Study Department, University of Chicago, Chicago 37, Ill.

Notable Papers on Aging. Outstanding presentations originally made for a limited audience, considered worthy of wider circulation by the National Committee on Aging (of the National Social Welfare Assembly), 345 East 46th Street, New York City. The first six are: "A Twentieth Century Philosophy for Homes for the Aged," by Ollie A. Randall; "A Foster Home Program for Older Persons," by William Posner; "Keeping the Older Person Employed," by Elizabeth Hatch; "Religion and the Aging Process," by Seward Hiltner; "Rehabilitation of Older People," by Murray Ferderber, M.D.; "Retirement and Pension Planning from a Labor Viewpoint," by Willard Solenberger.

INDEX

INDEX